the WICKED current

A MESSAGE

the WICKED current

A MESSAGE

Robert Ray Self

Buffalo Mill Press
Hohenwald, TN

The Wicked Current
A message

Copyright © 2002 Robert Ray Self.

Printed and bound in the United States of America.

ISBN 0–9717598–0–4

DB &BW
DhKAA Θ கh

Acknowledgements

Cover sketch and lettering by great friend and neighbor, Chuck Fuerst.
    Special thanks to Billy Ray Cowen and Sarah and Kenny Thomas for hosting a great day on the Current River so we could photograph Martin's bluff for the cover.

Introduction

"I wonder why Adam Troop never sent me and Bob a postcard from Venezuela."

"I don't know, Mom . . ."

This was the last exchange between my husband Ray and his mother Jennie. She died shortly thereafter in May 1999 at 83 years. Although Ray knew who Adam was and a little about him, we didn't know that he'd soon seem like an old friend.

After Jennie's funeral, Ray an overwhelming urge to write the story of his life, especially concerning aspects that caused him to lead a rather paradoxical existence. But he is not a writer, never had any aspirations in that direction, and is not exactly known for his proper spelling, pronunciation and grammar. Most of his surface life was spent logging in the Northwest, farming, sawmilling, and other outdoor pursuits with no interest in literature. So, I was surprised when he actually sat down one day with a legal pad and pencil and began to write.

That day, he wrote what amounts to the first two or three pages of this book, beginning a story his father Edd had told him years ago. He then set the legal pad down by his chair where it sat for weeks. I figured that was the end of it for I couldn't imagine this physically active outdoorsman type sitting indoors for hours on end writing.

About late July, Ray started experiencing extremely vivid "dreams." He explained to me that our bedroom would be full of people dressed out of time and his half-Cherokee grandmother, Lillie May, was speaking to him. Most were speaking in a language he didn't understand.

The "dreams" clearly disturbed him. "I know it was dream, but it was so *real*," he would say.

This happened on several occasions. Sometimes Ray would ask me in the morning, "Didn't you hear them?" I never did.

Ray said the message his grandmother Lillie May was trying to convey to him was, "Learn the language, tell the story." He assumed the language she meant was Cherokee. But the story? Surely not the story of his own life he'd started a few weeks ago.

Early in the morning on August 13, 1999, Ray became impatient and irritated with his "visitors" and told "them" they were causing him to think he might be going crazy. He asked for a sign to prove to him that what was occurring was genuine and not just his mind playing tricks. He told me "they" simply laughed and disappeared.

We discussed that morning about what sort of sign it would have to be—definitely something with no other possible explanation. Then we then started laughing and wondering about ourselves, talking about all of this as if we were taking it seriously. We don't conjure, are not into strange religions or seek out any sort of mystical experiences.

Three days later, Ray got his sign in the form of a perfectly carved lancehead (like an arrowhead but longer) left in the upstairs back bedroom on his workout bench that he'd used three days before. We had no visitors nor went anywhere. There is no possible explanation for it being there.

Needless to say, this got our attention. He again began to write. Immediately, his "trances" began. A copper colored dust appears before his eyes and he will then write, usually for hours. He writes in pencil on a legal pad using little punctuation, capitalization, or paragraphs. He can go into these trances at will and doesn't have any idea what he's written until he rereads it.

At first, Ray was writing a story that took place thousands of years ago about the origin of the lancehead. Soon, he was just writing odd symbols that made no sense to us. (It was not Cherokee syllabary.)

After three legal pads full, Ray felt compelled to destroy them and threw them into our large wood furnace. The fire it created from a handful of dying coals got so hot that it cracked our huge chimney all the way to the top. Even the inner glass of the old water heaters Ray had used as a liner for the chimney's rockwork melted.

He then decided to pick up the original story he'd started a couple of months before. He dug out the legal pad by his recliner from under the gardening catalogs, hunting and trapping magazines, herbal medicine books, etc. Continuing to write in a trance, the story picked up right from where Ray had left off but quickly transitioned into a different and unexpected direction.

This book is the first in a continuing series. As of this writing, Ray has completed the third. The writings begin to increasingly turn darker and toward subjects that are considered mysterious, outlandish, and bizarre. There also appears to be an urgent message for someone, somewhere about the very survival of humanity. There are only a couple of brief hints about something so dire in *The Wicked Current*.

Ray does not attest to the accuracy of any of these stories that come to him through A-wo-ye-na. Although he did know some of the basic facts surrounding the events concerning his mother Jennie, he did not know anything close to the details given in this book.

We both tend to believe this first book may have been a reaction to what he burned in the furnace. The initial writings that he destroyed were perhaps just and little too much too soon, so he was given a story about places and folks he knows well to captivate him long enough and slowly ease him back to the original purpose.

As Ray would say, "This book is just the pacifier to lay the baby back down in the dark."

—AMY SELF

part
ONE

THE BORNIN'

chapter
ONE

The River Crossing

My story began the day of my birth, January 31, 1943, in a shanty in the Ozark Mountains. The mountains are so old nothing is left but poor, rocky hills and hollers that are even rockier than the ridges. The shanty had cracks large enough a cat could crawl through. When it snowed, Mom would shake the snow off the top comforter at first light.

My mom was old as time, even older than the rocky hills. She was all of 27 years at my birthin'. I am the fifth of her six children.

Pap and Mom were married in '33 right at the height of the Great Depression. The damnedest thing was, if you were born an Ozarkian, you never knew when the Depression came or went. Most lived as hunters and gatherers, squattin' on company ground, clearin' them off a small plot for corn, beans, and squash, along with huntin' squirrel, rabbits, coon, possum, and trappin' wild hogs for meat and lard. The deer and turkey, as the Old Settlers would say, was "kilt off" years before.

When one writes it down, it seems like the livin' was good. It's simple to write, but nearly impossible to do.

At the time of my oldest sister Susie's bornin' in November of 1934, my folks lived on the old home place on the Current River. Crystal clear, cold, and swift, the water still holds a winter chill as late as August.

It was a typical cold, wet November and the rain had continued for days. By this time, even the dry hollers were ragin' and roarin', runnin' like a scalded dog down into the creeks, and the creeks to the Current. The Current had swollen up out of its banks and was running from ridge to ridge.

Well, as the saying goes, bad weather makes a mare foal, a cow calf, and a sow farrow, as well as the rest of the beasts, tame or wild. A human woman ain't nigh a bit different.

Mom's labor pains began right at the height of the flood. My pap was 19 years old, 6 months older than Mom. Young and strong—too young to yet know fear—he took Mom's saddle horse, Ol' Bird, to go fetch the old midwife, Aunt Ellie Stewart. Hill people pronounce the letter "E" like "A," so Ellie came out "Alley."

Aunt Alley lived on the opposite side of the Current. Now remember, it was still a-rainin' hard and straight down. This means the river was rising like the floodgates of heaven were left open and Mom's predicament sure won't wait until the river goes down. Crossing at this time was perilous at best. A horse with any less spirit would have drowned along with its rider.

The horse was not named Bird for nothin'. She had earned it many times before and would have to prove worthy to the name again in a few short hours—twice. First, while crossing over with a single rider. Then, when crossing back double—the old woman on the mare's back and Pap holding fast to the root of Bird's tail. There would be no rest between crossings for there was no time to spare.

During the first crossing, Ol' Bird and Pap were struck hard several times by trees, hard enough twice that Pap knew the little mare would be lost. Each time, he slipped off her back grabbin' her tail so she would swim higher in the water. By working his way up to the root of her tail, he could help guide her along with the flow of the uprooted trees until they could free themselves from them.

Aunt Alley's cabin was six miles upriver as the crow flies, but was actually eight or better on the ground. A crow flies straight over the ridges and hollers; the little mare had to pull every hill and keep her footing on the descents. Going down proved the real test for she had to fight to keep not only her footing, but also her balance.

Ol' Bird was what was known as a five-gaited horse. The five gaits, from slowest to the fastest, are: running walk, canter, foxtrot, pace, and singlefoot. Nowadays, they'll call a horse five-gaited if it can walk, stumble, and fart. It's a shame for even in a running walk, a fast horse can cover ten miles in an hour.

The old midwife was in her 80s, the best Pap could recollect. Pap said she figured she was about 82 or 83 years old. The old woman herself wasn't "fer shore." Anyway and anywho, she was too damned old to be settin' a horse and crossin' the wicked Current.

Pap soon arrived at the Stewart's cabin. If there had even been time for him to dismount and go in, he wouldn't have. Pap was already soaked to the bone and cold from the first crossing. Warming up is the worst thing you can do once you've adjusted to the elements.

Uncle Jim and Aunt Alley "done and knowed" what he was comin' for. There wasn't nothin' in those days before the "giverment" came that wasn't already known to all your neighbors. Everybody knew, had discussed at length, and nodded in agreement that this bad o' weather would "shore 'nuff" bring Edd and Jennie Self's baby on. Even before Pap reached the cabin, Aunt Alley had her bundle ready to go. She knew there was no time to lose, especially since the rain was still pounding down steady and hard. The river was gaining force by the minute and Bird would have to pack the added burden of the old woman and her bundle.

Since leaving the cabin, the conditions didn't make for hearty conversation. The rain was driving into the ground, looking like green sheets. I have gauged 9 inches in 3 hours. Judgin' from Pap's description, it was all of that and more.

They made their way back to the ford road where Pap normally crossed. All that could be heard above the maddening roar of the river was uprooted trees snapping in two, sounding like the crack of a high-powered rifle.

5

At first, Ol' Bird refused to enter. She would paw, put her head down, sip at the water, and paw again—not a sign of thirst, but of nervousness.

Then, Aunt Alley spoke. "Edd, Ol' Bird was bornt and raised 'ere. She's a wise ol' river hoss. Ye give 'er 'er head, and let 'er go in on 'er own. She'll put in when and whor she know hit's right. We'll both come out on t' other side, safe and sound. Iff'n ye force 'er in, we ain't gonna e'er see nary side agin."

Pap tied the reins together and put them over the saddle horn. Bird headed upriver along the bank, but not in her usual running walk. She went along slowly and deliberately. Pap said to himself, "Hell, she'll soon have us clean back to the Stewart place!"

The going was slow. At times the ground was almost impassable. Earth that had been thousands of years in the making melted into gorges of water, the water's force cutting down through the top soil, tumbling and carrying off even the rocks, exposing the red clay. The red clay then turned the clear rainwater into a reddish brown sea all racing its way to the Current.

Two miles upriver, Ol' Bird finally put in to begin the crossing. Bird's choice damn sure wouldn't have been Pap's. There were large grapevines and thorn trees in their way that had paired up 100 years before, each in an attempt to ensure its own survival and together ensuring their own destruction. One not familiar with the river as Pap would not have known that there were limestone bluffs submerged at this spot under 6 feet of water. These bluffs were 16 feet high, so the river was up 22 feet.

A 19-year-old boy who was scared—not of the river, but for his young wife and baby yet to be born.

An old woman in her 80s with her small bundle of things to help bring the yet unborn into this world—a world that would experience changes in the course of the infant's lifetime more fearful than the river a thousand fold.

The old woman's bones ached with the cold. The rain had long ago soaked her last dry thread. Both of them were so chilled that upon entering the river, they got the false sense the air was colder than the water. It only seemed that way because they were no longer in the elements with the wind whipping their soaked bodies.

The little mare swam low and fast in the swift water. Instead of fighting the current, she allowed it to carry her, but all the while working her way toward the opposite bank. Putting in two miles upriver made the crossing less strenuous. However, with the 22-foot rise, there wasn't an inch of ground gained that wasn't fought for tooth and nail.

Ol' Bird came out on the opposite ford directly across from where Pap had first tried to make her enter the river; the same spot where Aunt Alley told Pap to "give 'er 'er head." How did Bird know? She'd never made a crossing in this high of a flood.

How does a salmon spawn miles up a freshwater river, go out to sea, then return to the same river year after year? Even a goose can fly thousands of miles at migration time and return to the exact same location generation after generation.

Pap would always shake his head when relating this story. "Damnedest thing I ever seed. How in the hell did she know it'd take her jest that far to come out on the ol' ford road?"

Here they were, all three wet as drowned rats, only difference being they weren't dead. They were much alive and very cold—the type of wet cold that makes one's teeth chatter and body shake uncontrollably.

The young wife, Jennie, was not worried about her own condition for it had come on day by day, for nine long months. She could scarcely remember what it was like not to be pregnant. But she knew how treacherous the river crossing would be. And it would have to be done not once, but twice. She had stayed glued to the window. These few hours had been the longest wait in her life.

chapter
TWO

Charlie Rides to the Rector Post Office

In the hours that passed, her mind had wandered back over the unlikely coincidences surrounding her and Ed's meeting, their marriage, and having his first child.

It had been just two years since Jennie's cousin Sammy, with her husband Calvin, and six other young couples who had come to spend the summer on the old home place, were settin' around the fire that Sammy's brother, Charlie, had built earlier in the evening to heat kettle water for baths. In early May, the river is too cold for bathing, especially after working all day. Plunging in the ol' Current would be enough to frost the balls off a brass monkey.

After everyone had bathed, they ate their fill of cornbread, beans laden with smoked pork, potatoes that had been fried in lard 'til golden brown, a large platter heaping with fried eggs and all sorts of relishes and chow chows, along with sauerkraut and 14 and 21 day pickles made the old way in large stone crocks. They both packed a fizz that tickled the taste buds into eating more than one should. This was all topped off with cakes and pies. There were three large meals cooked each day, but we will return to talk more about all the work involved in coming up with one's daily sustenance when it's raised and preserved by one's own hands.

The fire by now had burned down to a bed of coals. The coals were still red hot, and every few seconds would flare up with an almost supernatural flickering flame. During one such flare-up, cousin Charlie could no longer contain his troubling thoughts. They had consumed him all day.

Actually, just most of the day. He'd ridden to the Rector Post Office, 19 miles away, starting out before daylight. At first, he tried to laugh off what he overheard at Rector. But on the ride home, his imagination took over completely and at times soared higher than the eagles. If he wanted to sleep that night, he needed others to laugh with him at such a tale.

Charlie poked at the fire, but didn't see the coals nor feel the heat from the flickering flames. He only saw the witch woman and a huge 60-gallon kettle of boiling molasses. He knew what just a drop from the boiling container would do to flesh and bone. He'd been trying to erase it from his thoughts, but he kept hearing over and over the words of the gray-bearded hunched-back man:

"Yeow, boys," said the old man, "did ye hear ol' Bum Powell done an' went and got his new Sears an' Roebuck saddle et up by a pack o' hawgs? Yeow, he rid o'er to the ol' witch woman's shack o'er in Foot Log Holler. Him an' a pack o' deputies, and by gad I don't blame 'im for not goin' alone ary bit. I damn shore wouldn't o' wanted to go a-trapsin' 'round, jes spilin' fer a fight with 'er, jest to please a bunch of churchies. No how, by myself. I'd a-swore in the whole damn county and half of Coxey's army before I'd a-went up agin her."

chapter
THREE

Union and Confederate

Well, ol' Sheriff Bum Powell and the sorry bunch of spit and whittlers rode the next few miles to Mahan's rail-fenced fodder patch. Spit and whittlers are the men in every small town who loafed around most of the day, whittlin' on cedar and spittin' tobacco juice, anxious for any excitement to add to their otherwise dreary lives.

Bum got off his horse and slipped off his new saddle, planning to hide it by a corn shock. He turned to his freshly sworn-in admiring followers and said, "Let the ol' bitch tell me whor's my saddle. Hell, boys, I know thar's some of ye right here with me thinks deep down she has power to tell ye who ye'll marry, kids that'll be bornt to ye, which ones'll live and die, their names, and the day, hour and how ye'll go to your maker."

Bum took an extra long swig from a quart jar of moonshine liquor and laughed, but not out of amusement. It was a laugh of downright gut nervousness.

"Hell, Bum," said one of the new deputies, "didn't she tell ye yer own daddy would get drowned a-crossin' the Current?"

"My ol' man was shit-faced drunk, was all!" replied Bum. "I figger it was jest a lucky guess and I'll prove 'er to ye. She won't know I got my new saddle hid, fer when we get peart nigh to 'er cabin, I'll ride in on Tom's hoss and he can stay back with mine."

All seemed pleased with this arrangement except for Tom. He hadn't gotten up before daylight to ride clean up on the Current just to hold Bum's damned horse. He'd only let Bum swear him in so he could make the trip in hopes of seein' Mandy, Lillie May Goforth's oldest daughter. *Redheaded gal she was, with odd green eyes. The hair and eyes just didn't go with the dark olive skin. Now, damned drunken Bum, damn him to hell! I'd been better off to o' stayed back in Eminence and loped my mule. That's about all the chance I'll have for sex!*

Tom was jerked abruptly out of his thoughts and fantasies by Bum's loud mouth, the mouth that had been supplying his brain with spirits of double-run 180-proof alcohol—ol' 180-proof "blabber mouth"—the juice that makes weak men strong, the small extra large, and the fearful brave. Right at this moment, Bum felt bulletproof—close to it, anyway, for limbs and mouth were starting to abandon their posts wantin' to be Confederate. Why should they be Union? Here, his mouth had become so mighty and superior over his legs, the foolish legs that couldn't take the most basic command. Nor could his arms that had the hands a-hold the pecker, the same short limp prick that stuck out in front of the white churn legs attached to the extra large belly—the belly with the red, white, and blue stretch marks. That damn little pecker stuck out not from an erection, but because it was so short that gravity had no law over it. So, there it stuck, trying to do its job, but because the mouth had guzzled most of the quart fruit jar of 180-proof liquor, his legs had got in the way of the stream of piss. Good, strong, yeller piss. Piss that had never been diluted by the mouth taking in water. Its yellow stream had made it almost halfway through before having its chance to get reacquainted with those fat butter-churn legs and flat feet. Here they had another reunion. Yes, this definitely was not their first nor last of many, many meetings.

"Okay, boys!" bellered Bum. "Let's go show that ol' witch whore who to fuck around with!"

All laughed except for a young man who spoke up with a nervous tone. "Bum, iff'n ye keep a-blackguardin' Missuz Goforth, I'm a-goin' home. She may be a fortuneteller but she ain't no whore. There ain't no more decent woman than her. Yeow, that's fer shore. And, I'll tell ye what! Ye can go ask ol' Jake Fersman what come his way when he bumped her up fer some pussy."

There was a long silence for most there already knew not only that story, but many more from relatives dead and alive who had personal experiences of their own with the woman the sheriff was about to serve the summons to. All were secretly wishing they hadn't been goaded into being deputized by this loud-mouthed bastard who couldn't even make his stream of piss over his churn legs to the ground. But, here they were. Each were making excuses in their minds why it was right for their presence, yet all wanted more than anything to be back in front of ol' Doc Oody's drugstore, jest a-whittlin' on their favorite chunk of cedar. *Damn Bum to hell!*

They were startled back to attention by Bum's next bellerin' at the young man who'd defended Lillie May Goforth. Bum was beginning to realize his posse was experiencing not only doubts about this mission, but something that has conquered the strongest and bravest throughout history—FEAR.

Fear, the master of all. Fear, the great whip capable of reducing any and all living creatures to a whining, quivering mass of submissive flesh.

"Dammit, son, you don't believe all that ol' shit, boy? Do ye? Hell, Fersman come in and tried to get me to serve papers on 'er when his cow's milk turned to blood. Said she put a spell on 'em. I told him I don't believe in no spells. Course, he said that don't make his milk a damn bit whiter and iff'n I didn't go and fix matters, he was gonna go kill the ol' Injun like they did in his pa's day. The damn dark heathens shoulda all been kilt years ago. Well, I told ol' Fersman, 'here's my gun and I'll throw in a box or two of bullets. Ye'll shore need 'em agin that pack o' heathens!'"

Bum laughed his shrill, maniacal laugh. All present were well acquainted with his various laughs. This one definitely had the clear sound of the "great whip of fear." Even with the whole quart of 180-proof nervine and all twelve of his fair-weather backers, there was a double-fisted knot in Bum's gut. *Why had he let that bunch of damn churchies get him, a good man, out here a-meddlin' in others' affairs? Damn 'em to their fiery hell, damn 'em to hell no how!*

Bum wiped the fine beads of sweat off his brow, hoping no one would notice. He knew that in this especially cool early May, it was too chilly for even a fat, liquored-up man to break a sweat—sweat brought on by old memories. Things he had buried, fears he had drunk to, laughed at, twisted, and made mockery of until he'd put the whole nerve-rackin', gut-wrenchin' scene not in its true perspective, but in a form that "brave mouth" could still fool an audience, even with those damn Confederate legs and bastardly arms that owned the trembling hands that gave themselves away to Bum's brain. His mind must always be on guard; his mouth must constantly shoot out darts of great deed, self-sacrifice and valor above and beyond the call of duty. He'll have to convince ally and foe daily to keep drawing strength. A gallon of double-run sour mash is the oil that keeps this great machine up and running under these sorts of circumstances.

Today, Bum was very excited, but not enjoyably so. This was the other kind—the kind that brings up acid from deep down in the gut. All of the sudden, there it is—that half-cup of bitter acid just behind the tongue. You can't swaller it down and if you bring it up to mouth, you'll puke shore as God made little green apples.

And now Bum was out of the fine oil—the oil that kept his great machine running with dignity and undying courage. He remembered all too well the day Lillie May took her arms and in front of a crowd of people . . .

chapter
FOUR

The Fine Oil

Of course, Lillie May didn't give a tinker's dam if Bum had been there or not for she had been a-grievin' fer a spell. *Hell, thought Bum, I don't blame her. She'd been married to Bressler, I can't remember his first name now. Heard she was barely 15 and he was 45. I reckon it might've been since he was a Mason and all. Don't know what them Masons are about, but they shore put one hell of a spell on that purty little gal. I reckon she'd defend him to her dyin' breath. Yeow, him and her come out of Kentuck, him makin' big money settin' up sawmills. There were large company steam mills bein' set up to log off the virgin forests. He didn't ever have money enough fer a $6 fare. Nope. Drunk up every red cent soon as he laid his mitts on it. Never keepin' a nickel fer her to buy grub. Jest squattin' here and there in dwellings not fittin' to be called a shack.*

Bum remembered the stories of how Lillie May and Bressler got married and hitched a train that morning before noon, unsure where they were going or why. After that first ride, so many followed, she couldn't remember them all for at times they would spend a day, maybe a week, then move on to another job.

Yes, Bressler made good money, big money for that day and age. He always picked up his pay and promised to her and to himself that he would come home first. But each time there was some excuse that called for a drink: a wedding, a birthing—hell, even a death called for a drink. Should a celebration be the only time one is permitted to numb their senses? Isn't a sorrowful occasion also a sufficient reason? Did the occasion really matter?

Oh, the oil. The oil that makes your mouth spew, each trying to talk louder and faster than the other; never hearing, only thinking of what you'll say next to impress all within earshot, even those not caring to hear about your greatness. Sharing your wisdom and philosophy with everyone. No, not sharing—*forcing* the magnitude of your accomplishments, opinions, sorrows, and injustices on one and all. Take the quietest, meekest, shyest human. As soon as his brain is saturated with this good oil, his mouth joins the contest to try to outrun everybody else's.

Bressler was a well-educated man in anyone's day. Quiet and dignified, he kept his aloofness to about the fourth shot. At times, to keep an audience, it cost. The price was such that he often returned home with nothing left but his gold watch and chain and, of course, his Mason ring: his badge of honor and outward sign to the world of his basic superiority; above the mill owners, the shopkeepers—all. Unless, of course, it was a fellow Mason.

He had thrown up a shack in the Ozark Mountains for Lillie May. From there, he'd go to another job that was going to change everything. She was pregnant, but unaware with triplets, and already had a pack of little ones. Each day the triplets grew in her womb with insufficient nutrition to sustain their mother, let alone the three yet to be born. The long months of little if any food had taken its toll. The triplets were born dead.

Lillie May buried her babies and piled rocks on top of the grave. There, she lit a fire and stayed up all night to keep the wolves away from the tiny corpses.

Even with Aunt Mae Hollins coming and taking her in, it was already too late. The malnutrition, the mental shock, the loss of blood. All were too much on any living creature. Lillie May refused all food and liquid. She had not eaten or drank for several days. Everyone knew she would soon die.

It was late summer. In the Hollins household, there remained the chore of canning and preserving several crops yet to be put up for the oncoming winter. They had bountiful crops this summer and their sorghum cane was ready to be milled. First, they would take wooden paddles and go down the standing cane rows knocking off the blades that stuck out from the stalks. Then, with their cane knives, they would hack it down, bundle it into shocks, load it into wagons, and bring it to where the sorghum grinder and press were set up. After the press has squeezed out the clear juice, it was boiled down in a large kettle. The Hollins's used a 60-gallon kettle.

This kettle is what Bum's memory was working over just as plain as the day it happened so many years ago.

They had got the kettle boiling way too hard and the molasses would be ruined if it scorched. All capable hands worked to bring down the boil by stirring with a long, wide, wooden paddle, taking extra care not to splash the molten hot liquid out of its rim—not for fear of waste, but of the injury they would wear for the rest of their life.

Bum was older than Lillie May, though in her presence he always felt like a boy. She'd seen so much of the world he knew nothing about and had married a genius, even if he did let the jug get the best of him. Bum could recall the scene so plainly because he had gone over it step by step hundreds of times and these recollections were never voluntary. Each time it was brought on by a sight, sound, or especially, smell—the lingering scent every fall at sorghum-makin' time, or the sorghum smell at breakfast, dinner, and suppertime.

Lillie May walked slowly out of the Hollins' cabin and stood before the large kettle. A dozen or so stupefied faces watched trance-like, too petrified to move. It was too late to intercept her, to restrain her. Lillie May slid both arms all the way into the pot clean to her little thin shoulders. She showed no sign of pain. She simply stood there singing a strange chant, a chant of her mother's people, the Cherokee.

Still, no one moved. Everyone there would later claim their limbs and legs were heavy as lead and they had no control over their tongues to even holler out.

All was deathly silent except for the boiling and bubbling of the large black pot and the young girl's strange foreign worded chant.

Years later, grandchildren and even great-grandchildren of the witnesses there that day have heard it said that when the wind blew, and a dead tree lodged just right in another would scrape together and moan its lonely, eerie sound, "I heard that at a 'lasses makin' many years ago." That pot of hot molasses burned hotter and scarred deeper than any flesh wound they could have received on that late summer day.

Bum had an uncontrollable shiver. His whole body made a trembling jerk for a fleet second before returning to normal. But his thoughts did not return to normal. They stayed there at the molasses making. At that time, Bum Powell was big and strong, young, hard, and lean; not yet with the red, white, and blue belly with pones of flesh that overhung each other in folds; before the huge churn legs and persistently swollen ankles that required his boot tops to be split to admit his flat feet.

"In those days, I was quick as a cat!" Bum often bragged. "I had no fear of man nor beast and very few haints." Bum had gone over and over the scene, each time positioning himself in a different heroic role. Bum, the one who restrains her from the kettle. Bum, who leaps to her aid when all the other brave men grow faint of heart. Bum, who runs his own strong muscular arms under her cooked young brown slender ones, the flesh of which had to be falling away from the bone. Bum, wearing deep puckered scar burns that would be worn like a badge proclaiming each day the courage, self-sacrifice, and bravery that only he, Bum Powell, had mustered when the others could only stand stupefied like a pole-axed steer at slaughter time.

Damn it! Bum thought. *Why did I stand there with my eyes bulged out like a bullfrog in a hailstorm? Why don't these bastard cowardly churchies go serve their own papers? Them a-sayin' she's doin' "no good" and "jay hawkin'" folks out of their hard-earned money. If only they coulda been there that day and seed with their own eyes: her arms down in that boilin' kettle, jest a-stirrin' 'til the rollin' boil came down to a bubblin' simmer, and heard with their ears the demon chant of the heathens.*

The next scene, however, is what always made Bum have the short, uncontrollable spasm.

If Lillie May would've pulled her arms out and fainted with no flesh left; if the bones had separated and stayed in the cooking juice of the sorghum, Bum could've simply concluded the poor girl had gone mad. Then, she could be buried, maybe even proper. In time, all could be put in the back of his mind.

But this did not happen. Lillie May's voice changed. "Sounded like a whole pack of 'em!" folks would later say. Some were deep, with a bear-like tone. Others were higher pitched than any Holy Roller anyone had ever heard at a brush arbor meetin'.

She began to bring her arms out of the boiling kettle slowly, chant-ing as she withdrew them from the amber liquid. It seemed to the onlookers it took an eternity. They remained petrified, wanting but unable to avert their eyes from what they knew would be the horrify-ing, gruesome sight of her arms.

When they were completely out of the molasses, the witnesses stood in stunned silence. There were no ghastly cooked arms. Rather, her arms were young and supple, more so than they had ever been.

Lillie May then raised her hands to the complete height over her head as though reaching clear into the heavens in search of something. As the molasses ran down her arms, her fingers kept feeling as if there was something she had to grasp.

Aunt Mae Hollins always claimed there had been a tan object like a thin narrow bird and it turned to stone. A handful of the others said later, years later, they thought they remembered her putting something into her blouse.

Lillie May walked back through the frozen forms of men, women, and children. Still no one had moved. Their eyes stayed fixed on the simmering black 60-gallon kettle, even as she spoke.

Her voice changed. It was now commanding as with one accustomed to giving orders.

"SONS! GO TO YOUR FATHERS!"

The boys stood and stared as though their ears had been sealed—all except for an undersized, skeletal, ragged little 6-year-old. The child had a deep purple and green bruise over his left eye. Lillie May had watched the child on many occasions. He had never run, played, screamed, or wrestled, as is the nature of boys. He always sat off to himself, head down, small thin shoulders hunched, staring at his feet.

It was this boy alone who seemed to have heard and understood the command. Maybe he'd been too far away from the rest to see what had happened at the kettle. It was the first time Lillie May had seen the boy show any sign of life. The child turned and started running toward his tormenter.

chapter
FIVE

The Tormentor

Yes, Tormentor. The one who took deep diabolical pleasure in putting his large rough hands over the boy's face, especially when the boy was an infant, and feel the little body fight for air, wrapping his small help-less baby fingers around any one of his father's. The infant would pull and struggle with all its might with the instinctive power born in all flesh and blood creatures to stay alive. It was during this struggle that its Tormentor's hatred would mount to the type of feverish insanity born of jealousy. When the little body would go limp, he would often slap it in the face causing a nosebleed so when the infant slept, its nose and mouth would produce little bubbles of blood. In the passionate throes of hatred the father would growl at the helpless little form. "Where's your nerve, you little worthless bastard? How did you like the treatment? Don't worry! I'll be back to give you another one, bastard!" At this point, the Tormentor's face would be pressed up against the child, eyes wild, veins bulging from his long scrawny neck, Adam's apple bobbing uncontrollably up and down, breath coming in short pants.

All the while, the boy's mother looked on. At first, the Tormentor dealt such treatments when she wasn't around. But there wasn't the same gratification nor could he experience the full hate release when only by himself. He felt real pleasure the first time she walked in. Now there was no satisfaction at all unless she was there.

The first time she witnessed this behavior, she had come in from outside through the open door. The Tormentor was so mentally involved in torturing the infant he never heard her approach. He was holding the baby, the "squirming little vile bastard," by the head. His large, calloused hands had the small head completely encased. When he looked up, there she was—her eyes wild, mouth open with trembling lips that could not produce even the lowest sound. He hissed between clenched teeth how much he despised the tiny infant.

It was impossible for her to overpower him. If she even tried, the girl knew he'd break the baby's neck.

In a panic, her natural maternal instincts took over. With no conscious thought, she began to undress. He flung the baby back into its cradle, the cradle her father had made when he found out that his first grandchild was on the way. Each prideful comment the grandfather made to his son-in-law was another stab, intensifying the yet unexpressed hatred until it finally warped him into a demon obsessing over the "bastardly parasite."

The Tormentor would make sex rough with the mother right up to the night she gave birth, hoping it would make her miscarry. He'd forced her to drink different teas rumored to bring on abortions, but nothing worked. He would be saddled with this "filthy little abomination" the rest of his life, so he swore to have his pleasure with it.

But, he had known. She'd never lied or tried to deceive him. When they first met, she had told him, and only him, that she was already pregnant.

He beheld his wife's naked body not with lust, but with revulsion. She was the only woman in his life who'd ever cast a glance his way. Even he could not deny his own strange features in the mirror.

At the first of the marriage, the sex was enough. It was so different. Sure, he'd had sex before. Lots of sex. But not with another human. As the child grew in her womb, the lust and the urge died out until the only way he could obtain an erection was to become violent. Eventually, even this new method of pleasure failed him. He would go limp before they could even get started. So, he had to hold her down and get rough. Really rough. She told herself that as soon as the child was born, things would be better.

After the baby was born, he tried to get her pregnant himself. However, his mother had confided in her some personal matters about him that in those days were not openly discussed; she was relieved about the pregnancy because her son had mumps in his eighth year of life and they had "gone down on him." His testicles swelled to such a huge size that they were in fear he'd lose even his scrotum. When he was over the mumps, his testicles shriveled and never grew. "I praise the Lord night and day fer lettin' this happen," she told her daughter-in-law.

The infant lay unmoving in the cradle. It had already learned to avoid crying and lay perfectly still if it could hear or even smell the scent of its Tormentor.

The girl stood lit by a shaft of sunlight that came slanting through the doorway, highlighting every detail of her body. All the man could see were the stretch marks the other man had brought to her slim stomach with the little bastard—the bastard who was gaining strength every day and could now pull himself up.

chapter
SIX

Back at the 'Lasses Making

A voice interrupted the Tormentor's deepest satisfying malignant thoughts. It was the same voice that had just ordered the sons to go to their fathers.

"FATHER! GO TO YOUR SON!" commanded Lillie May, now speaking of only one father and one son.

No one moved, so she repeated the command. Again, no one moved.

"The father who claims his son not will perish before the sun sets!" Lillie May proclaimed.

A young, single man who appeared to be in his early twenties stepped forward with his head bent as though in prayer. Lillie May pointed her finger, the finger that had been transformed into a tool of authority and power. The strong young man now felt his knees weaken and his voice was barely audible. He fell to his knees.

Oddly, the child who had run to his Tormentor was now running toward the young man. The young man's arms embraced the child.

"The bastard child is no longer a bastard for he is in the arms of his father," said Lillie May, in a voice so low that only father and son heard.

"Lift your son's shirt," she continued.

Upon lifting the shirt, the father's eyes filled with tears that swelled like a river whose banks could no longer hold the pressure of the onrushing current. He wept with deep uncontrollable sobs as she put into his mind the cruel life the little fellow before him had led. Lillie May told the father to take his son, leave home, and not return until the season was right. (The young father returned only once more, years later in death, to be buried in the old Tripp graveyard.)

Lillie May turned to address the crowd. The sorghum makers had composed themselves enough to comprehend what was now being spoken to them by the young Indian woman. She announced that from this time on, she had received power from her mother's people, the "ancient ones." Anyone desiring to know the future, past, or present could come and she would do their bidding. Payment would never be mentioned; they were to leave whatever they saw fit in their hearts.

All folks had to do was bring tea or coffee. Once it was brewed, Lillie May would sing a chant, a chant so old even her mother's people no longer knew the words. She would look into the cup of the one who was seeking. In the same monotone, she would chant out the answers to all that was asked. Lillie May would only answer once and had no memory of what she had chanted so the receiver had to listen closely, for the words were theirs, not hers. Most visitors were young couples wondering about their prospects for the future. They seldom received the message they had hoped to hear: that the future held prosperity, health, and happiness, for this fortunate state of affairs seldom marched hand in hand with real life. "For every laugh there will be a thousand tears" was more typical of Lillie May's message. After their reading, many even decided against marrying.

chapter
SEVEN

The Fate of Bum's New Sears and Roebuck Saddle

"Hey, Bum, damn ye! Are ye gonna stand thar with yer pecker hangin' out all day? Are ye gonna hide that derned Roebuck saddle or ain't ye? Let's go serve them papers or let's go home. I'm a-gettin' tarred o' this ol' shit. My ass is gettin' sore as a turpentined dog!"

Bum's mind had cleared. In fact, it was too clear. The quart hadn't been nigh enough. *Damn them churchies*, Bum thought. *Damn them to their burnin' hell fer makin' me forget the rest of my liquor!* Before the journey had started, he had set out three more quarts of that good fine clear 180-proof. When it's straight run, a man can cut it to his own taste.

Of course, the churchies didn't cause Bum to forget his liquor any more than they made him bring the one and only quart. But, they were very handy to blame. Someone had to be at fault and it was never Bum.

The shocks of corn that the Mahans hadn't used that winter for fodder made the perfect setting for his trick on the "ol' injun woman." Bum liked to call her that even though he was little older.

Bum slipped his saddle off at Mahan's rail-fence enclosed fodder patch, taking his time, holding it aloft on his beefy shoulder so his grumbling followers could admire the new Sears and Roebuck top-of-the-line saddle made with special best-grade cowhide. This was its first time in use. He loved the smell of the expensive oil-tanned leather. The sheriff would take deep breaths every so often so the aroma would be drawn deeply into his lungs, just for pure enjoyment. He had always coveted such a saddle, though he'd never turn loose the money when it could be put to much wiser use. This thought made Bum cuss to himself again about the other three quarts of whiskey.

Bum took the saddle and placed it with utmost care to avoid scuffing the new shiny leather. He tried to position the shock of fodder so as to conceal the saddle completely, but the ends of the cut corn canes made a small scratch at the horn. He instinctively made a quick swing and brought the treasure out of harm's way. The strenuous effort of the sudden movement made in a half bent-over position, along with the hundred plus pounds of belly put the strain on his lower back, which in turn put a hot flash of pain down the large churn leg that exploded in his swollen ankle. This brought on a sudden fit of cursing that brought Bum help without his asking.

It was finally decided to place his most beloved possession on a golden throne of fodder. Straightening up and letting the pain subside, Bum got caught up in the admiration of his saddle and the contrast of its color against the golden fodder.

Bum wasted no time. The party was anxious to have the business at hand resolved and start the long ride home. They quickly rode the remaining distance with few words spoken. Only Tom would grumble now and again about his ill fate of having to hold the High Sheriff's horse.

The sheriff's party rode on until they were within 1,000 feet of the cabin. Here, Tom was left holding Bum's horse. Not only were the sheriff's nerves at the breaking point, so were those of all the spit and whittlers who were still secretly wishing they were back on their favorite bench in front of the court house where it was much easier to be a brave man.

There it loomed before them, their destination: a little rough hand-hewn cabin chinked with red clay and buffalo grass. The wider chinks were further filled in with the largest chips from where the broad ax had scored deeper causing the ax to take larger chunks off the once round logs.

In its day, the cabin would have been impressive to the eyes of a craftsman. However, the builder, Lillie May's previous husband, Jim Self, had been dead for four years, during which time the cabin had fallen into disrepair. Times were hard since his passing. This was the reason she'd been doing readings.

In front of the cabin to the right of the door was a 30-gallon, 3-legged kettle used for everything from scalding a hog to be scraped to canning and heating water for body and clothes. Today they had put out a large washing, not only for themselves but also their visitors, the Martin boys: Tucker, the eldest, Arnie, who was courtin' daughter Mandy, and the youngest, Elvie.

The Martin boys figured it was a good time for a "vacation." They'd been running a large still and it had sprung leaks. So, to repair it, Tucker had his "associate," Ivy Kelly, who was at that time Mandy's "man," crawl into the huge copper vat. When the dome was placed on top, the inside was dark as a black cat's ass. Ivy could see the smallest ray of light shining through the tiniest pinhole. He'd peck the spot where there was a leak until Tucker could find it. Once Tuck located the hole, he would bore or use a hammer and punch to open it up to receive the rivet. It was slow work at best. Tucker, or Uncle Tuck as everyone called him, was fond of the jug. Being on the outside gave him ample opportunity to fulfill his desire.

As Uncle Tuck was reaching for the jug to take another nip, he looked up and "lo and behold," here come the revenuers from out of Dent County. Every moonshiner feared them for the simple fact they couldn't be bought off. Tuck lit out as fast as his Ichabod Crane lookin' legs would carry him. Ivy was still inside peckin' and sayin', "Here, damn it!" and getting madder by the second. His pecks were growing feebler until they were barely audible.

Ivy decided he'd make ten more pecks before opening the dome and comin' out on Tuck. At peck number eight, the revenuers reached the still. One of them took his pick ax, reared back, and brought it down with a mighty blow at the exact spot where Ivy was pecking, rupturing the still's side. Ivy was so angry he came up through the top, knocking the dome off. He grabbed the first revenuer by the throat thinking it was Tuck.

"Ye damned drunken fool!" Ivy screamed, choking the T-man. "Ye done and gone and ruint our still! How in the hell are we gonna make a decent livin'?!"

So, this was the reason the Martins were layin' low at Lillie May's cabin. Bum and all his fresh sworn-in deputies had at one time or another bought liquor from the Martin boys. Bum was relieved and overjoyed to see them, but his enjoyment was short lived.

Sheriff Bum Powell spoke to Tucker in an undertone. "We got some talkin' to do, you and me. Tuck, don't go to slippin' off, fer if ye do, I'll have yer ass if I have to go to the bowels of hell!

Bum then bellered, "Is Mrs. Bressler, I mean Mrs. Self, hell, I reckon it's Go—"

Before Bum got the name "Goforth" completed, Lillie May stepped through the cabin door. She usually wore her long hair in a coiled pile atop her head held secure with hair combs. But for this occasion, she'd let her hair down, hair that reached the floor—hair that one couldn't keep from staring at when left to its natural flow.

The talking among the deputies and the visitors came to a complete halt. Those who owned watches swore they could hear them tick.

Lillie May walked out a few feet to where the black kettle stood, still steaming lightly from the heat of the water they'd used to put out the wash only an hour before the sheriff's arrival. Occasional wisps of smoke would rise when a dying firewood ember that hadn't been completely consumed got enough oxygen to feebly ignite and hold a flame for a few seconds before giving it up in a puff of smoke.

The setting was eerie, and conveyed a sense of the supernatural.

Thirty-six years ago, Bum had seen her with her hair hanging down in a wild, haunting fashion. Her eyes that were kind and understanding one moment could become intense, piercing and frightening the next. Here it was again for big, brave Bum, the one who had no fear of "man nor beast and very few haints." His legs suddenly experienced a queer weakness; his breath came in shallow pants. *Why am I so dizzy? Damn, I need a drink. Damn those friggin' churchies. What in the hell am I doin' here no how?*

Bum opened his mouth to speak to her. At first, nothing came. Then, in a hoarse whisper, he said, "Mrs. Bressler, uh, uh, uh, Mrs. Self . . . uh . . ."

Before he could correct it to "Mrs. Goforth," the old Indian woman raised her hands over her head which in turn stopped Bum's heart. He knew he was going to black out. He was fighting for consciousness when he heard her words coming through to him in a hazy mist, her finger pointing directly in line with his bleary eyes. He was in her power, as was the case with Fersman, the Tormenter, and Bussart, the father of the son, 36 years before: the physical body is there but the mind that controls it has abandoned its duty to let all parts fend for themselves.

The pointing finger had commanded the High Sheriff to dismount when speaking to a lady. In Bum's present mental state, the feat of dismounting Tom's horse and standing on those churn legs atop the flat feet, all expected to hold up the mountain of belly, would have been as possible as pissin' up a greased rope.

"Bum, Bum! I order you to get off of Tom's horse!" Lillie commanded.

Upon hearing "Tom's horse," Bum snapped out of his trance-like daze. He dismounted and always claimed the horse "sidestepped" which is why he ended up on his knees. Of course, he never mentions that he stayed on them the whole time she spoke to him.

"Bum!" continued Lillie, "you and your party has said things about me, words that I, who is supposed to be an evildoer, would not let be upon the tip of my tongue, much less in my heart."

Turning to the youth who stood up to Bum in her defense, her eyes became motherly kind for a moment. The youth felt her thoughts; no words were necessary. The rest of the party never knew it happened or that there was even a break in her message to the sheriff.

"Bum, your new saddle is being et up by the hogs as I speak. The summons you have rode so far to give has also been consumed by the beasts."

It flashed into Bum Powell's head. He'd forgotten the summons in his saddlebags in all the confusion of trying to keep his "pride and joy" from being scraped or scuffed, and along with the pain in his back and legs he'd rode off without another thought as to the purpose of this mission.

Lillie finished up short and brief, telling him she no longer was doing readings—she had accepted the Lord. The International Bible Students, who were traveling missionaries, had convinced her with logic that her power was wrong and of the burden it put on the receiver.

Everyone was eyeing the sheriff so intently that the party later claimed she just vanished into thin air. All except the youth who had defended her. They exchanged a slight wave of hands as she went back into her cabin.

Bum's head finally cleared. Seeing the coast was all clear, he raised up on two wobbly legs, turned to the youth, and ordered him to go fetch Tom and his saddle horse. He then turned away from his party and sought out Uncle Tuck. As soon as he found him, they walked out of earshot.

"Okay, Tucker, I want a gallon of your best."

"Best what?" Tuck inquired.

"Damn you, Tuck. I'll take yer ass in right here on the spot. I ain't in no mood fer ye, ye hear. Them Dent County boys are a-lookin' fer ye. A gallon, and I mean pronto, or I'll cuff you and yer two brothers."

"My brothers ain't got nothin' to do with 'er."

"They will have iff'n thar ain't a gallon a-hangin' on the crook of my finger in five minutes!"

Tucker beat the deadline by half and was enjoying watching the High Sheriff take long pulls out of the gallon crock jug.

"Say, sheriff, I'll be a-needin' that jug back when ye empty 'er."

"Wrong, Tuck, yer damn dead wrong, Tuck." The sheriff then informed Tuck that the T-men through the Dent County Sheriff had sworn out a warrant against him. Bum had also got it straight from the horse's mouth that Ivy was gonna turn state's evidence, not only on Tuck, but several others, for everything from stealin' hogs to bootleggin'.

"Ye'd better light out," Bum said. "And if I was you, I wouldn't let the sun set on my ass unless you want to take a trip with Ivy."

The sheriff led his saddleless horse over to the chop block and with some effort, mounted and rode off not caring whether his spit and whittlers followed suit. He was anxious to retrieve his saddle from the throne of fodder and be on his way.

Tom looked long and hard to catch a glimpse of Mandy. He had stayed to the last. Finally, one of his friends who'd figured as much broke his bubble.

"Tom, let's go . . ."

Tom told him he wanted to see Elvie, the younger brother.

"Let me tell ye, Tom. Mandy'd been a-livin' with Ivy. He's in jail, and Arnie's done and took over. He's been a-roddin' her since the night they hauled Ivy off. If ye'd a-been thar ye coulda had a chance to kivver her. Ye jest as well come on back now. Ye'll stay and try to tool her. Them Martin boys'll cut yer guts out like they did ol' Terrill's. Ye remember? Hell, ye was standing in ten foot of him when Elvie opened him up at the Paint Rock schoolhouse pie supper."

They reined their mounts after the others, set them to a canter and were back with the party just before they reached Mahan's fodder patch. Bum by this time was feeling no pain. He had returned to his loud, boisterous nature and was telling them the story of the molasses making. No, not the first part. That part he never wanted to be in his mind or on his lips. He did, however, always look for an occasion to tell the story about Fersman, the Tormentor, and Bussart, the real father of the boy, and how Bussart took the boy Henry and went west.

"Heard Bussart ended up a-workin' fer the Army at old Ft. Boise," Bum explained. "He first trapped mustangs, broke 'em and sold 'em with the Army till he died. They even shipped his body back. They put him away real proper and paid his son's fare both ways to see his pa put away. Now that boy turned into one fine man. Young Henry come into my office inquiring about his ma. I took a natural born likin' to him. I shore hated to have to go and tell him his ma was dead. I quizzed him to how long he was a-stayin' and he said he had to catch the train out at Winona the same evening.

"I didn't figger it'd do him ary bit o' good with a fresh buried pa to learn his ma had kilt herself in the same week him and his pa left when he was a little feller. He wanted to know if I knew how she died and I said, 'Shore, typhoid. Typhoid kilt her and all her people since I never knowed what Bussart had told him about their sleepin' arrangements.

"Young Henry jest said, 'Well,' just stood thar fer a good minute, then shrugged his shoulders and walked out, and I never saw him again."

One of the spit and whittlers spoke up to tell what the boy's dead mother had told his own ma. Well, actually she hadn't just told only his ma. His ma was at church when Henry's mother came in the night before she hung herself and confessed to the Lord all the evil she stood by and let Fersman do to little Henry when he was first bornt and about the fiendish delight he took in his punishment. He remembered one his ma heard about where 'ol Fersman would tie the boy backwards on the back of a heifer.

The heifer part of the story started Bum to laughin' and talkin'. "Yeah, ol' Fersman was shore fond of the heifers alright."

After the young woman's burying, Bum remembered the punkin pie his own mom had baked, left in the pie pan, and put into a brown paper sack. Paper sacks were rare and hoarded back for such occasions. Few things came in them. Folks furnished their own tote sacks and containers when you went and got your bill of goods.

Young Bum's ma placed the pie and paper bag into a tote sack made of washed burlap and told him to take it over to the young widower saying in his time of grief, "a body jest don't feel like cookin'." Bum had to walk the five or so miles since his pa had rode to the county seat on business on their only saddle horse. Young Bum took the sack and picked up the single-shot Stevens .22, puttin' it in the crook of his arm, and set off. Bum, like everyone, always took a gun for the game you could kill was a necessity of life.

Bum's trip there was uneventful. But when he got to Fersman's, this all changed. Young Bum knocked at the open front door but there was no answer. He'd hoped Fersman was in the cabin so he could give him the pie out of the pan and start right back toward home since he always had a complete dislike for the long turkey buzzard necked bastard. He started to holler out for him, but then heard a commotion out at the barn.

Bum set the tote sack in the doorway and propped his .22 up on the cabin wall, and walked out to the barn, figurin' Fersman was milkin' and doin' his evening chores early.

What Bum saw next had him shakin' his head to clear his eyes.

There Fersman stood with a heifer looked to be about a yearling. He had her head in the cow's milk stanchion and he was behind her with his overalls down to his knees and his shirt tied in a knot at the waist. The young widower wasn't showing much grief. He was making sounds and they were far from those of mourning. His grunts became louder as his hips thrust faster. He would bow over the heifer until he would lay belly to back. Then he would straighten up and throw his head back.

Bum could see he had his eyes shut and had worked himself up into such a frenzy that his overalls had fallen clean down to his ankles. His bony legs were making wild moves to keep up as the heifer struggled. Not only was her head in the stanchion, but she had kicker irons on her rear legs.

Then, in one of Fersman's passionate, heated movements of his lovemaking, his legs knocked the kicker irons off the calf's right leg. She could now move them independently. And move them she did. In a wink of an eye, she had her right leg entangled in his overalls.

Fersman saw that she had her legs free. He noticed his legs were now pinned to the barn's dirt floor, but thought she was just standing on his overalls. He never realized her leg had found the same hole he had his leg through. To make matters worse, one of his overall's galluses had made a perfect half hitch around her ankle.

Fersman became enraged with his lover when he felt he was in a permanent union with an unbreakable tie—the tie being his new overall gallus that was binding man to beast. He tried to reach the gallus thinking he could loose it enough to slip her hoof from the loop. Yet with all his humanly effort, he couldn't break this bond with the young cow. Her hoof had gone completely through the overall leg to the dirt floor and the gallus had now formed a perfect clove hitch. After several attempts, all in vain, he reverted to his old nasty self that had always worked for him whenever he had a weak, helpless subject in his complete power.

Fersman went to beating the heifer. At first, with slaps and fists. He then reached for his goad stick and started getting wicked. It looked like the heifer would break her neck in the stanchion. She would lunge far enough forward until the boards formed a yoke, then lunge backwards till she should have broken her neck.

Then, it happened. In one of her severest, mightiest strains, the thin green shit flew. It came out with such force it sounded like water coming through a pipe. It hit the formerly horny young widower square on his knotted shirtfront, coating his now limp noodle till his undersized scrotum sack disappeared from view.

Since the calf's dung had started, there seemed to be an endless supply. The fresh, green shit mixing with the stirred-up dirt floor from their former lovemaking session would be the cause of his imminent downfall.

She finally emptied her colon. As she retreated back, she pushed her human partner to the farthest limits from the head stanchion. Next, a fear and adrenaline fueled lunge forward brought Fersman down, ass flat on the cow shitty floor and sliding hard toward the stanchion, so hard that his entangled legs brought the heifer calf into a sitting position atop her lover's little limp tool.

Fersman was still hollering about how he was going to give her another treatment when young Bum Powell turned toward the cabin, his presence never detected. Taking the pie out of the pan, Bum laid it in Fersman's doorway, retrieved his gun, and started the journey home.

"Hell, Bum! Look, Bum! Damn, Bum! Look whor your saddle was!" snapped Bum out of his thoughts of Fersman's merrymaking. Bum tried focusing his eyes, straining them to see the spot where he'd left his new saddle. There was the golden throne of corn stalks and the rest of the fodder shocks in their exact places. He told his men not to enter the field till he gave the word.

"Some bastard's played a trick, done and went and moved my saddle. I'll have 'er ironed out quicker than a deacon in a cathouse. I bet ye that, since I've got ol' Uncle Hokie right here on the spot."

Uncle Hokie had been and still was a highly revered tracker and trapper. He could track a mouse across a gravel bar. Hokie's motto was, "If hide or hair ever touched the earth, it could be tracked down."

Bum had his men stay mounted, and told Uncle Hokie, "Go find 'er."

Hokie didn't enter the fodder patch the way the sheriff and the rest of the men figured he would. Instead, the old tracker walked the outer perimeter of the rail-fenced field till he came back to the party. Looking up to Bum and the rest of his mounted comrades, he made his declaration.

"Thar ain't been a rabbit stir, much less a pack of hogs. If thar's even one critter, it's still in ol' Mahan's field."

The fodder patch was small, no more than an acre. They could look over all of it in a glance. Hokie climbed over the rails where the sheriff had walked earlier and pointed out where the others had scurried to Bum's rescue when his back had gone out while trying to keep his new Sears and Roebuck saddle from being scuffed. He proceeded to work his way in circles in the small fodder patch, making the golden throne the bull's-eye. While Uncle Hokie worked out the field, Bum worked over his new gallon jug of liquor. He never got impatient as long as he had this good oil to keep everything in harmony.

When the old tracker zeroed in on the throne, he squatted down and went to studying the earth. He got up, walked behind the fodder shock, squatted and studied the tracks. Getting down on his hands and knees he smelled the tracks, the fodder, then rose up to smell the piece of wood left on the throne. He frowned, scratched his head, and once again studied the tracks. They all pointed toward where the saddle had set. Not a single track of the dozens there was turned in the opposite direction. Something had devoured the leather of the saddle, leaving only the wooden tree and the tacks that had fastened the newly oiled tanned leather. Even the decorative tacks that were only for show, intended for the pure vanity of its owner, were left untouched. Not one tack had been displaced.

In his many decades of hunting and trapping, even being a renowned tracker for the cavalry when he was a young man in the Army, Hokie's eyes had never seen anything like what he'd just beheld. *Even if the tracks had led back a few feet . . . Even if one had pointed in the opposite direction.* No. Whatever made these tracks was large and very heavy, weighing several hundred pounds. He could read the signs the tracks left in the pounded up earth as easily as a scholar reads a primer book.

Uncle Hokie walked back to where the men had been left, retrieved his horse, mounted up, and started to ride off. Just prior, the sheriff had walked off by himself out of the circle of men and was trying to make his stream. He was straining, concentrating on water running from rocky brooks to shake roofs, and was on the verge of making it flow when he heard his men hollering at Uncle Hokie riding away. Bum, turning on his heels, hastened back and cut off the old tracker.

"Whor the hell ye think yer a-goin', Uncle Hokie? Whor's my saddle?"

"It's et up Bum." Hokie told him what he'd just seen and added, loud and clear enough for all, "And it was not et up from a livin' beast of this ol' earth and ye don't need to be no tracker. A blind man could figure it out. I've had all I want. I'm a-goin' home. I wouldn't touch that saddletree fer all the saddles new or used this side of hell. I figure that's whor them beasts come from that et 'er up. It's yer show from here on, sheriff. Ye do as you please."

Hokie reined his horse around and proceeded off. The others fell in behind the old tracker. They too had had their fill of playing lawman that day and for many days to come.

Bum went the few paces back to where his horse was tied to the top rail of the fence and started to cross over it to the fodder shock. A small breeze came up at the far end of the field and turned into a dust devil whipping up fodder leaves, weeds, and small pieces of corn cane, all coming straight toward him. The wind it created made a low, whispering moan.

Bum popped the slip hitch of his bridle ring, climbed up on the rail fence, mounted his horse and, holding his jug so no harm could come to it, rode after the rest.

The Reading

Cousin Charlie finished telling the others all he had heard about the molasses making and saddle. Most of his narrations resembled what the reader has just read, although like any piece of information that is passed on many times, inaccuracies and embellishments creep in.

Cousin Charlie fell into much the same category. But the dying embers, the night sounds of owls, coyotes, whippoorwills, and insects, had enough effect on all the young folks' nerves to make up for whatever was lacking in the story. At times the listeners would gasp. Some would state their disbelief. This was especially true of the young men who would frown, shake their heads, and confidently declare that it was all a bunch of bullcrap, hoping their uneasiness was not detected.

The girls made up for their counterparts' reserve by squealing, clutching each other, expressing physically and vocally both their excitement and fright.

After much deliberation, it was settled. They would all ride over to Lillie May Goforth's for a "reading" on Sunday if all the work could be caught up by then.

All hands put forth full steam in hopes of having the spring planting brought to a close by Saturday. It was Monday when cousin Charlie rode to the Rector post office, so they had five days to bring it all
to a close. If the weather stayed dry, it would be no problem. Only
once in the next five days did one youth have to quit work in the
planting fields to go hunt up one of the farm's milk cows. She hadn't
come in to be milked the night before or the following morning,
which was too long between milkings. A heavy milker such as she was,
especially with a calf, could get mastitis, which ruins the udder and
makes the milk taste salty. So, the search couldn't be put off, even for
the plantings.

It was decided that Calvin would take the task. This gave him his
first break since he'd arrived at the old home place for his summer's
vacation. He gladly accepted the opportunity knowing the rarity of this
chance. There would be few moments if any like this to be idle until he
and his wife Sammy returned to his job in Washington, DC.

Saddling up Bird, he planned first to set out toward the sinks, make
wide half-circles, eventually hitting the river. He would make Uncle
Jim and Aunt Alley Stewart's cabin by noon, eat with them, then work
his way home.

He never found any sign going toward the sinks. He headed back
toward the river in hopes of finding better luck. No sooner had he
made the river and was heading toward the Stewart's cabin, than he
rounded a bend and came face to face with an old Indian woman and a
blind man.

Calvin dismounted to make conversation. It was the Ozarkian way
to show respect to your elders, especially when in the presence of a
woman. As she made some inquiries, he thought what a striking contrast. The man so blind where he once had eyes—the eyes now only
bloody red blobs whenever he half opened the lids that covered the
sunken sockets. She, on the other hand, had eyes that looked deep into
one's soul.

Calvin had the unsettling feeling she could read his thoughts. It
made him feel like a child who had done something wrong but didn't
know what the nature of it was. The blind man never spoke. The old

woman didn't give their names, but she called Calvin by his. Later, he thought, *how strange*, for he could never recall introducing himself.

She asked Calvin if he had seen anyone on the river. He told her he hadn't but that he'd keep an eye out for anyone and relay any message she wanted to pass on. Her message made Calvin uneasy, and he wished he'd cut his search short and had never made this meeting as she told him her story about a riverboat party taking her food and possessions.

Calvin was trying to think how to make his departure when the old woman said, "Hit ain't the grub and fixins, hit's Tucker and Daner's oldest son. He'll be drowned iff'n they ain't stopped. That cow yer lookin' fer is up behind the Blowin' Spring with a bull calf."

Calvin was still standing in front of Bird staring at the pair as they went out of his sight around the bend of the river. He never stopped at the Stewart's cabin that day. He rode straight through, circled the old home place, and went the quarter mile west to the Blowing Spring. There was the missing cow with the newborn bull calf. That night, Calvin didn't relate any of his experiences of that day, especially how he located the cow and calf. He figured for now he would keep it to himself.

As the week drew to a close, the young ones knew they'd be riding over to the old Indian witch woman's cabin in Foot Log Holler come Sunday. The tensions mounted to a fever pitch since each evening after chores, supper, and bath, the topic of conversation was always about what cousin Charlie had heard at the Rector Post Office.

Jennie Smith's brother Bob was the youngest though always the most observant, quietly listening to everyone else's stories and tales. Rarely did something miss his ears or eyes, and he noticed Calvin had become quiet ever since he left to find the cow and calf. It was completely at odds with his nature. From that night on he seemed lost in his own thoughts.

There were five horses being ridden double to the "reading" on that warm pleasant day in May. The ten young girls and boys were in a lively mood and not only because they were engaged in such a self-inflicted scary journey. It was also pure satisfaction and enjoyment to let their tired young muscles recuperate for a full day, especially in May. In those times, if folks didn't get their crops in on time, the resulting hardship would be hunger for themselves as well as the animals in their care.

They rode at a brisk running walk to make the distance as quickly as possible so there would be plenty of time for those who wanted a reading.

Jennie rode with her little brother Bob on her mare, Bird. She'd filled the saddlebags full of items to give as barter. She stuffed them so full that her brother's short legs stuck out at a comical angle making the rest laugh heartily several times. Each time the laughter was so catching that brother Bob laughed hard as the rest, always being of good nature. The miles passed quickly in their happy state of mind.

The cabin suddenly appeared before them. They never had time to gain their composure. The setting was the same as the week before when the Shannon County sheriff made his visit, including the black 30-gallon kettle with its continuous fire. There was some job or other that called for its use almost every day of the year.

The clan was settin' outside; some on a long wooden bench while several others sat on blocks of wood that eventually would be fed into the kettle fire. As the riders approached, the clan grew silent. The small children quieted down and the fretting baby went to sucking its thumb, its large eyes looking intensely at the horses and their riders.

The young riders were settin' their mounts, each wishing, and waiting, for someone to speak. The young people of Jennie's party, one after another, opened their mouths, but no words came forth. First, they would stare at the kettle. Then they took to looking at the ground, each hoping someone, anyone from either side, would make openers.

Brother Bob, sitting behind Jennie, was in a perfect position to observe this scene without any detection from either side.

An old man was settin' in the only chair. It was a rough hand-hewn white oak with a split hickory caned woven bottom. It looked as old as its occupant. Both had weathered many a rough year. The man had lost the old cracked leather appearance a decade and a half ago. Now his face and neck had taken on the appearance of a dried, wrinkled prune.

He was whittlin' long, even shavings from what was once a large cedar limb. His Barlow pocketknife worked intently as though life depended upon each shaving having the same length, depth, width, and curl. The only other movement came when he'd change the cud of chewing tobacco from one jaw to the other.

The baby was held by a woman, young enough still to be thought attractive by a 13-year-old boy. Her reddish hair turned the color of gold when she advanced out of the shade of the porch which let the sun play on it as well as the baby's face. This would make the infant squirm; its little face with the large eyes would hide under the old washed cotton flour sack. The young woman had olive skin and her eyes were green. Bob was captivated by her unusual features but there were so many others that merited equal attention, such as the children. There were two of them, completely naked, playing in the dirt at the cabin's south end, their little brown bodies soaking up the sun. He couldn't tell whether they were boys or girls since the whole clan wore their long hair parted in the middle, letting it hang down Indian fashion. Bob thought one of the younger men, with his goatee and handle bar mustache, looked like the Wild Bill Hickock picture he'd seen in a book. He stood straight and seemed taller to the boy than what he really was. Brother Bob would come to know him well in his lifetime. Actually, he would come to know all the clan here and become closer to a few of them than his own younger siblings.

Then, his eyes caught sight of a girl who looked to be 7 or 8. He realized he had forgotten to breathe. She was simply the most startlingly beautiful child he had ever seen. Lillie May had always said she "bornt her fer a movin' star." As Bob looked at her from his concealed position, he would've had no argument with her statement. She was the darkest person he'd ever seen. Her hair was raven black. She had just washed and rinsed it in a maidenhair fern solution that gave each hair a sheen all its own. Her dress had been sturdy cotton flour sacks once, but it had been washed and boiled in the big black kettle too many times until the sturdiness was long gone.

There had been a good five minutes of dead silence. It seemed that Jennie's party and the clan would stare indefinitely. It was broken when someone finally said something. The speaker looked to be in his early twenties. His words were offered purely for the purpose of breaking the long silence and not intended as an invitation.

"Light down, come on in, we'll make a bite to eat in a little while you rest."

Johnny "Wash" Counts, the old man whittlin' on the cedar limb, never looked up or missed a stroke. "What ye gonna do, Frankie, be like Moses? Get manna from Heaven? Ye better go ketch yerself a fish!" Laughing, Johnny continued. "Pray over hit like the good Lord? And hope ye can feed this here multitude since that Martin boy took all the vittles and most o' the pots and pans to cook 'em in. They're both long gone down the river. Don't reckon we'll see hide nor hair of either fer a spell."

The old man shook his head, spit a long amber stream of tobacco juice, and returned to his cedar. The red cedar gave off the faint aroma of its oils which mingled with the scent of the wood fire that was ever-present under the kettle in the daylight hours.

The riders turned their attention to the man who broke the silence. Frank sat on a limb that had been dragged in and never made its way to its final destination under the kettle. His voice had a character all its own. Some would call it high-pitched, as in his first greeting to the riders. Then when he spoke low, where others' voices would have been inaudible, his words and sentences came as clear as if holding an ear horn to one's head. The tone of his voice commanded man and animal alike. He had a black and white shepherd dog settin' at his side. When he saw the riders approaching, he had signaled the shepherd, whose name was Watch, to come in, set, and make no sound.

Frank and the riders' eyes met. He kept a steady gaze, meeting all their eyes and holding them as long as they would look, which was not for long with the exception of Bob, whose hidden position still allowed him to stare.

At first, Bob thought he'd seen him before. He knew the face, the long black hair cropped squarely across the shoulders and the black piercing eyes, one with an old injury. Bob couldn't have looked and studied this one eye, this evil looking eye, if it hadn't been for his vantage point.

Frank had been kicked in the face by a horse when he was five. Without proper medical care, the cheek had healed faster, tugging open the eye. This gave it a mean, fierce look, just like the Indian's picture that Bob had seen in the same book in which he'd seen Wild Bill's. Bob thought at first, *Yes, here he is. He has escaped the Cheyenne reservation.* It was a letdown to the young boy when he remembered the picture was from 1880.

Frank, knowing and feeling their hesitance, told Watch to go "greet 'em." The shepherd walked toward the party until he was within fifteen feet of them. He then stood on his back legs, placed his front paws together and made a dancing motion, swirling around several times. Throwing himself flat on the ground, he rolled over, sat up and made several different barking noises while raising his right paw for a handshake.

The young riders dismounted, dropping the bridle reins as the horses were trained to stand in place when both reins were dropped. They approached Watch, shook his hand, each in turn making their own different greeting.

The last to approach was the youngest of their party, brother Bob. When Bob reached out his hand, Frank gave Watch another signal. Soon as the boy grasped the paw of the dog, Watch stood up and walked Bob back to his master. With his other paw, Watch made motions as if making introductions. By this time, all the young men and women of Jennie's party and the clan were laughing and all talking at once.

Frank was born with the gift to take command of these types of situations. His sayin' was, "If ye can't say nothin' good 'bout someone, don't say nothin' at all. When there's too much tension, ye gotta make 'em laugh or cry." This time it was laughter.

Brother Bob and Frank Self bonded there that day. Frank became Bob's older brother—the older brother he'd always wanted. The baby with the large, fawn-like eyes, held by the redheaded woman, drew the girls like a drummer's cart does the ladies. They were making a fuss over the infant—the natural emotions born in the female that keep our species alive.

No one saw the old Indian woman as she approached. She had a knack of her own knowing when to appear for introduction and how.

All the talking and laughing stopped. The ensuing silence was the same as it had been on Sheriff Bum Powell's visit—the type of quietness in which one can hear their own pulse throb in their temples as the heart beats.

It was hard for Jennie to get this meeting clear in her memory. Her fuss was also directed at the pretty baby. Unexpectedly, there was a little brown hand made strong and rough by years of long, hard toil, keeping so many fed and well. The hand stroked Jennie's platinum blond hair back, away from her deep blue eyes. The old Indian woman was studying the girl's face. Jennie alone could see the several tears that ran down her cheeks though all present heard her words.

"Daughter, I don't make readin's no more since them travelin' missionaries from the International Bible Students come last winter, stayed right here with us fer nigh two weeks. Reckon we kivvered the whole white man's black book. I reckon it's too much fer most to pack, knowin' what's ahead of 'em. My daughter, ye go in peace, the road ye'll travel will be long, the journey yer soon goin' to start is goin' to be hard. Thar'll be very little easement come yer way, ever."

While Lillie May was talking to Jennie, the young men and women gathered in as close as possible so as not to miss a single word that she spoke. All except young brother Bob. He had returned to their horses, relieving the saddlebags of their contents. He would later claim he'd only done it to make for a more comfortable ride home.

Bob never said a word as he stacked all the commodities they had brought for barter. The only one at the clan's cabin to witness any of brother Bob's act of generosity was the old weathered man, still whittlin' on his cedar limb. He looked up, caught Bob's eye and gave a knowing wink and slight headshake. An outright acknowledgement of thanks would have brought embarrassment not only to the old man and young boy, but to all the clan. These were the days before the government came, came to take away one's pride, making a generation, now generations feel that handouts were acceptable—nothing to be ashamed of. The clan with little had all. They had their pride, their dignity, respect and self-respect. This was all coming rapidly to a close.

They started homeward, riding silently, each with their own train of thought. Every so often, the silence became too uncomfortable. Holding in what was on their minds was as one trying to carry the whole boat. You have to set the load down, cry out for help, or risk collapsing under the weight. Soon as one of them openly expressed their feelings, the floodgates were opened.

Calvin wanted the water behind his gate to rush forth, clearing his mind of his encounter with the old Indian woman and blind man on the day he had gone to search for the cow, especially after she had asked him point black in front of everybody, "Was the cow and bull calf okay?" Most of the party were teasing Jennie in good humor, asking which one she would marry to become "daughter." Jennie laughed hearing the other's laugh, but was so preoccupied with her own thoughts about all that was said she heard only words, missing the structure and meaning of the sentence.

Calvin finally blurted out about his meeting at the river with whom he now knew were Lillie May and her husband, John Goforth. He revealed to them the details of his experience. When he was through, the rest rode as silently as Jennie for the remainder of the trip. They didn't stop for their picnic lunch as was planned, since brother Bob had already given all they had to eat away to the clan. Everyone was secretly relieved.

Jennie was thinking about Mr. and Mrs. Payne—the same International Bible students who had convinced Lillie May to quit her readings, and the same good people who had come to her aide also just two years ago. No, Jennie had never accepted the Lord. She felt just as strong about her atheist beliefs now as two years before, when the traveling missionaries had come to her rescue.

Her thoughts flashed back to her father dying. She was 11 years old, and he had to be taken across the river to be buried. The Current River had a slight rise, just enough to make it difficult to transport the body across. The rain was falling gently but steadily and had been for the few days before he died. All this misery heaped upon their grief.

When she recalled his funeral and burying, the reality would equal any nightmare she ever could have had.

46

chapter
NINE

The Burying of Jennie's Father, Little Fiddling Jimmy Smith

When the johnboat finally made the opposite bank, neighbors had a team and wagon waiting. The handmade coffin was scarcely above a rough box. The rain had seeped through, soaking the corpse's clothing. In the interior was a new comforter, donated in good faith. But it would've been better if the donator had kept it for herself for the coming winter. It was saturated to the point of runoff.

When they reached the gravesite, the pallbearers lifted the rough box. Water ran out from the soaked cloth. They tried to keep as much distance as possible from the coffin's stream of water and still carry their friend to his final resting place—or, in the minds of most, to his last miserable spot here on earth.

The funeral could have proceeded with a little less anguish if only the preacher had let them bury him with a regular funeral sermon. But the High Reverend had the chance of a lifetime and he wasn't going to let it slip through his fingers. He didn't care how wet the mourners got, or how much water ran into the grave. Some of the men were trying to keep it bailed out. They stopped out of respect for the grieving family, figuring the preacher would make things quick under the circumstances. They guessed wrong. He had come prepared, donned in his dress raincoat knowing no one else would have one. Most had never even heard of such a garment.

The reverend had an intense loathing for "Little Fiddlin' Jimmy Smith." Fiddlin' Jimmy had never gone to church except to play music for a square dance, pie supper, cake walk, or any other gleeful occasion. *Here he lay dead today and I'm going to put him where he belongs, in the bowels of the burnin' hell. I hope he burns forever, damn him* thought the High Reverend. How many times had he dreamed of this day?

Over the years, it seemed whenever he was at some doin's, with the sole attention and admiration of all, in walked Fiddlin' Jimmy. From the second Fiddlin' Jimmy arrived, it was as if the reverend never existed. At the least, his position was no longer the most exalted.

The good reverend began his sermon. He explained how multitudes of men, women, and even some children were just like Fiddlin' Jimmy Smith. "They are burnin' as I speak! The same way Jimmy is going to be by the time I finish things up with my Lord here today!!"

As he was getting all heated up with his hell fire and brimstone, the hand-dug, six-foot deep grave was receiving one hell of a drenching and was now filled with four feet of water. The rain started to fall hard—hard enough to start washing away the red clay earth that had been excavated to make the sepulcher, the graveyard being on a slope.

The grave would have filled to the brim and the dirt washed completely away had the good High Reverend not lost his voice. He'd gotten very carried away saving lost souls and had put the fear of the Lord in many that day—waving his hands, dancing, shouting, at times speaking in tongues. Only he knew the mystery that was being revealed to him. And if the sinners didn't come forth and confess, they would die and burn in Gehenna, the fire that burns day and night forever and ever.

Soon as the preacher lost his voice, he shook a few hands with the ladies, bowed to some of the younger women, made his way to his horse and surrey and departed with as much haste as one in his elevated position could muster without being too obvious.

Oh, if only my voice would've held out. I would've gone on till dark, he thought on his trip home, since no one had invited him to stay overnight. *That must have been the will of my Sweet Jesus.*

The men couldn't wait for the family to leave to fill in the grave. It was late, and many had yet to cross the Current. There was no time to be lost. In daylight, it was dangerous enough. After dark, there would be more bodies to search for and bury.

The water from the downpour was now filling the grave faster than they could bail. It was out of the question to hold his remains over until the weather cleared. It had already been held out too long as it was. There were no lengthy, days-long processes to the ritual. Usually, the burying took place within 24 hours—sooner in hot weather. Winter would let for more leeway if it stayed freezing or below.

The family hadn't stirred during the Good Reverend's kindhearted sermon. His words had put them into a daze of despair; the foul weather only adding to their misery. Their limbs weren't heavy. They felt as dead as the one being buried. From the old to the young of Fiddlin' Jimmy Smith's people, his love for life was contagious to all in his presence. As the folks at the Old Settler's Reunion would say, "There could be a ruckus a-goin' on. Let Fiddlin' Jimmy Smith jest ride up, pull out that fiddle, and the time it took a cat to lick its ass everybody would be a-tappin' their foot, and most likely the two who was about to go at it would be a-giggin' each other in the ribs a-laughin'."

Here today, he lays in a rough box soaked through and through, saturated with the falling rain, wet as the earth they are so desperately trying to have receive him. If he had been alive, he would have given one of his sly winks out of those expressive eyes, and said, "Wet and cold as I am, hope they throw some more coals on the Good Reverend's 'burnin' hell.' It's gonna take a damn good fire to ever warm this mess up and dry it out."

Shit. The great fire of Gehenna could not have touched it. They took the coffin and set it afloat on top of the watery hole. His friends, the pallbearers, broke and wept. They cried in despair not knowing what to do.

Their open weeping kindled, then fanned the flames of the pent-up grief of the family. It was as the stillness before a bad storm. First, a slight sound. Then, within seconds, it rose to a mournful wailing that carried its way to the heavens. It couldn't have traveled far toward the High Reverend's burnin' hell. The earth would've been too dense with the soaking it had had this day for sound to carry down. It could only make its way upward. As hard as the rain was now falling, heaven had better start at twelve feet up, or all would be lost again.

While everyone lingered helpless in their anguish, nature had taken its course. The green pine lumber that the rough box had been built of, along with the thick cotton comforter and the weight of the dead, had started the coffin to sink as it took on water, expelling the air, taking on more volume till it stabilized. It submerged till the coffin's lid was level with the red clay earth. There it stopped, having equalized its weight with the pull of gravity.

The men in their zombie-like state started carrying large stones, placing them carefully on the rough box's top, making it sink straight, not hanging on the grave's walls. The rain that had been coming down in driving sheets stopped abruptly with a brisk wind that arrived with a chilling force.

By the time the coffin met the bottom of the grave, the rough box had only a few air pockets left to send its scant feeble bubbles to the water's surface. The runoff that had washed around the red mound of earth, dug out to receive its dweller for eternity, had become a sticky, slimy mess. They dipped and bailed frantically, alternately pushing the clay earth and piling stones of every size into the gaping hole until the grave was closed.

Jennie, standing as tall as her little frame would allow, had never cried. Her pain had turned to a numbing shock at the sight that greeted her at the graveyard. Before her grief could return, the High Reverend's words made her heart and mind hard and cold as granite. She proclaimed that day she would become a nonbeliever like her Grandfather Bealert, the old medical scientist. His family was originally from

France, and was known to most of the hill people as "old infidel Bealert," even though he'd saved many of them and their children with his medicine.

The grieving family returned home that night unaware that their sorrows and troubles were just beginning.

chapter
TEN

Jennie's Doubt that Turns to Fear

It was fall. The corn was still in the field and would last long in low humidity. However, it was far from the dry, ideal weather needed for saving the corn and would have to improve to even be considered bad weather. With the rain coming one squall behind another, all would soon be lost. There is no way to crib wet or even damp corn and there were hundreds of bushels to gather in. They waited out the next few days. And the days dragged into weeks.

The corn finally dried in the field sufficiently. This was where their troubles first started with the Riley clan.

There was the old man, Pa Riley, and his three grown sons—Osrowl, and the twins, Cletis and Clytis. They came with teams and wagons, cut the fences, and went to gathering load after load of corn. When they figured they had enough, the Rileys turned out their hogs, cattle, horses, and mules to finish what they had started.

Jennie's mother, Susie Smith, went through all legal measures, but the grind wheel of justice turns slowly. This grind wheel had several broken cogs. Nothing was ever done.

Fiddlin' Jimmy Smith had been as good a farmer as he was a musician. He'd built his fences with woven wire topped with two or three barbed wires, and used the most modern horse-drawn equipment of his day. He rotated crops and was the laughing stock of the river people for raising green manure crops such as white clover, rye, and buckwheat. He read every farm publication, putting to use their knowledge to his advantage. People would laugh openly, arguing with him even though he proved time and again these methods raised tenfold more than they that robbed the soil of all its nutrients.

This is what saved the Smith family the first year. Before Fiddlin' Jimmy died, he had laid up enough the previous season. They could squeeze by. Even after death, he was still providing.

Soon as the Rileys saw that the legal system didn't give an old rat's ass one way or the other, they become braver to the point of belligerency. Even with all of their stealing, the corn crop wasn't enough to satisfy their greed or need for very long.

Next, the twins, Cletis and Clytis, decided the grieving family's Berkshire boar (which was the only one in the whole river county that was purebred stock) was theirs. They rode over, bringing their maul with them. They used it to beat the boar's pen to pieces when all they had to do was open the well-made gate. Everything Fiddlin' Jimmy Smith made was done with pride. Even his boar's pen was a work of art and pleasing to the eye.

Cletis was born having fits of anger that would grow into such rage his father and his two brothers would have to hold him down till he went into a coma-like stupor. Upon awakening, he never remembered the incident. This day, here at the boar's pen, Cletis would soon be in the grip of a titanic one.

Clytis was beating the south side, the side that held the well-made gate. The gate was proving to be stronger than Clytis's blows with the large maul. Cletis saw this and it triggered his insanity to its boiling point. In minutes, the steam had built till there was no turning back. Cletis blew.

Charging his twin and throwing his full weight upon Clytis, he knocked him down till he sprawled flat, lying in the hog's manure.

Cletis grabbed the heavy maul with eyes set, nostrils flared and slobber running from his open mouth. He walked right over Clytis, never seeing or feeling him underfoot, and made his way to the strongly built gate. Here, Cletis set himself to battle, becoming more enraged with every blow he dealt this abominable thing that had become his own personal enemy.

Clytis knew all too well the fitful state that Cletis had worked himself into and felt it was high time that he and the boar hog made their exit. There was still time if he worked fast. He knew Cletis could turn on him at any second, taking the large maul and pulverizing him beyond recognition.

Clytis had brought a whip with him to help drive the boar home. Since the boar had been raised from a piglet with tender loving care and knew only human kindness, he'd humped up in the farthest corner he could find, away from the twins' action from the moment Clytis had first started beating the pen earthward.

The hog is the smartest barnyard animal. Despite its keen intelligence, the hog has this little quirk: it will always go to the same opening it has learned to cross for access in or out of its pen. Cletis was wildly thrashing at the gate so the boar stayed put, even though the fence was gone.

Clytis's own adrenaline was running through his veins at a fairly fast rate, hearing Cletis bellerin' like a mad bull as his hammer swung again and again at the unyielding white oak gate that had, unbeknownst to Cletis, been put together with wagon bolts.

Clytis, now frantic, decided to take the boar and leave his twin brother to his task. In his rage, there would be no reasoning with him. Clytis kicked and hollered at the boar, making "Ol' Berk" do what most all hogs will in the same predicament—hug the ground closely, grunting, emitting a high-pitched squeal when Clytis's whip either stung or cut his flesh, leaving long welts.

The twin's fright gave him uncharacteristic power and strength over his whip. Clytis was known to be on the lazy side, but hearing, more than seeing, his brother's insane frenzy gave him an edge. He gave Ol' Berk such a brutal lashing the Berkshire boar could no longer stand the punishment. He headed for the gate, the one he had passed safely through for four years since he was a fresh weaned pig off his mother.

Cletis was still doing great battle with this same gate, holding and swinging his maul like a Viking wielding the long sword. Clytis saw the boar making its way headlong toward the gate even though there were no fence boards left on the pen. Still, he couldn't whip the hog across where the fence used to be, where there had never been access before. The boar ran toward the gate with Clytis whipping his head, trying to cut him off and make him cross the torn-down pen boards. The boar ran blindly in his fright hoping to escape his agonizing torture.

Cletis, swinging the great maul, brought it down with superhuman force. He completely missed the gate and connected with the boar's head. The boar had been paying no attention to Cletis, only to Clytis, the one with the power to brutalize him with the whip. The fear of the whip is what brought death to Ol' Berk. Cletis's maul struck him squarely between the eyes as though he had taken aim.

It wasn't a pretty death. The Berkshire boar weighed over 400 pounds. In his death struggle, blood flowed from his snout and mouth, puddling on the earth of his pen. His front and hind legs kicked and pawed the air as the life force left his dying body. A spastic forked hoof dug into the ground, spinning his large frame. He'd quiver, then kick out violently again.

Cletis still didn't realize what he'd done and was readying his maul for another blow.

At the same instant, the hog caught his front hoof on a partially submerged stone. He half spun and made his mightiest death kick with his back legs, bringing them up flush with his belly and letting them fly back out hard.

Cletis's swing and the boar's kick all connected perfectly. The large swine's legs hit Cletis, one hoof striking him just below the knee and the other striking his Brogan boots. The power of the dying kick swept Cletis off his feet with such force his head and shoulders slammed into the earth, leaving his head in a puddle of boar's blood. He sat up, dazed, the blow having knocked the sense back into him.

Cletis's head was now throbbing. His ears and brain were shot through with a sharp pain each time his heart beat. He saw all the blood on the ground and had blood running down his face dripping into his eyes. Thinking the blood was all his, and he was running dry of it fast, he set to squallin' long, loud, forlorn wails for Clytis.

Clytis didn't realize that Cletis was back to normal. He ran to his horse and leapt on its back. Cletis was staggering with the maul, bawlin' extra loud, coming toward him. Clytis grabbed Cletis's mule's bridle reins and turned the two steeds toward home in a brisk gallop, fearful Cletis might do to him as he'd done to the boar.

Jennie and brother Bob, while doing the evening chores, found the boar dead, its house and pen demolished. The only thing left was the gate. Jennie trudged back the quarter mile to the old fort house their family called home since Great-Grandpa Bealert had been awarded it for fighting in the Black Hawk Wars. The only gun they owned was his muzzleloader. It worked well for shooting the steers for beef, but usually the men pole-axed the beefs same as they did the hogs.

Jennie, thinking hard on her walk home, realized her grandfather wouldn't be much help. He was, at first, right after her father Fiddlin' Jimmy died. Now his health and mind were in a dead heat to see which would go first. Her mother already had enough to break the spirit of most, being pregnant at the time of her husband's funeral. After the birth, she had a nervous breakdown that lasted only a few weeks. Her mother Susie finally managed to pull herself up, telling herself, "I have too many little ones that depend on me to stay like this."

No, Jennie thought, *Mom doesn't need to know any of this*, and swore brother Bob to secrecy.

She turned to her grandmother. Grandma Bealert's mind was sharp, her movements quick, and she'd been known as a high-spirited girl in her day. Jennie had high hopes her grandmother would help her with her idea.

Jennie had Bob go gather the eggs, reminding him to be sure to double bar and lock their door. As soon as the chickens had gone to roost, she turned toward the house. She went to her room, took up the Sears and Roebuck catalogue and returned downstairs to find her grandmother. She then gave a sign with her eyes and gestured with her head for the elderly woman to follow her outside.

When they were out of earshot, she told her about the boar being killed—his house, pen, everything being destroyed except the gate. Her grandmother merely pursed her lips and nodded her head slightly, letting the young girl know she fully understood the meaning of Jennie having the mail-order book open to the guns as she spoke. She had circled a .32 caliber owl's head pistol and a Mossburg pump .22, along with hundreds of rounds for each.

She then turned the pages to its order form, which was already filled out and tallied up, and handed the catalog to her grandmother who studied the figures for a few seconds, then turned and walked away. Jennie had to go help her younger brother finish the evening chores before dark, mindful to not be careless with their movements since the Rileys had grown so openly aggressive with their stealing and vandalism.

They ate their supper in silence, wanting only to get it over with. In the past few months, their meals had become just another chore. It was not the height of enjoyment they once looked forward to when after supper their father would take out his violin, and fill the house and its surroundings with his lovely music. Now, they wanted to get the dishes washed, dried and put away, burning the kerosene lamps no longer than necessary. It wasn't because kerosene was five cents per gallon. They still had more than enough to get by on, yet. It was fear of the Riley boys doing something foolish to them in their own house. No one openly admitted it, but everyone felt it.

This feeling, Jennie thought to herself later, was what soon made her grandfather take their money, gold, and jewelry and walk out and away from the house while they were working. He buried it, returned, and informed them casually that "bushwhackers" were coming and that he had "saved the day." Grandfather Bealert's saving of the day would drastically change their lives.

Jennie took her lamp, lit it, and went upstairs to her room. Soon as she entered, she saw the Sears and Roebuck catalogue lying in the middle of her bed. The money that was needed for her order was resting neatly on top of her order blank, the envelope addressed and stamped by her grandmother's hand.

Later that same week, Jennie made the 19-mile ride to the Rector post office and obtained the money order for her mail-order purchase. She asked the postmaster how long it usually took. He informed her it would be 3 to 4 weeks, saying these sorts of orders came only once a month, if that.

The postmaster knew by heart when folks tended to show for their mail. In fact, he seemed to have a better handle than anyone else on the state of the whole county. The post office was the main place local news and information was shared, gathered, and exchanged.

As Jennie mounted Bird, the postmaster walked out so the constant loafers that hung around the post office couldn't overhear their conversation. The postmaster talked low and quick. "Jennie, you all take heed. That no 'count Riley bunch was in here jest last week a-braggin' what they'd done and was gonna do. Don't be cow or hog huntin' by yerself. Tell yer folks to stay clear of yer winders at night. I don't think they've nerve enough to do ary a thing when they're sober. That's the trouble. All three boys and their old man was lit up when they were here last week."

Jennie thanked him and reined her horse toward home, her light weight placing scant burden on her spirited mare's back. She held her in at a running walk on inclines, letting her out to a singlefoot when the going was good and easy. She wanted to be home before the evening chores to avoid leaving her brother with the whole responsibility.

The next three weeks rushed by with the demanding, hectic time of year. There were fences to rebuild and mend where spring floods had washed them out or the Rileys had destroyed the prior fall. This all had to be done before planting could begin. The fields were turned early to make for easy tilling when it came time for them to receive their different crops.

Jennie knew she couldn't take the time off to make the long ride to the post office since the weather had held up the planting for a week. She turned to her brother, once more swearing him to secrecy, and had him make the trip while she worked doubly hard filling both billets.

Bob returned that evening with the order Jennie had been so anxiously waiting for, making it back in time to help her with the evening chores. As soon as the family had finished supper, dishes, and kitchen tidying up, Jennie took her lamp and hurried to her bedroom. Not waiting a second, she tore open the box from the Sears and Roebuck Company.

The young girl's eyes beheld for the first time the objects that might finally bring a measure of security to her and the entire household since her father had died. First, the .32 owl's head pistol was taken from the oilpaper the company had wrapped it in. Next, the Mossberg .22. She turned it over and over feeling with her hands and fingers this strange instrument, wondering about the procedure taken to load and fire it. She'd never thought there would be so many moving parts to contend with.

Her drafty bedroom brought life to the kerosene lamp's dim flame. At first, it flared, giving a false pretense of illumination. Then it spluttered, almost extinguishing, casting grotesque pictures on the walls of her room.

One of the images she would pack with her the rest of her life was of herself and the gun's shadow being united, becoming one in the light of her oil lamp that night.

The girl would first feel relief from having in her possession these instruments of power. Then the next moment, she'd experience overwhelming doubt, a feeling of inner uncertainty, and was afraid she might never master either of them.

Looking at the .32 pistol and the .22 rifle in the flickering flame of the poor kerosene light filled her with such insecurity she couldn't keep her emotions in. She took the two weapons and hid them between her mattress and feather bed, then crawled in beneath her comforter. Jennie made her little frame into a ball down deep in the large feather bed, letting all the held-in emotions of fear and doubt flow out in tears. She silently cried herself to sleep.

Jennie did not soon again touch the cold steel or the oiled wood of those strange contraptions. She did not want to admit to herself the doubt that turned into a fear that kept her from retrieving them from where she'd hidden them four months ago, finally convincing herself there wasn't time to get acquainted with the pieces, much less practice with them.

Spring came and went, and drew into middle summer. The field of corn had been planted. The middles were busted out twice, then were laid by. There would be no more work in the fields till fall picking time, which wasn't to say there was any sort of idle time. Before summer's official onset, there were at least a half dozen garden crops that had to be dried, canned, or preserved and stored for consumption in the coming seasons.

July and August were the busiest and the hottest months. The heat and long days of toil had taken its toll on the family and their beasts of burden. Even their well-trained gentle draft horses were growing edgy. More than once in the last few days, before the fields were finished, they had to pop the check lines across the large wide rumps of their Clydesdales to keep them stepping on out so they could finish everything on schedule.

Jennie and all had been terribly overworked that summer with her father dead, her grandfather going senile, her mother and grandma taking care of the garden, canning and tending her newborn brother, J.B. It seemed there would never be an end to summer. The only time Jennie and brother Bob made it to the old swimming hole at the river was to take the teams to be scrubbed and washed. The Clydesdales, being river horses born and raised, also enjoyed the water.

The earth kept spinning, days turned into weeks, weeks into months, and finally summer was over. It had been a good year. There was a bountiful harvest. The cellar under the old fort house was full.

They had just begun to dig their potatoes. They never used their riding equipment for the garden or truck patches because it couldn't be turned short enough at the row's end that met up with the fence. So, taking a single horse, they hitched it to the little 8 Oliver turning plow.

They would keep the handles high, making its point dig and stay deep in the black sandy fertile soil, turning out bushel after bushel of the largest tubers they had ever seen anyone raise. There would've been three to four wagonloads if they could've brought them in right after they were plowed out. But, it was first necessary to carefully gather up the potatoes and place them in long rows to air dry a few days. This kept down spoilage when they were stored with a light coat of slack lime in their potato bin for the coming winter.

There were enough large white and red tubers for three families if they could've been brought in immediately or if the Riley boys had never been born. Either way, they would've been set for potatoes this coming season.

chapter
ELEVEN

The Fightin' McAfees

Cletis, Clytis, and older brother Osrowl were going to a school pie supper a few townships away with high anticipation of making promising contact with the opposite sex. Clytis and Osrowl had groomed their horses by currying and brushing their coats. They mixed drops of linseed and olive oil and rubbed it on their mounts, making them shine. They then cleaned their saddles and bridles, donned their martingales, and stood back trying to peer at their reflection in a windowpane. The wood around the window had dry-rotted several decades ago. The ancient glass could barely manage to reflect the warped image of the two who desired admiring their primp and tuckered reflection. Even the slightest movement would distort their image. First, they appeared tall and thin. With the slightest shift, parts of them turned short and wide. Then they'd become as wavery looking as the scrub board on which they'd worked over their newest overalls the week before when they heard at the post office about the pie supper and square dance. Cletis had done nothing to his gaited riding mule or his tack.

The three brothers had been in high spirits all morning. After the noon meal, they caught their trusty steeds up to get them prepared for the ride to the hooraw.

Soon as Cletis saw his mule, the gaiety flew out of him like a fresh-flushed covey of quails. He hadn't taken the time through the summer to spray or swipe his "Sunday mount." Now his transportation was in somewhat of a shambles. The mule was infested with mites. The tail and roached mane were hit even worse. Its underside even showed signs of where it had straddled low scrub bushes to scrape and scratch itself, trying to get some relief from the itching, burning, and stinging of the mites. The mule had managed to rub off large, matted patches of hair and flesh. The root of her tail shown the worst since it was the most visible; it was red bloody raw, not even any short hair left and no sign of new growth. This had come mighty close to throwing Cletis into one of his "spells." His brothers knew he'd have one before the night was finished. Woe to whomever he wound up taking it out on. The brothers were holding their breath, hoping to keep him pacified until they made it to the doin's.

Clytis and Osrowl rode out ahead keeping silent as possible. When they did speak, which was seldom, it was in a low whisper. They feared producing any spark that might ignite the powder keg that was building in brother Cletis.

As they were riding toward the Paint Rock School, so were the McAfee brothers—Homer, Lankern (Lincoln), and the one they called "younger brother," also known as "Fightin' Walter McAfee." These young men were from the far side of Shannon County, fortysome-odd miles south as the crow flies. Folks would've liked to hope they were coming to see girls, dance, buy a pie, and have a good time. But, no. These ol' boys were coming for one reason and one reason only: *to fight.* They were known as fighters over on the south side of the county. In surrounding counties, they were also known all too well.

Birchtree was having a big shindig on the same Saturday night as Paint Rock. Birchtree was the McAfee boys' stomping ground, so they had little reason to be in Paint Rock. However, two weeks earlier at the Little Shawnee School cakewalk, Lankern arrived by himself. The Carr brothers and their cousins decided this was the golden opportunity of a lifetime—a chance to settle old scores that ran back a half decade or more.

The Carrs and their allies fell in on Lankern as soon as his brogans touched the ground. Lankern, figuring something like this might happen, had fashioned himself a little whindig that featured a nail driven into a 3-foot hickory sapling. His first and only swing plucked out an eye of one of his unfortunate adversaries. The blood and screaming from his fallen victim had startled and stalled the mob long enough for Lankern to leap on the back of his fleet-footed friend and gallop off, getting a good head start while his foes still stood in shock.

The McAfees had heard through the grapevine that both the Carrs and the law were laying for them since the sheriff was a cousin to the Carrs. The McAfee boys had parleyed and decided to make long rides in and out of the county to have their fun.

Clytis and Osrowl spurred their horses from a running walk to a canter hoping to gain some distance from their brother while trying not to make this too obvious to Cletis. They were hoping that in his dejected state, he would just give up and turn his mule toward home, flogging it all the way. They feared that if Cletis made it to the schoolhouse, and some young buck there made jest of his mule, even innocently with no knowledge of the power that Cletis possessed in his fits of anger, how many might be hurt before the night was over.

Soon as Clytis and Osrowl arrived, they spotted the Martin boys. The Riley boys had been fairly steady customers. Their father, Pa Riley, had sent money and his empty container with Osrowl with orders to fetch him a gallon jug also. Pa knew at least Tucker would be there, if no one else, selling his wares. Pa Riley was gettin' in desperate need of this fine oil. His last words to his three sons were, "Stay clear of trouble and dad-bratted don't ferget what I sent ye fer."

Osrowl made contact with Uncle Tuck and got right down to business, purchasing his quantity early in fear Tuck would sell out like he had at the brush arbor meeting. He took no chances on having to ride home empty-handed or, in this case, empty-jugged to face the wrath of his old man.

Cletis never turned back like his brothers had hoped. He dismounted only once to whip his mule, but before he could get himself really worked up, he heard riders coming up on him. So, he remounted and took it out on the mule by holding her in a fast pace for the last mile with most of the distance being on a fairly good incline. When he arrived at the school, he tied his mangy-looking mount at a respectful distance, hoping she wouldn't be spotted.

The riders that Cletis had heard were the McAfee brothers. They also wanted to keep a low profile in order to simply look things over. They rode in, saw Cletis's mule, and started to tie up by it. But after seeing the mite-eaten raw condition the poor beast was in, they decided immediately to hitch up a good distance away, mites being such a contagious parasite.

The full moon was on the rise by the time the McAfees had unsaddled their mounts, got their sleeping tarps and tack all arranged, and gathered a supply of firewood consisting of fallen limbs, dead saplings, and twigs. They planned to stay the night on this far of a ride and head for home at first light since a round trip would be too hard on their horses.

They settled back, rolled and smoked a few cigarettes, and waited for the music to begin. Being old hands at this sort of game, they knew when the music and dancing started, all eyes would be on the caller of the square dance. Folks would pay little heed to a stranger, especially if one at a time ambled in and came up on opposite sides, then moseyed around, mingling with the crowd before flockin' up later in the evening. This way, they could gather information on what they'd be up against.

Homer had an easy way with people when it came to obtaining information. He'd look around, find the oldest looking man or woman, and ask them how they were feelin'. After an hour or two of listening to them cataloguing their ailments, one could get down to the business of drawing out whatever information was of interest.

The old man Homer was talking to and quizzing pointed at Cletis, who was standing talking to a turkey-buzzard-looking older man settin' on a broken-legged, cane-bottomed chair. Every so often, Cletis would place a leaning hand on the chair, causing its occupant to fan his long scarecrow arms, his hands clawing the air for balance. No sooner than gained, the one standing would forget, putting the buzzard-looking one back to struggling to keep his balance on his perch.

The old man told Homer, "Son, watch out fer that 'en," pointing again at Cletis. "He's Cletis Riley and the other feller is Jake Fersman, his uncle. Both o' 'em is sorta strange. Ol' Fersman was married they say years ago. She kilt herself, the story goes." The old man gave Homer a sly, knowing wink, pursed his lips, and with these two motions said more than words about his doubts concerning the actual fate of the late Mrs. Fersman.

Homer's thoughts were swirling. The name Fersman he'd heard before. Looking at the scarecrow man's appearance with the turkey buzzard neck, he knew it wouldn't be a story of a former reputation fighter. While his thoughts were still in a jumble, the old timer said, "You being from down yonder in south side o' Shannon, ye seen ol' Bum Powell lately?"

That's all it took. Homer now remembered how the sheriff had got to laughing and telling a story about way back when he was a youth and delivering a pumpkin pie. Of course, telling the whole truth as to why he never gave Fersman the pie personally always made his listeners laugh and gig each other in good humor, especially when the jug had been passed around several times.

Homer shook his head, then realized the old man was telling him what he had rode so far for. "Cletis," explained the old man, "has fits of anger and most every doin's 'round these here parts dread to see him come fer he'll get liquored up, and if everyone don't pussyfoot around him thar's gonna be trouble. His brothers, one a twin to him, Clytis, the other the oldest, Osrowl, has done went tippin' most fellers off to be right careful what they was talkin' 'bout when Cletis was in earshot.

Make him mad and he'll whoop everyone here fer his fancy gaited ridin' mule done went and got herself et up with them thar mites. She's all bloody from asshole to appetite." Saying this the old feller laughed. When Cletis looked their way, the senior citizen stopped abruptly, dropped his head, and quit talking.

Homer got up, walked the circle of dancers, made contact with brother Lankern, and told him to go fetch "little brother" Walt—he had a "job" for him.

Upon returning, Homer filled them in on the turkey buzzard looking man. He didn't have to go into detail about the calf since Bum had at one time or another told every man in the south side of Shannon County the story. Besides, the one they were interested in was his fit-throwin' nephew, Cletis.

Homer told Fightin' Walt what to say, explaining to his younger cousin what he'd learned from the old gentleman. The old man was still sitting across the dance floor, head bowed, not daring to look up and meet Cletis's stare. Cletis was forming one of his hands into a fist, bringing it back then slamming it into the palm of his other hand, loud enough to start drawing attention to himself, which was his plan since his arrival that evening.

Cletis was feeling the rage start. *All these here sons of a bitches dancin', laughin', havin' themselves a good time a-merrymakin', not one of 'em carin' a whit about me and my mule.* He'd already convinced himself that each burst of laughter, especially the most contagious ones that left everyone roaring, and the girls' high-pitched giggles, were aimed directly at him and his mule. He wanted to be mad and was just look-ing for things large or small to rile him to anger; looking, feeling, sens-ing for the right moment to explode so as to put the fear of God into all, old and young alike. They'd better not get in his way or have too good of a time. It would be better for everyone in attendance here this night to have no enjoyment at all. Only then might he let the old gen-tleman he was still glaring at get off with just a few good slaps instead of the beating and mauling he'd already decided to give him.

Finally, Cletis screamed, cursing at the elderly man. The body of the old man started trembling, knowing there would be no help for him at first. All there knew Cletis's nature, like that of the great cat, was to have satisfaction with his helpless prey before six to eight strong young men piled on top of him and pulled him off while others consoled, pleaded, begged him for mercy, hoping and praying aloud that his mighty anger wouldn't return. Hopefully they could pacify him long enough so everyone could just hitch up and leave.

Young Walt was keeping a close eye and knew exactly what was comin' down. He worked his way to the other side of the dance floor. Cletis's attention was on no one except his prey. The only one there making any sort of sound was his Uncle Jake Fersman, who was chuckling and grinning, making gestures of support and cheering for his nephew with his long scarecrow arms. He was so comical looking that Homer and Lankern couldn't help but watch him. When they realized who he was, they started laughing. The longer they laughed, the louder the two brothers became, which was just the opposite of the onlookers. They were growing silent and holding their breath, but also sighing in relief. They knew Cletis would take his wrath out on the two laughing men for sure, and hoped he'd run down before it came their turn.

The enraged twin stopped his long swift strides, still pounding his fist into his palm, and slowly turned letting his anger reach its peak. He felt his body fill with the uncontrollable power that always accompanied the rage. He snarled and glared insanely at Homer.

Lankern gave the sign for Walt to begin.

Fightin' Walter McAfee walked to the middle of the dance floor and bowed mockingly to the crowd. He then called to Cletis, stopping his advancement.

"Hey, Cletis!! Is that yer flea bitten mule out thar tied in the brash? I sorta figgered yer ol' Uncle Fersman thar woulda showed ye how to keep 'em from rubbin' all the hair off'n her tail, since he's sorta perfeshunal with his young heifers and all!"

Uncle Fersman quit laughin' and crowin' and eggin' his young nephew on to beat up the old man. Now his oversized Adam's apple was bobbing up and down with the panic and fear that seized him immediately upon mention of the heifer. But no eyes turned toward

Fersman. They were all fixed on the two standing on the now vacant dance floor.

Cletis stopped beating his fist into his hand and started bellerin' as he'd done at the well-made white oak gate, except this time he was charging flesh and blood, not wood held together with four wagon bolts. The only thing the gate had in common with the man Cletis was about to charge was both were strongly built in a way the eyes of their adversary would not detect until it was too late.

Cletis charged with a roar—the same charge accompanied by loud animal sounds that had worked so well all his life in paralyzing his weaker opponents with fear. He had worked out his plan of attack as soon as this apparently slight-built man had so openly made fun of him and his uncle. First, he would crush him with his size. Then he'd stand up and stomp and kick with his steel-toed brogans. He'd tacked worn-out horseshoes to their outer edges just for this purpose. Once he had this mouthy bastard's head pummeled into a bloody blob that his own Ma couldn't recognize, he'd turn his attention to the old man, giving him many times the punishment than he would have originally. This way, people at future parties and gatherings would know that when Cletis Riley was having a bad day, they would all have hell to pay and he was ready and able to dole it out as he saw fit.

Suddenly, Cletis found himself lying on his back. There was a slight ringing in his ears like when the clapper strikes the metal and the vibration has all but left the iron. He was confused trying to remember . . . *Hell, had the school bell been rung? For any purpose? Why is my vision so blurry?*

At this moment, Walt bent over Cletis. The crowd gasped, thinking Cletis was putting on the coy act to draw in his opponent. He'd been known to do just that on several occasions in order to toy with some unsuspecting youth who felt he had put the big bully down.

Walt grasped the hair of Cletis's beard, pulled him up to a sitting position, and slapped his jaws as one would slap an unruly child—not hard, but with a light sting. This helped clear Cletis's vision and the ringing subsided somewhat, although Cletis still didn't know what had happened. The crowd starting moving in closer, some laughing out of relief that Cletis wouldn't have to be pacified, at least not on this night.

Walt deliberately turned his back, making Cletis think Walt was vulnerable for a clear shot. The crowd gasped again, this time moving back getting as far off the dance floor as possible. Cletis sprang up and leaped through the air, which is what Walt was hoping he'd do, only this time he wouldn't hit Cletis with such force. He would hit fast, drawing each punch so as not to stun him again. As brother Lankern always said, "Thar's no fun to a fight iff'n thars only two hits—one's on a feller's jaw, the other's him hittin' the ground."

Walt let Cletis swing. Walt ducked, sidestepped and lunged, ending up behind him, slapping his ears hard enough to burst his eardrums, which made Cletis dizzy enough to lose his balance. Then Walt proceeded to work him over, most of his licks occurring faster than the eye could follow. The spectators were spellbound.

Clytis and Osrowl reluctantly decided to come to the aid of their brother. Homer had pointed them out to Walt before the battle started. Walt had kept an eye on them, knowing this time would come. Homer and Lankern started to move in to cut the Riley boys off. Walt, seeing this, gave them the signal not to interfere; he had it all under control.

Osrowl came first. Clytis, seeing how easy this slight-made man handled his bigger brother, figured he'd let his oldest brother connect first. Well, the connection was all one-way. One hard punch and Osrowl was lying flat on his back. Poor Clytis was whipped before Walt ever slapped him down. Walt never actually struck Clytis with his fists. He wasn't taking pity on him. He was a fighter in a new territory and knew a "no fist" defeat would build for him the reputation he wanted to establish as legend—not that Walt's reputation was lagging behind in the south side of the county. This was not simply brawling; fighting was a sport like any other and was considered a contest of skill. Most hill people had utmost respect for fighters.

Clytis and Osrowl, smarter and wiser than Cletis, lay or sat where they fell, giving open sign of submission, hoping their part in the tussle was over. Cletis, by now, had somewhat regained his bearings, enough to make one more final charge to even the score for him and his brothers. Walt knew Cletis wouldn't be able to come back for more punishment after this session. And Cletis had seen his two brothers, his only allies, on the floor. Cletis also foggily remembered his Uncle Jake slipping out the door when he had gained consciousness after the first bout.

Cletis rushed head down like a bull. Walt, making like a bullfighter, sidestepped again, stuck his foot out backwards and tripped Cletis, who sprawled headlong, smashing his head on the oiled pine floor. He laid there trembling, crying, saying, "Don't the people know they've done it all wrong? Supposed to hold me down? Be scared of me?"

He was still mumbling about all the procedures expected from the scared audience when Walt nabbed Cletis's overall galluses where they crossed his back. He led Cletis on hands and knees to where the old man was still sitting. Walt ordered Cletis to beg the old man for forgiveness.

Cletis said, "I apologize."

Walt said, "What?!"

Cletis growled, "I'm sorry!"

Walt kicked him square in the rear with the inside of his boot, sending Cletis into a belly flop, head up, arms and legs sprawled in a strange position. One among the crowd spoke aloud, more of a comment to herself, saying Cletis looked "jest like a big toad frog layin' thar lookin' up."

The crowd's roaring laughter drowned out the rest of her sentence. This was more than Cletis, the bully, could stand. He was still bawlin' when his brothers led him out of the school door. They were overly anxious to be mounted and on their way.

The McAfee boys didn't have to make camp that night. They had more invitations than they could ever accept. This was a turning point in their lives. In less than a year, they would all be married—Homer and Lankern to girls who were as close as sisters and were there at the pie supper. Walt married a woman who was a cousin to these two women and was not present that night, but grew full of admiration when the story was recounted.

chapter
TWELVE

Mashed Potatoes

The Riley boys made haste the first few miles on their homeward-bound trip, pulling up every so often when they reached the crest of a ridge. The moon was full and the night air cool and crisp—the kind of night in which sound would travel far and fast. Osrowl and Clytis, cupping their hands to their ears, would hold their breath with their eyes squeezed shut, straining to hear the faintest noise, wondering why the McAfee boys let them off with so little injury—other than their pride.

While listening for any possible pursuers, they repeatedly had to reprimand Cletis. Whenever they stopped, he'd commence his bawling, blubbering about the ringing in his ears, how dizzy his little head was, the no 'count bully, and what all he was going to do not only to him, but to every living man, woman, child, and beast here on the face of the earth. The other two, figuring the McAfee brothers were riding their way to overtake them, would yell at Cletis to shut his damn mouth, setting Cletis off into a longer, louder bawling fit of self-pity. Finally, Osrowl unhitched the jug, his daddy's jug, thinking Cletis would sip a few ounces and quiet down. Osrowl would then stop at the

Blowing Spring on the Smith farm and refill it, no one being the wiser. He told Clytis his plan since they'd have to ride a different route than they had come, only taking them a couple of miles out of their way. And, if they were being followed, this would throw their pursuers off.

Osrowl and Cletis figured they might as well have a few sips also, since it was just as easy to refill the jug at the Blowing Spring for three sippers as it would be for one.

They would've made the ride in half the time had it not been for their Pa's jug being passed around as they rode. At first, their fear kept them moving at a good clip. But soon, the liquor settled their nerves, giving the three renewed courage. They talked loud and for the most part all at once.

This was the scene when Osrowl's horse spooked. His mount threw its head forward, ears pointed in the same direction, eyes rolled back showing the whites with nostrils flared. His horse snorted, then abruptly jumped sideways and backwards just as the jug was being passed to Osrowl, who had his arms outstretched to receive it. As his hands touched the gallon jug, the lunge took place. It seemed to his two brothers that their eldest sibling was floating on air, suspended in space. It lasted a split second.

Cletis and Clytis's eyes were on the jug. The spooked horse's lunge was so quick that in their intoxicated state, they never saw the horse leap—just Osrowl settin' in space holding Pa's jug. He should have hovered longer for when he hit the earth, Pa's jug struck a limestone rock, shattering the bottom to pieces. Osrowl floundered a time or two finally getting stable on his feet, and went to catch up his horse. Clytis dismounted and ran to retrieve Pa's jug, which was lying on its side. He was worried its precious contents would spill, oblivious of the fact the bottom was shattered. Relieved to have it safely in his custody once more, he swore not to let the other two touch it again, and tied it to the saddle horn of his horse.

During all the commotion, Cletis discovered what made his brother's horse spook: white and red potatoes—several long rows of the largest spuds he'd ever seen. His mule had stretched her neck out to nibble at them. Cletis called to his brothers. The three inebriated men stood staring at the robust tubers. Osrowl's horse, still nervous from its recent scare, snorted and pranced back and forth over the drying potatoes.

Cletis noticed how easily they crunched under the weight of the gelding's iron-shod hoofs and entered into one of his rare laughs. The crazy high pitch made Cletis's mule start the same stomping dance, back and forth over the potatoes same as Osrowl's gelding. The mule was well versed on his master's laughs and knew this type of humanly sound usually signaled a thrashing coming. It was becoming hard to hold her. Cletis got back astride the mule, and began running her up one row then back down the other.

Initially, Osrowl and Clytis simply watched. Then they joined in the chase, even making rules for their spontaneous game. They rode till their animals were worn out and on the verge of being wind broken. Their steeds' bodies turned white with hot lather, and steam rose from their heaving, panting flanks as a fog rises from a warm brook on a cold, frosty morning.

The potatoes were stomped back into the earth that had produced them. Most of the tubers were so pulverized by the iron-clad hoofs they turned to liquid, soaking back into the rich black loam they had come from.

The novelty soon wore off for the Riley boys. But even if they hadn't tired of the game, the fun was over since there were no potatoes left to be destroyed.

The moon was low by the time they reached the Blowing Spring. There, they would refill Pa's jug of double-run straight 180-proof "white lightning." Clytis had taken command of Pa's jug when Osrowl levitated toward heaven off his gelding. He wasn't about to trust the other two with his Pappy's fine oil of life. Unhitching it from his saddle horn, he held the jug in a tight grip, scared in his drunken clumsiness he'd lose it in the Blowing Spring's gushing stream of water.

Clytis retrieved the gourd dipper that hung on the old maple tree at the spring's edge. He carefully set Pa's crock gallon jug on the large flat stone that had been placed there over half a century ago to receive a container being refilled or a full one so one could catch their breath before laboriously carrying it back.

Clytis squatted down and commenced to pouring dipper after large gourd dipper of the cold clear spring water into the gallon crock jug. After several dipper fulls, he stood, backed up, and walked a small circle to relieve the ache in his lower back. He returned, this time getting down on all fours, trying to peer into the crock jug's open black spout, sticking his finger as far as his hand would allow into the small opening. He then leaned over the jug to reach the stream of boiling gushing water. Dipping frantically, he poured dipper after dipper into the stone gallon container. Even as slow-witted as his twin brother Cletis was, he realized something was wrong and slurred, "What the hale ye gonna do, Clytis, dip the whole friggin' spring dry? Hit's only a gallon and ye already done and went and poured 50 or better through 'er."

Cletis's comment didn't deter Clytis from his objective of filling the jug. He fanned his dipper from water to jug all the faster, pouring now as rapidly as the dipper could scoop up the water and ladle it out, not caring if it hit the jug's mouth square, just as long as there was water being transferred toward the stone object he so fearlessly labored over.

Osrowl had drunk the least and always was the quickest witted of the Riley clan, which was still a few leagues behind the rest of the world. Osrowl walked over, snatched up the liquor container while Clytis was still dipping and pouring and said, "Here's the matter. I've found the problem!"

He proudly declared that the jug's bottom must have been busted out when Clytis set it on the large square rock to be filled.

Adam Troop's Missing Round

The next morning Bob was sent to fetch enough potatoes for their noon meal. Running back to the house and bursting into the kitchen breathless, he saw his mother and tried to speak, but no words would come. It was then he saw Jennie through the kitchen window entering through the yard gate. She'd just milked the cow and was coming back with the pail of milk. She went by the chicken house and opened the door, wanting to finish the chores early so she could devote the rest of the day to gathering wagonloads of potatoes and storing them in the their root cellar for the coming winter.

Bob tore out of the kitchen door and ran toward Jennie who sensed something was terribly wrong. She set the bucket of milk on the gatepost as Bob charged toward her, still trying to speak.

Finally, he said in a hoarse whisper, "Potatoes all gone! Come!" and he went as fast as his feet would pack him back toward the potato patch, nearly a quarter mile from the house. They had chosen this spot knowing the fertile loamy soil would produce a bumper crop.

Jennie saw the mess that was the field and knew the mass of destruction the potatoes would be in if there were any left at all. Entering the stomped ground that had once been the carefully laid long neat rows, she fell upon her knees, digging with her bare hands deep into the loose, black soil—the soil so woefully plowed up by the animals. Their iron-shod hooves had destroyed an entire summer's work, their year's crop. Bob's words said it all: "all gone."

Jennie trudged back up the gradual slope the quarter mile to the yard gate, retrieved her pail of milk, went into the kitchen and strained it, put it into its container, carried it out and placed it in the spring box.

She then went to her room, reached under her feather bed, and grasped the .32 revolver and .22 rifle.

There would be no potatoes gathered that day. Her doubts that had turned to fear of her weapons left her forever there in the middle of the potato patch.

Jennie began to teach herself to shoot, starting with the pistol. Brother Bob taught her what he knew, which was a fair amount since he often went hunting with his Stewart cousins. She practiced loading and unloading the cylinder, first on foot in a standing position, then running, then astride her horse, Bird. When this came as natural as breathing to her, she familiarized herself in the same way with her pump .22.

A large white oak tree stood in the middle of one of their hayfields located by the river just below the Blowing Spring, the same spring where the Riley brothers had tried to fill their Pa's jug. She chose this spot to learn the art of shooting. She practiced every evening after returning home from the one-room country school. She would first do her chores. Then, if there was any light left at all, she would race to the field with the large oak.

It was a Saturday in late March. She had not practiced lately since the field had to be turned on the upper and lower farms to ready them once again to receive their different crops. It had rained just enough to make the earth clot. It would do more harm than good to turn it when the ground was this wet. The March wind was blowing steadily and an occasional gust would give rise to whirlwinds. Watching one come toward her and her target—the giant old oak—she thought how she and brother Bob, as children, would run and play, trying to stay in the swirling wind. Now she was 13 and Bob was 10. She had taken, or rather was handed, the responsibility that had fallen to her upon their father's death. Grandfather Bealert died a year later. Before he died, he took what money, gold, and jewelry there was and hid it all except for an old Spanish gold coin she'd found while plowing the upper Gladden Valley farm's field—the same field in which she found the silver bullion stamped with an odd insignia. Her mother's sister Frankie took it to the Rolla School of Mines. She laughed aloud thinking Grandpa should've hidden it also, no more good than either of her treasure discoveries ever did the family. Soon as the word got out, "Sunday treasure seekers" came by the droves, literally stomping the ten-acre field of corn back into the earth. *So,* she thought, *we lost again.*

Looking at the small owl's head .32 in her hand, she wondered if this would turn out to be a loss also, no better than it had gone so far. She cocked, aimed, and fired. Seeing she had missed not only her target, but also the huge tree it was nailed to, she held its trigger down fanning the hammer, letting the other four shots go wild. She never put all six bullets in, letting the hammer rest on the empty shell cylinder.

Soon as the last bullet left the barrel, there was a voice so close to her ear she felt the breath of the speaker on the nape of her neck. She whirled around with empty pistol in hand, arm dangling limp by her side in fright. Her hearing had always been extra keen. While firing, she would put cotton balls in her ears. In spite of this, she should have heard the tall, lean, grey-headed stranger's approach.

He wore buckskins and moccasins that were not the back-east city type. The pack on his back caught her attention. It was so neat, so uniquely made of willow and rawhide, cleverly put together with everything having its place down to the 94 model lever action 30/30 Winchester and the large Colt black-powder pistols strapped on either side.

The pack had been designed so the guns could be retrieved immediately without having to remove it from his back.

His hair was long. His smoked tan headband made his neatly trimmed white beard and hair seem all the more silver-white. Everything about him had an odd, mystical feel—even his eyes, as they stood staring at each other for those few seconds. Jennie thought, *I've never seen any human more pleasing to my eye.* Yes, even his eyes were strangely different. One was a pale sky blue, the other as dark as the one was light, it being the color of fresh-brewed strong coffee.

"Son," he addressed Jennie, not realizing yet her gender, "if you plan on being a gunfighter, I hate to inform you you're about 40 years too late."

This made both of them laugh. Soon as he heard her, he declared, slapping his leg, "By law! You're a girl! What are you doing out here with a gun?" He then turned red in the face; she could tell his last words brought embarrassment.

He started to apologize for his last statement, but Jennie never let him finish. All her fears and doubts she shed forth to this complete stranger, not even knowing his name. As she talked, a bond arose instantly between them. She told of the Riley boys, the hardships they'd brought through their destruction, and even of her own grandfather going senile and then dying. (She never admitted his senility to anyone else right down to her own death at 83 years old.)

He asked her about her father. When Jennie told her memories of his death and funeral, the silver-headed man turned away, pretending to study the massive white oak tree to hide the tears that ran down to soak into his silky white silver beard.

He stretched his arms over his head, cleared his throat, and spoke again—this time in earnest tones. He took his heavy pack, loosened its shoulder and waist straps, slipped it off, and laid it on the ground. Reaching out his hand, he took her gun. She handed him the bullets from her father's ragged blue cotton work coat. He went to the tree, picked up six small pebbles, placed them into the bark, and walked back to where they were hardly visible. He asked her if she owned a belted holster. She reached under her coat and unbuckled the wide belt. The belt had never been cut down and had ample notches to receive his lean waist. He strapped it on and adjusted it to his liking.

Watching, Jennie for the first time grasped the meaning of the old adage, "The hand is quicker than the eye." She never saw his hand move, thinking later she must have blinked at the precise instant he drew. Five small stones out of six were busted. She was awestruck, speechless. The tall man was confused also, talking aloud to himself, walking toward the tree. Upon reaching it, he inspected the holes where the pebbles had been, peering and looking for the sixth.

By now, Jennie had made it to the target tree, staring wide-eyed at his skill as a marksman. "I wonder what happened to the sixth," he said, more to himself than to her. It was then Jennie realized the silver-headed man wasn't looking at his shooting in pride, but just the opposite since he had missed the sixth, the largest stone of all.

She giggled, saying, "I have it figured out." He was still looking for some sign of a bullet hole when the girl informed him she'd only given him five bullets, a habit she acquired when she started her practicing. He laughed and slapped his knee, one of his many habits she would get to know so well in the coming year.

He started their first lesson on this clear windy March day, telling her to quit sighting her pistol, to leave that type of shooting for her rifle. He began by having her aim with her hand as if she were holding the small owl's head pistol and her index finger was its barrel. She did this hundreds of times, at dozens of different objects. He observed all this with his keen marksman's eye.

Finally, she said, with hand trembling, tense arm cramping, that her shoulder wouldn't let her go any longer. Grinning, he spoke for the first time since she had started drawing the imaginary gun from her holster.

"You have learned the most important lesson of a gunfighter."

Jennie thought, *Have I? What was it?*

"You know now, young lady, you have been tense, straining as if you were holding an anvil in your hand. I want you to practice now with your pistol empty, and soon as you get out of the habit you've cultivated, we'll make the next lesson live. Now, if it is permissible with you, take me to your mother. I would like to speak with her in private."

As the two turned toward the old Spanish fort house, the young girl felt the first relief she'd known since her father's death. She didn't even know the stranger's name yet felt as though she'd known him all her life. He slowed down his long strides and still made the youth hit a trot at times to keep up. The old man grinned to himself, thinking, *This girl's got grit, okay. Never seen any kid go that long that fast.*

Leaving the stranger standing on the porch, Jennie entered the house, went to the kitchen, and approached her mom. "There is a kind gentlemen waiting on the porch to speak with you." Her mother Susie went to the porch door and invited him into the parlor. Jennie never entered—he'd said "in private." Besides, it was time to start the evening chores.

The silver-headed gentleman introduced himself to Jennie's mother as Adam Troop. Then, in his easy manner, he got right down to business, telling Susie Smith that he had stopped two days prior at the Rector post office, which was also a general store, to purchase supplies. He'd heard a loud-talking, intoxicated, belligerent young man making threats. "After he left," Adam explained, "I spoke to the postmaster about what I'd overheard." He chuckled and slapped his knee. "Actually I couldn't keep from hearing, since he made sure I heard by shouting the complete incident in my ear!"

"After the postmaster and I had our visit, I started to proceed on my planned journey. But . . ." Blushing, the ancient wanderer looked down, shuffled his feet, and then looked Susie square in the eye. "I have come to rent your cabin."

Susie Smith, never one who needed to be "beat over the head," accepted this act of kindness. She, too, felt as her daughter Jennie—a kinship, an immediate bond with this tall, lean old man.

This is the way Adam Troop came into their lives. He would have a place in their hearts and minds until their own deaths decades later. Here, this man's act of kindness is being put down for purposes unknown; perhaps for the kindness and the concern he felt for the underdog, or the knowledge he possessed to turn the weak and fearful into a force to be reckoned with.

chapter
FOURTEEN

Brother Bob's Book

Susie refused his rent each month pointing out to him all the labor he'd performed: the tasks of planting, mowing, mending of fences and buildings. He seemed to have a relentless supply of energy. He had whipped not one, but both farms back into shape. Each evening, Adam and his student would go down to the giant old oak tree.

One evening, he said to Jennie, "When you have it shot dead," pointing at the old tree, "you'll be able to go up against Wyatt Earp." He then stared off into space. Jennie could tell his memory was traveling back in time. All of the sudden, he laughed and slapped his knee saying, "I hope you get better than that, for it sure wouldn't take much of a gunfighter for the chore!"

The instructor had his student to the point where her weapons had become a part of her anatomy. The pistol with its sights removed had become her finger, the rifle her arm. They now belonged to her. They were part of her. He'd even told her she was a natural. She possessed the odd trait of what he called "eye to hand contact."

The crops were laid by early, but not simply because of his labor. He had organized each job, turning the work into a game, making Jennie and brother Bob look forward to each morning. With the onset of evening, his student and her kid brother would fetch in arm loads of scrap wood for their outside fire. They would gather around this nightly fire after the chores were completed.

One night, Adam brought his willow rawhide pack into the fire's circle. Ceremoniously, he untied the rawhide straps from around the sleeping tarp that held all of his unseen treasures. The two children sat breathless, as if it was Christmas time at their cousin's cabin. They'd witnessed this odd ritual once. This night by the fire, with the flickering light dancing off the silver hair of his beard and long flowing hair, he reminded them of stories they'd heard of St. Nicholas. Bob was still just young enough to want to believe in the Santa Claus myths he'd heard at school, and whispered to his sister while Adam released the straps and spread the tarp out to expose its contents to the shimmering light of the fire. The two brass carbide lights gathered the light of the fire, reflecting it into the boy's eyes as he turned his head back to gaze at the wonders of the old man's pack.

Young brother Bob, in his excitement, not realizing he was speaking his thought aloud, blurted out, "Hell, I knew he was Santa Claus all along! He's just lost a ton of weight is all!"

Jennie and Adam's eyes met, both trying to hold in their laughter. They knew it would explode any second and didn't want to embarrass the boy, loving his innocence. Jennie came this time to the rescue. "Bob, I'd bet Mr. Troops would like to see your book."

The boy leaped up from the fire ring and ran to the house to fetch his most cherished possession. While Bob was away, Adam told the girl about the cave he'd discovered, there being several caves on the old home place. None ran too far back into the earth and their entrances were extremely large. This made it easy for young explorers to go a short distance before returning to safety. He explained to her the danger in this one. The mouth was no wider than 2 and ½ feet, making a 90-degree turn in about 20 feet, opening up into its first small chamber. Thereafter, each ran into a larger living chamber. He briefly told her he'd been in hundreds of caves from Mexico to Canada and this one had him awestruck. He was going to explore it and would probably be gone for a couple days, wanting to travel its main chamber and, if there was time, some of its contemporary ones. He told her as soon as he returned, he would seal its entrance. Adam started to say more, but saw her younger brother coming toward them. He wanted to keep the cave a secret from Bob, so he changed the subject, pretending to explain the usage and care of the carbide lamps.

Bob came proudly, holding his book as if bearing the Arc of the Covenant, presenting his most sacred possession to Mr. Troop. Adam took the book and began looking at its pictures, bypassing most of the novelist's propaganda. He thought, *If I told this young boy I knew practically everyone in this book, he would be so excited he'd tell everyone he knew or met, and everyone would think and say that the old man was a "windjammer" or just another "old blowhard."*

Adam knew from experience in these modern times there was no way of making people comprehend that in his young days, the West was utterly vast with very few places the Caucasians called "civilized," such as forts. A few towns sprung up as the settlers started moving west of the Mississippi. If you were actually there, you were likely a trapper, then prospector, hide hunter, and later, Indian fighter. When all such occupations had been exhausted in order, many men prostituted themselves and turned gunfighter—either for the law or for hire to anyone who had the means to pay. He looked at each picture as you would a family album, visited by thoughts that had burned out of his memory over half a century or better, sometimes shifting his position, turning the large book to catch more light from the fire. He would frown occasionally and shake his head. Then, he'd chuckle to himself at the next photo or drawing thinking how true it was that "the pen is mightier than the sword." Seeing the image of a long forgotten face, then reading briefly what the novelist had written he would think, *Yes, there is a fragment of truth*, and the next moment he would experience actual shock, knowing personally how pathetic the glorified person really was.

He then turned to the page that was Bob's favorite—the Indian with the scarred eye. Here, Adam Troop sat up straighter, reached for one of his carbide lights, and lit it. Retrieving his bifocals from his pack, he read the story over twice. He then reached in the pack and got his magnifying glass and held it to the picture, studying it carefully. Turning his carbide light off, he handed the book back to its owner and excused himself by saying, "It's late and if I am to get an early start, I'd better turn in."

Adam looked at the boy. "Son, you keep everything going until I get back. I've got to attend to some unfinished business."

At this, little brother Bob took his book and walked toward his room and bed feeling very tall that night.

chapter
FIFTEEN

The Indian with the Scarred Eye

Before first light, the old explorer was already in the cave's entrance. He'd gone over his supplies the prior evening while packing. He moved a five-pound sack of cornmeal to get to the soda crackers he'd purchased for the journey. Picking up the cornmeal, the Old Mother Goose tale of "Hansel and Gretel" came to mind. He smiled, thinking, *Yes, I must be getting old. Next thing I know, I'll be playing jacks wearing out my pants knees!*

Taking the fresh ground meal, he put it in his pack, knowing full well he wouldn't use it and that it would just be five pounds of extra weight. Shrugging his shoulders, he started to take it out, and then remembered the extra carbide. He went to the cabin's outer room, brought back the carbide and put it in his rawhide pack, forgetting about the cornmeal and leaving it with his survival gear.

Crawling the short distance to the first small chamber, the air seemed cool, Adam having just come out from the warm summer's early dawn.

He slipped on the light wool shirt he'd carried for this very purpose, knowing his body would adjust to the cave's temperature in a few hours.

To keep track of his location, Adam used his combination watch and compass built back-to-back and his small waterproof notebook to set down the minutes and degrees. He had over the years in exploring scores of caverns become so familiar with this method it was now second nature, never failing him. He felt completely confident. As long as there was ground to walk on he knew he could make it back to his starting point.

An hour in, he knew this was no ordinary cavern. There were large offshoots from what he took for the main chamber. Realizing how easy it would be to get confused, he started leaving more sign and going more slowly. Since he would be spending at least 48 hours there, he figured he would run out of the cave's main chambers before exploring some of its lesser ones.

His light illuminated formations that Old Man Time had sculpted over millions of years. Within the first 24 hours, he saw stalagmites in one high chamber that were the most massive he'd ever seen. He first thought they were entrances to several small caverns before realizing what they really were. He started to return to change his bearing marks and symbols. He was mesmerized by the wonder and mystery of millions of years. The stalagmites and stalactites were revealing shifting sculptures from the illumination of the carbide light attached to his cap. Some were angels, their wings opening and closing as the light played across their height and width. There were myriads of warriors of old, marching ghost-like before his eyes. Some came in single file, others in battle. Turning to look again at the same formation, it would become an old man or woman bowed forward struggling with the burden they had labored under since the founding of the earth.

Then, it happened. His feet were no longer on solid earth. *How could this be?* He later wanted to scream these words to echo off the massive sculptured walls—this abode that would hold his remains forever.

He had just trodden this same path only minutes before. It was solid and almost level, not broken up as some of the other chambers he'd traveled through an hour before. This had laid the snare. Adam had put away caution, letting his guard down, confident that he knew this short length of the cavern's floor. He didn't see the black hole on his first passing. It lay there innocently as a bottle plant waiting for a fly—waiting for millenniums. It now had the old explorer in its grip. If the opening had been as wide as where the small protruding rock was that his foot caught, he would have fallen hundreds of feet down into another underground chamber system.

He was struggling for his life. Adam clung to the rim and clawed the cold, damp rock of the cave's floor, not feeling the pain or shock of the fall. His fingers dug frantically for life, plunging into the crevices of the opening. He managed to raise his own weight with superhuman strength; the type of power that one possesses, the hidden strength, that ebbs and flows in such mortal emergencies. Afterwards, it leaves the possessor so weak it can take hours to days to recover.

The old explorer had neither.

After bodily raising himself vertically, kicking and clawing until his stomach reached the rim of his would-be tomb, he lay barely breathing. An observer would have thought Adam dead—motionless as the limestone formations that surrounded his limp form. He'd been in many close scrapes with death in his 82 years. Here he lay, an old man exceptionally strong in health and years. He had outlived all he knew from his youth. Consciousness waning, his hands grasped his carbide lamp. Burning his fingers, he turned its jet lever till the flame subsided.

He lay in this great tomb too weak to even return the short distance to where he'd left his pack. He desired the warmth of his sleeping tarp and wool blankets and the security and comfort he drew from them. His instinct told him in this ebony black darkness that he was still among the living. But he was so fatigued, so drained of energy.

Adam knew if he moved now, he would die. This was the old man's last waking thought as he slid into semiconsciousness.

Before him stood the Indian with the mean scarred eye, the same one who he'd lit off his carbide lantern to study in depth at the fire just two days prior. Now the picture came swirling, turning into form, the form of the living, as much alive as Adam—maybe more alive than the old man laying in this cold black void.

part
TWO

ADAM'S SECOND CHANCE

chapter
ONE

The Living Symbols of Peace

Adam's body quit shaking and he felt a pleasant warmth engulf him. He tried to remember where he was. What year? For here stood his brother-in-law before him.

"Witch-ka," said Adam, "the white men have made you a chief."

Witch-ka frowned, looked puzzled, but never spoke, knowing his sister's husband would clarify his statement.

"Yes, they have your picture in a book—the picture that the black robed man took when you went with Kicking Bird to Washington D.C. to get the papers that were going to bring peace as long as the grass grew, the water ran, the sky—"

Adam never finished the rest of Washington D.C.'s propaganda speech. They were both laughing. They could laugh now. Each had waited several scores of years for this moment, remembering the strife, the division, the resentment, the doubt, even actual murderous hate. The going and bringing back of the document had erected barriers between families and friends, breaking bonds that would never heal. The scar remained tender, standing out, making itself—

Their laughter interrupted their thoughts again. Both remembered what was done with the peace medals and peace treaty document less than a month after the peace seeker's return.

The U.S. Calvary had charged the small hunting party's village, killing Witch-ka's wife and two children. If she had been white, they would have said three, since she was big pregnant. Too heavy with child to flee, she could not run and hide. The life she was about to bring forth brought death to the giver.

Now, the aged wanderer and cave explorer was not old. Adam returned to his youth, though only in this delirium.

He gets a second chance. Looking back, his entire life was but a glance, a fleeting moment. It was the day-to-day aspect that took an eternity. Young, the years turn slowly. In ancient years, they are as a blade on a buzz saw. As the black robe's book speaks it, a "twinkling of an eye."

Witch-ka remembered well what their people did to the peace medals and then to the treaty itself. They placed the peace medals under a forked crotch of a ponderosa pine top that had been dethroned from its lofty crown years before. It had weathered into a blue steel gray and was the perfect height, even better than a squatting position. It would be an affair for every member of the tribe. Man, woman, and child relieved themselves upon the large round medals and red, white, and blue shiny ribbons.

Then, the "living symbols of peace," as the Great White Father in Washington called the long, broad sheet of stiff paper, were used to swipe their rears. They had, at first, held the scroll in sacred reverence, with its beautiful elaborately printed surface. Only Mississippi's husband, Adam, the man with the strange-colored eyes, could speak the sacred message that it contained from the Great Chief who lived in the Great House from where it was issued. Their chief and the others who had made the trip told the squaws they could pitch all their teepees in the great room of the Great Chief's house, never filling it up, and that the ceiling reached into the heavens itself. Their language lacked the words to describe the magnitude of the riches, the wealth, and the food they saw their white brothers owned. No wonder Mississippi asked Adam over and over again until even he, with his good nature, grew impatient and wouldn't answer, refusing to try to further clarify another question.

"Why, Strange Eyes, does your people, with all, want what little we have? Not even satisfied to take our ponies, our lodges and kettles, but must have our lives also, not even wanting to allot us a space to rest after they have brought the sting of death to all. Why? Why? Why? Can't they ever get enough?"

Witch-ka said, "I will let you return to your thoughts, brother, but first I want you to make matters straight. I always wondered, Strange Eyes. I saw the slaughter with my own eyes when I returned. You killed the blue coats in battle when they charged our camp. If it had not been for you, they would have destroyed us all. Instead, you killed all 28, even their horses. Why did you not go relieve yourself on the medals, wipe on their treaty or their sacred cloth? Does it still hold great power over you? Think back, brother. From that day onward, your wife's—my sister's—heart grew cold toward you. We all knew where the dissention entered into your lodge. She spoke of her shame openly to her mother, the shame that eventually drove her to her death. Tell me this day so I too can rest. What was the great power of the White Father's things?"

Adam, for the first time in Witch-ka's long speech, realized what he was talking about: he was wondering why Adam never went forth and shit on the pile of human feces that had already accumulated on the peace medals. He remembered one couldn't even tell there was anything under the pile of dung. He then would've had to catch the shitty peace treaty or flag to wipe his ass. Knowing he would draw all eyes, Adam realized the act would be impossible. Even if he could have pulled it off, because he was the very last one, he would have the whole tribe's shit from elbow to asshole. Witch-ka's roaring laughter echoed along with his parting words. "Strange Eyes, Strange Eyes, so much grief from such small worry. May you go in peace."

The light and the scarred-eyed warrior were gone. The sound of water trickling, dripping, bubbling in the black distance of the blind, dark cavern made the old man stir, knowing he was still alive. He reached out to grasp his most treasured possession. Life hinged on this manmade invention: light. "Let there be light." Even the sons of the true God proclaimed, "Light is good." He withdrew his flint and steel, taking it carefully out of its case, knowing the loss of either would mean the loss of light forever.

Turning the carbide jet to the lighting position, he struck flint to steel, giving rise to a miracle in this large black void: light. Adam, born with exceptional vision, realized he had never truly seen until this moment. The cave's walls, ceiling, and floors took on a whole new visual meaning. He saw things trivial and great that he'd missed in all his previous years. It made him feel small. A prayer came to his heart; his mind received it and his lips transmitted it. He chanted the prayer in the fine deep tones of his voice. The words were of his wife's people—the morning prayer of the Mandans. *So symbolic*, he thought as he chanted. They are all gone—none left, the same as he, Adam, was the last of his kind.

He shined the now bright carbide lamp not on the walls or ceilings and the wonders exhibited there, but in search of the lowly waterproof notebook and his gold watch and compass, thinking as soon as he retrieved them he'd go fetch his pack and start his retreat. He wanted to get back to the entrance knowing it might take two days or better due the condition the fall had left him in.

He searched in a daze. Still very weak, he felt his awareness slipping again. His brain was giving up trying to save his tired heart, the heart that had blessed the old man with the extraordinary strength to pull himself out of the deep void, the bottom of which light could not reach. He had crept to its edge, looking, hoping the light would reflect off his watch's golden polished surface, betraying its hiding place. He knew the notebook would be there also. Feeling the weakness coming in waves over his semiconscious body, he realized now that he'd had a slight stroke. He must give up the search, go to his pack while there was still time, make a pallet where it was dry, rest, and force himself to eat, rest, eat, rest, till his strength prevailed.

Adam could never recall his short trip back to his willow pack or how long he lay suspended between life and death. He had been in a sort of stupor for several hours when he finally awoke. His hands felt the sleeping tarp and wool Hudson trade blankets that had kept the chill out of his old bones. Not having to draw from the little store of precious energy left in his now aged, ailing body helped him to recuperate enough to gain a small appetite. He felt around the perimeter of his pallet and located his pack. He sought out by touch the crackers and block of cheese. Reaching under his covers, he fumbled until his hand met with the hilt of his belt knife.

The knife was almost as old as he, it being one of his first purchases. He smiled as his hand pulled it forth to carve his block of light cream-yellow cheese. His old, weak hand had held the same knife—

His smile faded when his memory flashed the haunting scene of him astride a war pony, a fresh-gutted cavalry soldier hanging from his arms as he tried to get the knife unhung. It was razor sharp and entered the soft flesh of the soldier, slitting its way up to the rib cage, then entering into the sternum and making its way up between the ribs where it lodged. Adam was riding in a dead run, the soldier hanging from his arm. He was one of the last soldiers killed in the cavalry's own battle.

Still, the old man always wished it had never been. It is one of many memories of his youth he could have lived without, as his weak hand struggled to transfer another small morsel of protein to his mouth.

A sharp pain struck his chest like a blow from a sledgehammer, throwing him back onto his pallet as he felt a ball of fire run down his left arm and explode at the elbow. The blackness of the cave transformed into golden swirling lights, shooting out prisms of every conceivable color.

Then he saw her. She was standing with a buffalo robe wrapped around her shoulders covering her body completely. Even her feet were hidden from view. Her eyes were teasing him, taunting him, bringing both of them laughter the way she'd always done before the soldiers came to make their massacre.

Adam shifted to obtain a more comfortable position. She vanished, taking the lights and colors with her before he had a chance to explain, to state his case, his reason, why he had failed so many years ago. Then, he chuckled, reached down, slapped his knee and chuckled again, thinking of his wife who had drowned so long ago. *This is MAD. Witch-ka has been dead for years. Could all of our troubles have been so simple as me not wanting to crap publicly on the peace medals, treaty, and flag?*

Adam stared into the pitch-black darkness, not wanting any light to interfere with his thoughts. His memories were all there was to life now. He wanted to retreat back to his beginning, try to reason it out and make some sense of his life—at least understand this current, this wicked current that every living soul who has ever tasted life will eventually be caught in. He wondered whether death would be a release or whether it would flow indefinitely.

Adam tried to recall how his mother looked, but he received nothing but a large purple brooch she wore pinned to her bosom and the two matching gold-colored combs in her hair as she lay dead in her coffin. As for his father, he couldn't recollect what the man had died of, let alone any of his attributes.

His mother died when he was twelve. He could remember a large man in the broadcloth suit with a tall stovepipe beaver hat. No sooner than they closed her grave, the big man informed the boy he had him a job. He would be leaving out the same evening with a trapping party outfitted by the old Hudson Bay Company. It went by a different name then, but that was no concern of his. He would learn a good trade and be with respectable "God-fearing men." Listen to what they say and look to them for an example, and he would turn out all right.

The fat man in the beaver hat talked nonstop as they trod the muddy streets of St. Louis, Missouri, finally arriving at the dock where the ferry was getting underway. The man in the broadcloth suit shoved the boy on board hollering in French, causing an uproar and cheers. A skinny woman walked up, slipped her hand down into the boy's pants, then pulled it out making a mocking gesture as though she were fainting, which inspired another round of loud jeering and laughter.

At this time, a small, lean, mean-looking Frenchman by the name of Charbonne reached the boy's side and pulled out a long hunting knife. Adam knew he was a dead man. The Frenchman was speaking fast in his native tongue making threatening motions at the mob all the while.

Finally, looking down at the tow-headed boy, he said, "Fook 'em all, sos o' beeches, yu cam vith me!"

Adam stood with his mouth open, staring at the small sword the Frenchman called a knife. Seeing the boy's frozen expression of fear, he laughed, sheathed his weapon, placed his arm around the young boy's shoulders, and led him to the rest of the trappers who had congregated at the bow of the ferry.

Here this day, Adam was introduced to the world of the trapper, never looking back, never feeling homesick. There was nothing to look back upon. His entire little world now lay beneath the ground. Wherever he hung his hat, that was where he was from. It was home. He learned fast, never speaking or asking questions, observing every move the trappers made. He listened intently to every instruction, never having to be told but once. He saw what had to be done and did it, winning favor with all. This ensured him passage with the best of trappers in this large outfit.

By the time he was 16, he'd become a master of his occupation. The only drawback was that the trappers had penetrated so deep, harvested so hard, they almost wiped out the beaver. The market was set by fad and fashion, and the beaver hat had fallen by the wayside. The trapper had grown used to the animal's high value due to what gentlemen of high esteem were willing to pay for the finished product. However, the trend had turned to a manmade material. This was good for the beaver, which nearly went the way of the dodo bird.

Adam had saved almost every coin that crossed his palm. One year, many gold ones came his way. He sold more prime pelts of beaver, mink, muskrat, and ermine than any one party of men combined. He never bought liquor, gambled, or spent his money on women.

All the same, he craved to have, to hold, to be owned by one of those mysterious creatures, but not those he'd seen down at Taos, Mexico. No. He'd seen the Cheyenne maidens and the women of several other bands in winter camp. He knew what he wanted and hoped for, yet not one ever glanced his way. Later Charbonne would tell him all the young maidens had their eyes on him. He remembered his answer. "Hell, I must be stone blind, Frenchie. I don't even remember their dogs lookin' my way." This made the wiry little Frenchman roar with laughter, slapping the tall, good-looking young man between the shoulder blades, knocking the breath out of him.

The Frenchman informed him there were lots of women at the rendezvous he could have for the price of a coin. Adam said nothing, remembering his first trip with this same man. The Frenchman seemed to have forgotten the pain and agony he'd gone through. But the youth remembered all too clearly. Their party had been out for the better part of two weeks when one evening Charbonne was doubled up in spasms of pain trying to piss.

Finally, he called out to a giant Frenchman by the name of Sybane, who was a doctor of sorts known for concocting herbs, making salve poultices, cutting out bullets, setting bones, and even pulling teeth. Charbonne pleaded in French for something to bring relief. Sybane said, "Let us look at your ailment."

Charbonne unbuttoned his pants and brought out his red, swollen member he had wrapped in a young beaver pelt, trying to keep it from being jarred, rubbed, or touched. The slightest movement would set him into a wretched agony.

Sybane's voice changed. He spoke low, soothingly, as though addressing a young child. He informed the owner of the puss-filled, swollen, stopped up pecker he had the exact treatment—just the thing. He would administer a warm soothing poultice. Then, a drink of an herbal concoction would relieve the pain and discomfort. But first, Charbonne needed to lay "it" flat on the high block of wood they'd been using for a butcher block. This way he could administer the poultice.

Adam remembered he was standing straight in the line of fire—not the line that shoots flames, but the one that spews corruption.

Sybane looked at Adam. "You, boy, don't stand in my light."

The boy moved, thinking to himself, *There is no light.* About that time a scream and string of curses came from the little Frenchman's lungs that must have resounded into the bowels of hell, for they surely would not be granted entrance into the heavens. Sybane had struck the puss-swollen diseased cock, jarring loose the scabby scales that had encrusted within stopping up its urethral opening, releasing a stream of bloody puss and held in piss, but not the pain.

Charbonne was now on the ground vomiting. Adam, a mere boy of 12, vowed right then and there, standing on earth, stars overhead as his witnesses, he would be a virgin on his wedding night, morning, or whenever and wherever these sorts of matters take place.

chapter

TWO

Adam's Courtship

My money belt was full. It was heavy to the touch with $50 gold pieces, but I still lived as if I hadn't two nickels to rub together, always fearful of being destitute. I never bought fancies or frills. My clothing consisted of buckskins. I could've worn a broadcloth suit of clothes and tall felt hat and pretended to be of blue blood, but I knew the shine and glitter wouldn't last long. Your money is gone and your good-time buddies are not to be found when it's their turn to buy.

I went to my last rendezvous, which was held on the Green River in Wyoming. It was there I saw the most beautiful creation under the sun and it literally took my breath away. I would gladly give all the large gold pieces I'd saved in my five years, my full working life up to that hour. No, it sure wasn't the sagebrush barren-looking land. That was free for the taking.

Her hair hung long and she seemed to float across the level ground where we were having our games and horse races. I first saw her when the heat of betting was at its highest. No one had their eyes off the racers, thus giving me my greatest opportunity to openly gaze at her.

I would normally have been too shy to ever look upon these fairy creatures.

I wanted to get closer. Living the way I had in the open, becoming one with nature, my senses of sight, hearing, and smell became animal keen. I had now seen this lovely being. I had even heard her speak and laugh with her female companions. I wanted to ease my way in and pretend I was engulfed in the races. This way I could breathe deep, my nostrils close to her hair. This is the way I figured it out, not knowing one thing about the opposite sex, much less courtship.

I was nervous. Actually, nervous is what one feels when you are knife fighting three men at once. I can tell you, I have been there and this is on top of the mountain; the knife fighting is still at the base—that was my feeling that day. I would work into an ideal position, then the damn racing ponies in their speed-crazed frenzy would draw the crowd like the moon does the tide, coming and going on a beach, nothing ever stable enough for this delicate operation.

Finally, I was there. The slight breeze was in my favor. At the same time, but not to my knowledge since I was so preoccupied with my task, the banty-legged little Irishman on the blue roan runner was having trouble holding his steed in. He became furiously angry at the crowd's goading, jeering, and mocking. The Irishman was very intoxicated. The horse grew terrified of his rider's whip until it reared up to where it should have fallen backwards. Instead, it staggered on its hind legs straight toward the Indian maidens.

I never actually witnessed any of this. I could only see how her thick black hair hung straight to her thin waist, dancing in the breeze, a little strand catching then grouping with other pieces fluttering out, coming so close to touching me. I would forget to breathe, thinking if only one strand would fall, I would retrieve it, then I would slip away. I'd just closed my eyes to take a deep breath of her scent that I would let filter slow and long, penetrating my mind, body, and soul.

I never heard the crowd scream its warning calls. The next instant, there she was in my arms. The horse at first was vertical, then perpendicular over us. I don't remember any of these moves for I had my eyes closed, concentrating on the scents my being was trying to sort out.

I had this divine creature in my arms and I had leaped with her out of harm's way. I became very embarrassed, thinking the crowd's applauds and calls were aimed at me having been caught in my secret act. Now it was out, known to all. I was taking long strides, thinking I could catch up my horses and pack animals, break camp, and get the hell out of here. I had walked across what seemed a good acre of ground when I sensed something was wrong. There was a small pair of brown hands holding my face. I stopped dead in my tracks, standing still as a statue. Charbonne claimed I had one foot raised to make the next step. There I stood paralyzed, motionless, wondering *how did this lovely being get out here? Why is she before me? Have I done something wrong? Yes, I have really messed up this time! Damn, why didn't I just break camp soon as I sold my pelts and move out like I had always done before?*

It was Charbonne's voice that finally filtered through and brought me back to earth. This was the first time I realized I was holding her.

"Vat yu due Audam, hole 'er all yare?"

Everyone was laughing now, slapping me on the back, hugging and punching in relief. All had turned out well. I had unknowingly saved her from under the horse's killing hooves. I was still standing in the half-stride position holding Mississippi. For reasons unknown I looked straight into the beautiful face and said, for the first time in my life, "I love you. I want to marry you. I'll do everything the rest of my life just for you."

Charbonne was interpreting as I spoke, but not to my knowledge because of my love stricken state. Leave it to a Frenchman—he must have really put a poetic spin on my short prose for he was still talking long after I got myself composed and set her gently down.

I was still holding her little warm hand as Charbonne spoke. Every so often she'd give my rough callused one a firm and loving squeeze that made my heart literally do odd little flutters. My lungs were doing their own little antics, too.

Of course, it wasn't up to her. Since her father had been killed in a war party against the Crow three years before, Charbonne would have to go parley with Witch-ka (Knife), her brother. And parley he did. It went on for better than a week, and as custom would have it, the bride-to-be and groom could not look upon each other for any reason at anytime. If they did, woe would eventually befall the union.

I furnished everything Charbonne felt necessary. I must have bought all the trade liquor and strong rope twist tobacco west of the Mississippi. I asked Charbonne along toward the end of the week if it always took so long. The little Frenchman looked up in a drunken stupor and slurred, "Don't fret so! Yu have vest of yu life to greez yur pole an' ze trader's kegs are almost empty!"

chapter
THREE

The Sacred Pole

Charbonne's broken English was so slurred, all the lovesick boy heard was that he had to "grease a pole." Assuming it a custom of his future bride's people, Adam proceeded to purchase by barter a lodge pole and skin pouch of bear grease and gave the pole a good lubing. Not knowing where to put it or why, he punched a shallow hole and set it up in the fashion of a totem pole, and felt confident that he had properly performed the customary ritual.

As they passed by Adam's camp, the bride-to-be's people would do reverence to the greased pole, thinking it was some sacred emblem of white man's customs before marriage. Adam had let it be known to all he was going to have Preachin' Bill perform a wedding service making their marriage binding in both worlds.

Adam saw how impressed her people were with the pole. Some touched it and chanted. Some of the older squaws trembled, crying as they sang, falling upon their knees and having to be helped up by others, then were too weak to walk back to their lodge without help.

The young bridegroom-to-be thought, *Yes, Charbonne is a wise man, knowing all their customs. If it hadn't been for him, I could've easily got off to a bad start.* He peered out through his tent flaps. It was barely first light and already there were several old squaws making their morning pilgrimage to this newest, most holy emblem. He realized for the first time since he'd started handing over gold coin after gold coin to the wise and worldly Frenchman what a true friend he was. *Here I'd felt resentment when I first started doling out the hard earned coins,* thought Adam. *Yes, Charbonne can have them all if need be for truly he knows best.*

Fortunately for Adam's money belt and his postponed wedding, the trader's kegs had run dry. The bear grease was rubbed off the sacred pole as high as the old squaws and young papooses could reach. Charbonne had sobered up, not on his own accord or liking, but because the traders had pulled out. Most of the trappers had started to break camp.

Charbonne told Adam he was a lucky lad to have him as a go-between. He had purchased his bride for nearly nothing, telling him about the Indian custom of the more paid, the higher the esteem brought to the bride and family. The Frenchman told the boy to offer the young gelding that had fistulas to the bride's family since the horse was worthless anyway, as well as the old broken fowling piece since it was too dangerous to shoot, and throw in a twist or two of trade tobacco. He explained that Adam shouldn't give any sugar or coffee, that he should hold these back for his own fare. They would need these staples when the two set up housekeeping.

The two trappers approached Witch-ka's teepee. Mississippi's brother sat on a buffalo robe smoking his large red clay pipe. He had adorned himself with paint for the occasion, knowing already what barter was coming his way. He regretted the bargain he'd made, thinking how it might have been if not for the firewater, and how this damn little Frenchman had toyed with his desires. Witch-ka had been given all the drinks as fast as he could swallow, one after another, more than he ever had in his life. Then, his true friend, the wiry little Frenchman, Charbonne, held both hands before his eyes, square in his face and said, "NO MORE, NO MORE, till the bride price is set, then we are truly brothers, our blood will be as one."

All I, Witch-ka, could think of was the feel of this good nectar that dwells in the Irishman's barrels, wanting it, craving it! Witch-ka became angrier with himself. *I would have traded my own woman, my own children, the fruit of my loins! My mother, sisters, lodges, ponies, even the sacred ring I wear in my left ear! I would even have given the secret of my power that is hidden from all eyes and lay in my medicine bag. Here, I have brought shame to my lodge and to my little sister who I have loved since the day of her birth as my own. Damn the Frenchman, damn the liquor!* Looking at Adam, he thought, *Yes, he is the same as all his race.*

Adam never gave Witch-ka time to finish his resentful thoughts. Witch-ka and Charbonne were both astonished at what happened next. Adam, stepping around Witch-ka, opened the lodge's flap, secured it open, and entered.

There she sat on a ceremonial yellow tanned elk skin in her special occasion dress; her head to her feet were adorned in beauty. She sat poised like a fairy tale princess. Even the small fire to her right in the center of the lodge seemed ideally arranged.

The groom knelt before her and unwrapped his cache of golden chains, lockets, bracelets, rings, combs, and jewelry of every description that he'd purchased over the last three trips to the southern rendezvous in Taos, Mexico. As he adorned her with each article, he would brush long strands of black hair from her pretty face, kissing her forehead, cheeks, hands, and arms, softly and gently. Even Charbonne thought, *Hell, this boy needs no help! The great Casanova could do no better.*

Adam turned to his mother-in-law and before her piled present after present, and repeated the process with his new sister-in-law and her two children, his now nephew and little newborn niece. He then went back out to his pack animal. This inspired the Frenchman to give one of his musical laughs, knowing now the reason, the mystery, of why the boy wanted to bring the horse with the tarp covering its complete back. The tarp stood tall as if there was a lodge built upon its strong withers.

Now, it was his brother-in-law's turn. Adam presented Witch-ka with a rifle and a brace of fancy engraved pistols, tobacco, and a tall stovepipe hat. (The same hat he was holding in Bob's picture book that Adam saw as an old man by carbide light at the Smith's.) It became

Witch-ka's pride and joy. This was the signal for a gray-headed squaw to approach. She was one of the old women who had come early every morning to receive power from the sacred greased pole. She led 13 ponies, all young, sound, and in good health. She'd helped the young man pick them out and purchase them, then never let his secret out. Adam took the halter ropes as she had instructed, placed the ropes in a sacred symbol, made different moves with his hands and feet, then uttered the same phrase in their tongue to the four sacred directions. This completed the ceremony.

Mississippi's brother Witch-ka and his mother stood, shook their heads, and refused to take any more gifts, saying, "Too much! Too much!" over and over. It was more wealth than even a great chief's daughter would hope to obtain. Turning to Charbonne, Witch-ka told him to tell his "son" to stop. Surely he would be put into poverty.

Charbonne turned to Adam and crudely translated what Witch-ka had said by saying, "Hell, my own sister isn't worth much more than a sick horse and a broken gun . . ." He started to include "two twists of tobacco," but seeing the *eyes*, the anger, the mad rage that swept, that flowed in and projected out of those strange eyes—those strange eyes of two different colors—Charbonne cut his sentence short and interpreted word for word what was said, knowing now the love and respect his orphan boy felt for his new wife and first-ever family. He turned to Adam and apologized. This act for Frenchie was rare as a blue moon. He took the young man by his shoulders, got up on his toes, and made the French greeting, cheek to cheek. *Yes*, thought Adam, *truly this fine French trapper is a true friend.*

The bride price had been paid in such a way that it would be talked about for years to come by the women—it was never a matter for the male gender to dwell on. Preachin' Bill made the ceremony of Adam's people short and sweet, not at all as he'd planned the night before with the half-gallon of liquor the young bridegroom had furnished with his gold and Charbonne's generosity. Neither his spirit nor his head was in any gay mood for this. All he wished for now was sleep.

"Hell, let's all quit hoorawin' it up and go to bed," said Preachin' Bill. "Bed's what's on your mind, boy." He winked at Adam, knowing as fast as he said it, only the native English speaking young man would catch the double meaning of his last phrase, which he ended with "amen." He had Adam sign his name. Adam then placed his hand over her dainty brown one and helped her guide the quill and ink making the letters "M-I-S-S-I-S-S-I-P-P-I." The girl picked the bible up and studied the letters of her name. She took her index finger after the ink had dried and traced the letters over and over.

It was still early in the morning, 10:30 at best. Adam had spent the last seven days gripped with dilemma, and was glad to have Charbonne's wisdom and advice on what to do. He wouldn't have even known the simplest thing. For instance, the setting up of the greased pole—all these necessary procedures to acquire a bride. Now, his mind went to racing, thinking, worrying about what he was supposed to do next. Although he'd given a lot of consideration to this subject, the matter was now at hand. He took a deep breath, trying to stop all the words, sounds, and pictures that were bombarding his brain all at one time.

He had seen the "act" performed once between humans. He bit his lower lip and was deep in thought while all the rest were talking and slapping one another on the back. Mississippi was still deeply engrossed in the odd wiggly and straight lines that spoke her name and hadn't looked up from the holy book that bonded "Strange Eyes" and her together until death.

Charbonne's interpretation to the Cheyenne was a good ten times longer than what Preachin' Bill spoke. Charbonne was still heavily under the "influence." When he returned to his tent earlier, he found one complete jug that he'd overlooked the night before. Charbonne got so worked up and so into character interpreting and elaborating upon the touching drama he was witnessing that every so often, his lips would tremble and tears would well up in his eyes.

Mississippi and her people all hugged each other, walked forward, and stroked Adam lovingly. Preachin' Bill thought, *I'm damn glad those Frenchies never wrote the Bible. It'd take two strong packhorses to carry it as many words as it takes in their language to equal mine.*

This new worry had crept into the far reaches of Adam's head. At first, his mind tried shoving it out completely in order to hear these most sacred words of his fellow American. The harder he tried to concentrate on what Preachin' Bill was saying, the more his brain shut down to logic, screaming out to his body, *you know nothing about a woman!* Then he'd keep asking himself the same questions. *What is there to know about the female? Aren't they all the same? The same . . . the same . . .* kept echoing through his head. He never knew when Preachin' Bill completed his marriage speech.

Charbonne talked on another fifteen minutes. It must take a spell to say "amen" in French. Adam was jarred from his distracting thoughts when someone gigged him in the short ribs with an elbow. He stood there looking around, wondering what was wrong. Frenchie, his wise friend, whispered to Adam as he was wiping away his tears.

"Kees 'er, kees 'er."

The young bridegroom leaned over and gave Mississippi a little peck on the cheek. Adam stepped back a couple steps, blinked his eyes several times, bit his lower lip, and nodded his head as if to say, "Yes, I've done it."

Frenchie was now hollering, "Na! Na! Na good! Kees, kees, daum et!"

Adam, nervous now to the point of panic, leaped over, caught the girl, and picked her up. He didn't remember the kiss, only Frenchie's voice saying, "Enough enough! I said kees, not smahther her to death!"

In Frenchie's broken English, the boy had gotten the message, as had Mississippi. She grasped her husband's strong rough hand, holding it tight next to her hip, squeezing it playfully. This only added to his worries about performing the "act." He was thinking to himself that if only he had time to be alone for an hour or two, he could cipher it out.

His good friend Frenchie came to his aid once again. Mississippi was talking to her new husband and the Frenchman was interpreting word for word.

"My mate, I go now to prepare our lodge. It is better I be alone, it is not for man, it is for woman. Do not be nervous, my husband, all will be well."

However, Frenchie only interpreted a portion of her message. He left out the part about being "nervous" and "all will be well" figuring, *Hell, what was there to be nervous about bedding the prettiest gal he'd ever laid eyes on?*

Adam turned and struck out in his longest strides, knowing the short Frenchman and most of the rest of his trapping friends weren't likely to keep pace just to talk. Talking was the last thing he wanted to be involved in just then. His memories of the "act" wouldn't let him be solitary for long, though.

He'd seen buffalo, elk, deer, and studs getting wild with mares. He even remembered one fiery little paint filly biting and kicking so fiercely she broke the stud's front leg. He came right back, hobbling on three legs and finally mounted before he had to be put down with a bullet. *No, this wasn't helping much.*

Adam then drew upon images locked deep in his memory. He could still see the adobe canteen it happened in. He could even call up the scents, the couple's sounds of grunting, groaning, screaming, clawing . . .

It was on his first trip with the St. Louis Fur Company to the Southern Rendezvous. After the pelts had been sold and the money paid out in shares to its rightful owners, everyone drifted their separate ways till fall. When the time came, they would congregate again and head for the high country. Adam was thirteen and a boy no more, he felt, since he'd hit that magical number. It even had a ring to it: "thirteen."

He took his small share. When he got to Taos with Charbonne and Sybane, they went straight for the big painted up cantina and told the boy he could find them there. They were also going to get a room, and he was welcome to sleep on the floor.

Adam walked the street, went into several shops, but couldn't stand the thought of spending his coins on any of the appealing but unnecessary extras the owners tried to persuade upon him. He had plans for each coin. Each coin that left his skin pouch had to purchase an object that would turn its worth a hundred fold. But it cost nothing to look, and him being a boy, most never gave him a second glance.

Then, he saw the knife. It was large, like Charbonne's, and well made. The metal had a ring. It had been tempered in mare's urine, the shopkeeper said.

"Mare's what?"

The Mexican, speaking fairly understandable English, said, "Mare's piss."

"Why does it have to be a mare?" Adam was interested and wanted to understand everything he heard so he could recall it for good use later on.

The Mexican shrugged his shoulders. "Hell, I don't know."

Adam bought the knife—a large, Bowie-fashioned affair, not like the Green River trade knives his fellow trappers packed. As he started to pay, the shopkeeper said, "No, boy, no. That is not the way."

Adam figured he must be holding the coin in the wrong fashion, that maybe you paid only with your right hand here in this land that bore fruit in the winter. It seemed everything was just the opposite. He changed the knife to his left hand, the coin to the right, and offered it again.

The owner of the shop, being quite sharp, figured out what was going on in Adam's head and couldn't keep from laughing. He recognized and understood Adam's youth and inexperience. So, he enlightened him on the art of haggling. He explained to the boy he'd set the price four times the worth of the knife so the customer could dicker. Then the buyer, feeling good about his shrewd purchase, was sure to come again to do business. It was the middle of the week and business was slow. Actually, "slow" was putting it mildly. The boy was his only customer so far and it was almost siesta time—the high heat of the day. Adam and the shopkeeper sat on the bench in front of the store, visited, and dozed in the shade of its one stunted bush the owner called a tree.

Time slowly ticked away. Adam was used to working steadily, most of the time till after dark: fleshing fresh hides, pulling, scraping, shaping them first on his fleshing beam, then stretching them on the boards he'd made by using a saw, ax, hammer, drawknife, and froe. In what he called "idle time," there were pots and pans to be scrubbed with ash from their constant fire. His idle time jobs also included gathering wood and fueling the flame, and keeping the tools sharp—not just for him but for several of the more prominent trappers.

Sybane and Charbonne had become fond of this American orphan boy and went out of their way to teach him all the hidden tricks of their trade, old trapping secrets they wouldn't even share with one another. No wonder Adam would become so skilled in just a few short years. It usually took a lifetime to acquire such knowledge.

Not knowing what to do with all his energy, Adam walked the streets east to west, then north to south. Since the shop owner had closed down, everything else had closed down, except for the cantinas. There must have been at least three cantinas on every street in Taos. Adam had had his fill of looking at the buildings, which appeared much the same to him: either sand brown or whitewashed with slack lime that came off on his hands or buckskins, whichever first touched the structure.

Yet one building stood out from the rest. It was not only the largest, but painted up like a three-ring circus with every color of gaiety the past dozen owners had ever got their hands on. Adam walked through the always-open door. At least two score of men had flocked into this cantina, leaving most all the others empty. They were crammed in a tight circle around a long, heavy table they'd pushed to the center of the establishment.

Adam didn't take much notice since gambling never held an interest for him. He'd seen in camp how excited the Frenchmen and Indians could get just to lose their hard-earned money, pelts, horses, and occasionally, lodges and even wives. Adam had heard the players sing songs, holler out little jingles, and make every sort of call and whistle as they threw the dice or chose the hand they thought concealed the object of their bet. He thought the men in the cantina were simply playing the card game for this one always caused the spectators to encircle the table in an attempt to peer at a holder's hand. Then they'd try to rotate, hoping to see the other player's hands to know the outcome in advance before the betting and raising came to a close.

But this time, the onlookers were not saying much. Their breathing was even different. He noticed that most of those he could see had their hands run down in their leggings with their jackets covering their arms and hands.

This sight made the boy uneasy for he knew what was up. *There has been a squabble over the last hand of poker and now all friends and allies of each player were keeping their hands on their assortment of weapons getting ready to take sides, if need be, when the hand was finished.*

Adam got up from the bench at the far side of the cantina entry wall figuring on hugging close to the whitewashed inner wall, then cutting straight across to the open door. He knew he had to work fast. It was going to blow at any second. The breathing of the crowd was coming in shorter pants and gasps. He couldn't see the players, but the sounds of their playing were different than he'd heard before: groaning and breathing punctuated with grunts of satisfaction. The young boy knew each player thought he held a winning hand.

Then came the high pitch of a woman's voice. She was screaming, it seemed, but her words made no sense. Adam was no more than 12 feet from the ring of spectators. The players were now making louder, faster, stranger animalistic noises. Those who had their back toward him leaped back and to the side. Their sudden movement was unexpected. Adam immediately realized why they had made their fast exit. He became paralyzed, knowing it was too late. He fell to the floor and lay flat on its dusty hard surface.

Now only one was making any noise, sounding like he was trying to clear an object from his half-choked lungs. The boy heard the laughter and the calls, and saw the obscene gestures coming from the standing crowd.

He looked up just as it happened. There was a woman lying on the table. A man had raised his partially clad body to his knees and was kneeling above the woman's completely naked form still making choking, gasping, dying sounds. She now was kicking and giggling, trying also to get out of the way of his streams of lustful pleasure. The first stream shot out toward where the crowd had previously stood at the end of the table. His eyes were rolled back in his head showing just the whites, same as the stud when the paint filly had broken his front leg by kicking in her full heat.

This woman was now kicking her own stud. She'd stopped giggling and began screaming and cursing him. He was the same as the broken-legged horse. He didn't feel her kicks or the pain they dealt out, just the animalistic lustful release from his loins, the loins that continued to pump out semen over her nude body.

Adam knew she had broken her lover's leg, also. This explained why he hadn't moved or felt the punishing blows of her feet. Otherwise, he'd have leaped out of the way of her kicks as the stud horse would've done had his legs been sound.

The woman had wriggled her way free and now stood by the table letting the spent love juices shed to the adobe floor. Adam, still lying on the floor, had a completely different view than the rest of her admirers. Here was his first and only view of the "act" and a naked female body. She had skinny legs that had been given a double portion of knee joints with sockets that bulged out, threatening to break the skin over them. The legs ran up straight to a pair of flat hips that made the waist protrude a few extra inches. Her belly was quite large in proportion to her skinny torso. One flat breast hung down, the large black nipple almost touching the round watermelon belly, while the other resembled a small pocket turned inside out. Her neck was long with blue veins thick from all the screaming.

Her gaze had found the tow-headed boy lying on the floor. She smiled and reached one hand out toward him, beckoning, while stroking the still gaping hole of her vagina.

Adam now only saw a panicked fog. He wanted to flee. All eyes were still glued to this gloating prize, especially since she'd started rubbing her ex-lover's fluid with one hand and masturbating with the other. They were so engrossed with the grossly erotic act she was performing for the boy that only one among them noticed his presence and his hasty departure.

Adam was now 17 years old. The apprehension and trepidation that had been installed in him that day he had pushed, shoved, wrestled, and finally buried deep into the far reaches of his young mind. The memory flooded back with such force, he knew the great dam had been breached. It was time to seek out help to mend, rebuild, and strengthen the structure. With very little time left, he knew he'd have to be straightforward. There would be no going to the high country like he had with Sybane the next morning after he'd witnessed the "act."

He must go immediately to seek out advice about what to do in his situation. He was hoping there would be a few who would share their secrets on mating like Charbonne and Sybane had their trapping knowledge. He felt close to the two old trappers and they were his first contacts.

Charbonne, speaking in his normal loud tone of voice, grew more excited with each sensitive aspect of man's physical position in mating, which was master, while keeping the woman in subjection. Sybane, usually calm, was trying to tell his side of things, much of which was the opposite of what Charbonne was saying. His low voice, which was usually barely audible, was now as fast and loud as Charbonne's. He was also waving his arms and making all manner of bizarre gestures. This drew droves of smart men on the topic like a fresh summer gutted bison attracted flies.

The young groom should have been relieved to find so many were willing to share their sage insight on this delicate matter. But in fact, each of his newfound advisors considered his views on the subject as gospel and all seemed to contradict each other. They gathered around Adam, making the young man the centerpiece of their circle. He would spin slowly as a top losing momentum, trying to hear and understand the orator's speech. Meanwhile, a half dozen others were trying to cut the speaker off, certain their advice was the absolute final say on the matter, as well as relating their own personal experiences which were, of course, too vast to completely detail.

There was a grizzled old-timer who asked Adam if he had a pipe. A dozen other voices chimed in unison, "A pipe?"

The little banty-legged Irishman, who was on the rearing horse that had almost struck the young man and his new bride at the race, turned to the elderly man and asked, "What de hale ye think ol' mon, is he going to fook de pipe?"

This made everyone laugh, even Adam. As the old man explained further, the advice givers all nodded their heads in agreement. Yes, the pipe was surely a tool made for man. It brought an imposing dignity, and with it one could relax in a mysterious air of silence. Your wife and subjects would sense the holder of the pipe's power and wisdom.

He must have a pipe. Smoking is one thing he must learn immediately.

Charbonne took over the matter of acquiring a pipe for Adam. He traded the young gelding of Adam's, the horse he originally was going to trade for his bride, the one with the fistulas. An Indian by the name of Crooked Nose gave up his beautifully decorated red clay pipe for the horse. Actually, Crooked Nose was forced to, since he had gambled away his herd a few days before while under the influence of the trader's keg. Almost destitute, he needed any sort of beast of burden to pull what little remained of his once well-equipped camp.

Now, Adam owned the pipe. He already felt calm, the same serene sense a small child gets when it smells and feels the security of its own blanket.

Sybane bestowed upon him a strong black twisted hoop of trade tobacco. Now all was completed. The only thing left was to wait patiently for evening. He would then sit in his own lodge, smoke his pipe in silence, letting his power radiate out over his subjects, his whole domain.

Yes, these were truly wise men. Their advice was good.

The old silver-haired man lying on his pallet in the dark cold cave experienced a warmth and heard himself laugh as his thoughts traveled back to his wedding night. He remembered how later Mississippi and he would become weak with laughter when they were snugly wrapped together in heavy warm buffalo robes in their first winter lodge. Mississippi would tease her husband she called Strange Eyes. "Oh, master, shall I fetch you your most sacred pipe so you can sit in your mysterious airs of silent dignity." Then she would throw off her robe, standing naked before him. At this, they would laugh till tears formed in their eyes, remember their first night, their wedding night, when neither could speak a word of the other's language.

chapter
FOUR

The Wedding Night

Mississippi, along with her sister-in-law and mother, had taken the small, neatly made teepee a mile north of the rendezvous main campground. There was a spring located up a box canyon that came from out of the canyon's side before disappearing into the shale rock a few feet from its beginning. A few yards away spread a small, flat grassy meadow. This is where the young maiden chose to pitch their honeymoon lodge. With the help of her mom and brother's children, she gathered an abundant supply of firewood, not only to stave off the cold of the late spring nights, but for ample light. She wanted everything to be "just so." She had thought hours on this night and discussed it with all her childhood girlfriends, giggling, whispering, and at times, sharing secret thoughts about their deep felt desires that they could never discuss again, being too shy and embarrassed.

Mississippi repeatedly rearranged the lodge's furnishings, worrying she'd never get them just right. This made her mother, the part-Mandan squaw, laugh, saying her daughter was as a pup with its first bone, burying it over and over, each time in a different place, finally returning it to the nook, cranny, or pile of leaves where it had buried it originally.

This was Mississippi all right. After wearing out the others, she finally had her wedding lodge back to its original setting. She stood back, pleased with her accomplishment. It was ready to receive her man, the man the white man's holy book said she'd be sealed in union with for life. Even after death, they would remain each other's. There would never be another; she would never have to share her man. She liked knowing she was only his. The fact that he was hers alone made her feel happy, content, and loving. A slight warm pressure built in her inner thighs, making her blush slightly. Turning her head away, she pretended to look once more at the floor arrangement of the elk skin and willow couch, the fire pit, and it's kettle.

Seeing the kettle along with the heavy iron teapot, she remembered to have it ready with sweet smelling mints and spicebush. The herbs had been gathered in different parts of the country as they were migrating from one camp to another as the seasons changed. Mississippi and her mother gathered these not only for the sweet fragrance and the aroma they gave off as they were boiled in the heavy black iron teakettle. They were also welcome when one became nauseated, to settle a sick stomach, bring down chills, or even help bring on sleep. Her quick little fingers crumbled up the herbs, pouring cold water over the contents that lay in a small mound in the teapot's bottom, making them float to the top of the liquid and forming a miniature raft of twigs and leaves.

Her mother now departed, taking her sister-in-law, nephew, and little niece with her. Mississippi looked around for something, anything out of place, even minute as a grain of sand not laying in the right direction. She giggled for the first time, realizing, admitting to herself, *Yes, I am nervous.* Actually, nervous did not describe what she felt at this moment with the sun already down over the box canyon's west wall, making a false nightfall appear.

She'd tried to anticipate what the act of lovemaking would be like. She blushed, thinking back to when she was a little girl and how she had looked forward to camp-breaking time. It was when the lodges were unrolled that she first sensed this feeling, this warmth that swept through the lower part of her body. The first time was accidental. She had skinned up the bare lodge pole, climbing almost to the smoke opening where the lodge poles lay together. Then, it happened, as she slowly slid down. She had pulled her leather tunic between her legs as a buffer zone between her and the bare slick lodge pole surface. It first made a tickling that was entirely new and different. She soon figured out she could make the sensation change just by adding pressure. It was an enjoyable game, the most fun game she'd ever invented to play by herself. One day her mother noticed her playing, enjoying this newly discovered game of pleasure. She privately informed Mississippi on many subjects pertaining to this new game, the same subjects she and her girlfriends would whisper and giggle about when no one was looking or listening.

Now, this game was about to be played out for real. The mysterious unknown was finally at hand. It was just like the unpitching of a lodge. When she thought of the lodge having its covering stripped from its frame standing in a form of nudity, she started thinking about how to take off the soft doe skin, the heavily decorated yellow tan leather dress that she wore only on very special occasions. How? How should she remove it, leaving her standing completely naked, just as her mother's lodge at camp-breaking time?

Slipping her dress over her head was a job that never seemed to hold any degree of difficulty before. Now it loomed as the greatest task she'd ever tried to perform. Reaching down, grasping the fringed dress's tail, she brought it up inside out toward her shoulders. Its travel was stopped by the time the bottom fringes met her nipples, so she let it fall back into place. She then grasped the dress by its short half sleeves, pulling and tugging it gently till she had it off.

She never heard Adam's approach. He had walked up the box canyon's floor, something so far-fetched from a Cheyenne's mind. A Cheyenne never walked. Walking was only done when a warrior was destitute, poor beyond words. They rode from one lodge to the other, even if it was in their same circle, displaying their power, their grace, their wealth of many ponies.

Here was Strange Eyes, strange indeed for walking at least a mile up the box canyon, especially on his wedding day. The walk, he hoped, would ease his tension. The comfort the pipe had first given him started to diminish as he gained ground toward his honeymoon lodge. He stood outside its closed flap, wanting to peer into the interior of the most holy, wishing he could shed this fear of the layman and accept his rightful role as the all-powerful high priest. Then he could enter into the inner chamber that had been prepared for him with her, the offering, lying on his altar.

Mississippi, sensing the unseen visitor, tried to get her dress back on. At the same time, clearing his throat, speaking in a nervous tone in his foreign tongue, Adam spoke, saying, "Hello."

She didn't comprehend this word, but it created a panic that spread through her naked body. She clawed at her soft, fancy, quill-embroidered dress, but it caught her golden hair combs, one of the many gifts Strange Eyes had given her this morning. Now they were entangled with the dress adornments, keeping the garment from covering her nakedness.

She heard her husband's hands on the teepee's entry flap. He was talking in a soothing voice and figured he was supposed to now enter. This must be part of the wedding customs of his wife's people—this waiting—since he'd been standing there for over half an hour, all the while hearing her movements within. Adam didn't realize she was as nervous as he. She was completely naked, frantically looking around for something to cover herself. She grasped the new bright blue Hudson Bay wool blanket and wrapped it around her shoulders, letting it fall to the fresh-swept earth floor of the teepee just as Adam opened the entry flap.

Not knowing what to do, she walked over to the willow elk hide couch and sat down, drawing her bare legs up under her stiffly held upper body, trying not to reveal her nervousness, especially since Strange Eyes appeared so calm, so composed at this awkward time. The young bride looked at him now, studying his face and his tall, lean physique. The strange-colored yellow hair was freshly washed with a light oil rubbed into it, bringing out hints of red. This odd mix of color was set against the peculiar hue of his eyes. One was the color of a clear blue sky; the other was as dark as the eyes of her own people.

Indeed, Strange Eyes was a much more a fitting name for this tall young American than his civilized Christian one, which was pronounced "Adam" in their tongue.

Adam quickly surveyed his new abode. But because he was so tense, so ill at ease, he actually noticed little of the lodge's interior.

Mississippi, sitting on the elk skin couch, watched his every movement. Her eyes missed nothing. She turned her head slightly toward the opposite side of their round room and pretended not to be so keenly aware of his presence.

Adam was a few feet from the fire pit, which was always positioned in the center, not just for comfort, but also to allow the smoke to rise when first built. There, his young bride had made their wedding bed. The bridegroom, seeing the comfortable piles of robes, blankets, and cushions, chose one of them for his evening throne.

He settled himself, trying to impart the masterful air of dignity befitting his newly purchased pipe and tobacco. Taking the heavy red clay bowl and holding it in his left hand, he reached into the pouch that hung from his side and drew out the twist of strong, dark-colored tobacco. Adam tore and crumbled the leaves and small hard pieces that resembled little chunks of coal. He placed them in the bowl, tamping them down with his thumb. He exaggerated each of the movements of this recently acquired habit. Actually, this was the first and only time he'd ever partaken of real tobacco for usually the Indian smoked a mixture of willow bark, deer's tongue herb, choke cherry shavings, and any other herbs that suited their taste.

Putting the thick, long, highly decorative stem to his lips, he took short quick pulls at the large opening. Soon, the dark, strong smoke had made its way into the stem's chamber. Now, even with the slightest draw, Adam could blow out a dark, billowy cloud of smoke. He felt now that everything was going to be all right, even though he had difficulty in lighting his pipe with flint and steel and needed to borrow a small red-hot coal from the fire, which kept the pipe's tobacco burning more readily than it normally would have.

He smoked, blowing out impressive clouds of thick black smoke. As his confidence grew with each draw on the pipe stem, he experimented with new ways of making the smoke clouds leave his mouth. He even had the luck of blowing it back through his nostrils, but this made his eyes water. So, he held to just puffing and blowing for the next few seconds, which seemed much longer than the time lapse actually was.

Then, he started to feel different. No, it wasn't the mysterious airs of aloofness and wisdom brought by the pipe to its master. In truth, he felt very strange. First, his cushion felt as if it had come to life; that the hide and the animal it had been taken from were being resurrected and wanted to depart, carrying the burden that sat upon its back away from its position by the fire. He would reach out his hand to steady himself. Then the earthen floor would rise up toward him, turning itself into a swell more akin to ocean waves than solid earth.

He wondered what had gone wrong. Adam wished now he had secretly spit out the mouthfuls of strong amber juice from the pipe stem and tobacco that mixed with his saliva instead of swallowing them. He was thinking hard, thinking fast, trying to remember what all his "advisors" had told him before he'd made his advance to the lodge to take his rightful kingly position of all-wise and superior overlord of his household.

Then he remembered what the older, grizzled man had told him. The pipe was made for man, by man; it was man's best friend, always coming to his aid, settling nerves and comforting him in times of distress. Adam had forgotten to do the most important thing: *inhale*. Breathe in the rich, dark, smoke that travels down the large, beautifully decorated stem from the red clay bowl that held the burning tobacco. "Let the smoke soothe your lungs, and blow it out slowly. This will clear your head and make you think straight," the old man had told him earlier.

Adam thought, *That is where I went wrong*, remembering how the old timer had drawn the smoke out of his own pipe stem. When it left his mouth, the smoke still came out in wispy strings that caught the slightest breeze, making short, narrow ribbon patterns that would break apart then join to float over the head of its creator. While the lips of his advisor were making words counseling him, smoke would pour out of his speaking mouth. *That was an impressive sight*, thought the young man as he tried in vain to keep his balance on his swaying throne. The sweat on his forehead had started to bead, and gravity was pulling it down into his waiting eyes that strained to gain perspective on the distance to the dirt floor.

The objects in the teepee now seemed like more of an obstacle course between the king and his castle's leather door. That is, should he have to make a hasty retreat into the cold night air to clear his swaying head. Maybe, just maybe, he could even shed this great lump in his throat.

The lump had started out small—more of a slight pressure deep in the pit of his empty stomach. Now it had grown to the size of a buffalo bull's head. He could no longer swallow it down. Adam knew this all had happened just because he'd forgotten to inhale. The young man took a long draw, sucking it deeply into his tender pink lungs. The lungs rejected the tobacco smoke, needing time to adjust to this pollution that was trying to poison them and had already taken its toll on the body. His lungs felt like a thousand cats, all with freshly sharpened long claws, were trying to claw faster than the other to reach the safety of pure, fresh air so as to breathe again; to keep living.

Adam half rose, trying to recall where the entry flap was located. All the while the teepee was spinning fast and the earthen floor was bucking furiously. Mississippi saw his face in the firelight for the first time since he'd retrieved the ember from their fire pit. She leaped up off her couch, seeing how pale his face had become. He was coughing terribly and was unable to get his breath. Each cough brought smoke from out of his choking lungs, expelling it through his gaping mouth. He was moving his lips but no words would form. She was so scared seeing her new and only life mate in such a dire condition, she forgot that she'd been sitting all the while bare with only the new blue trade blanket so hastily wrapped around herself.

She stood up with both hands stretched out toward her husband and let the blanket fall. She forgot in her fright that she was now naked except for the golden-colored hair combs that kept her long black hair from falling over her eyes as she bent over, trying to stabilize the weaving, staggering, young man and prevent him from falling into the smoldering red embers. Only a few end pieces of wood that had been outside the fire's circle remained to put forth a feeble flame, creating a dim light as they'd catch air and flicker to life. The flame would then die as quickly as it had flared, making the nicotine-sick youth stagger toward the burning embers much as a moth flies into a candle's flame, burning its wings and body to a blackened crisp. His moccasin feet would be burnt, crippling him for days, weeks, maybe even for life. A bad burn could also create a serious infection, which usually spelled death.

She pressed her naked body up against his as they swayed together to and fro from the fire pit; two steps forward, one back, their only destination toward the entry flap and the cool, fresh air outside.

It was a crystal clear night and the half moon was already out. This was all the light needed for the staggering pair as they exited the lodge together. He made it out three to four rods, then fell on his knees with arms splayed out. He wretched, his stomach heaving, but only long streams of saliva came from his mouth.

Mississippi tried to hold his head, then remembered the tea kettle full of water and herbs she intended to place on their fire pit when the fire had burned low so as to unleash their different sweet fragrances. She ran back to the teepee, put the kettle on the live coals, then raced back to her mate, petting him, talking low and trying to make him understand that she had help on the way.

Adam was now gaining some control over his vomiting spasms. He saw her naked body in the light of the half moon, her tender movements, and smelled the sweet smell of her herb brew that was starting to simmer through its iron spout. He looked upon her in this half-light, feeling for the first time the foolishness at all his earlier worries. He promised himself he would tell her the complete story, down to the last detail, just as soon as he could speak her tongue. Yes, he knew, and thought to himself, *This is the only woman I will ever have. There will be only one and it is this Cheyenne girl. We have signed the book together, together for eternity.*

Adam got over his sickness with her tea and by replenishing his empty stomach. Soon he was as good as new. This first trial created a bond between them faster than if he'd spoken her language and had been an avid smoker. He never touched his pipe again. He gave it and the tobacco to his brother-in-law.

The rendezvous camp below broke up and everyone was pulling out. Some of the trappers headed south for Taos and other southern settlements. The Indians started their migration knowing exactly where they were headed. This had been going on since time immemorial, tracing as far back as their stories which were passed down from generation to generation. They went by the natural seasons; from the first green shoots to the time the ponies are fat. Leaf-falling season brought on the time of cold and the time of hunger if the men didn't hunt and the women hadn't prepared their lodges for the coming winter. The traders always left first like the lead gander that had to prepare the flock to start their flight to distant parts of the vast "uncivilized" world, as the eastern white man liked to call it.

The young white American groom and his Indian bride stayed in their secure little box canyon. They were deep in her people's territory, feeling safe as one could feel in these early times. Adam learned his wife's Cheyenne tongue. He picked up the dialect faster than he had French since most of the Frenchmen could manage some broken English. Here, not one word of his own people's language was ever uttered. In no time, he started thinking in Cheyenne, allowing it to come even more quickly. Now they could communicate, exchange ideas, and get more acquainted. Strange Eyes told Mississippi the complete truth about the pipe, how and why he'd felt so compelled to impress her, and of his boyhood fears and doubts about the "act."

Adam never forgot his promises to himself made when he was so sick he felt for certain he'd never live to see the rising sun.

chapter
FIVE

Buffalo Running and the White Buffalo

Adam and Mississippi were soon accustomed to each other and worked side by side, never out of arm's reach from one another. Taking a pack-horse, they'd ride out and select a young bison, elk, sometimes even a young spiked buck deer, shoot and dress it on the spot, then pack it back to camp and preserve the meat by several methods for the coming winter. They'd already decided to stay out, migrating south but keeping to themselves, not wanting to share even a second with the presence of anyone else.

Typically as energetic as ten men, Adam could never sit by idly watching his wife do all the hard menials tasks, such as laboring over the large buffalo hides she had staked out, then taking a large, flat shoulder bone and scraping the flesh side for hours on end. In the Cheyenne tradition, the man was supposed to sit on his rear looking important for having killed whatever beast his woman was laboring over. He was amazed when he found out the other warriors didn't even make the effort to skin or pack in their kill. It was the woman's job again to break camp, take up lodge, children, dogs, and whatever else, and move to the kill, then make all the necessary preparations before the next kill.

Adam told Mississippi there was enough work to keep an army busy, let alone one little lean girl, which made her laugh and open up to him. She shared thoughts that she was never even supposed to entertain, much less speak aloud, especially to a man. There were so many surprises and downright shocks for her. Her husband would actually grab the shoulder blade and with his superior strength and help, they'd finish in a day what should have taken her all week.

The work could have been finished even faster if it weren't for Strange Eyes. Right in the middle of their laboring over a large hide or jerking meat, he would rush in, pick the girl up, and go running with her on his shoulders. *Odd this was*, she thought, *each time he did this, we end up on a grassy spot*. Next thing she knew, they each would be naked, lying on their clothes, making love. Then they would lie, staring at the sky, sharing things about their pasts.

One of his first new experiences came during their first month together. Adam looked for an excuse to grab her. He hugged and kissed her all over until she'd grown as excited as her mate for this game. On this day, she had gotten carried away, becoming wild, saying to him, "Let's play 'bison in rutting season'." They both got down on all fours. He pawed at the earth, pretending to throw dirt upon his back. When he came for her, she would run away. Finally, she would stand for him, playing the part of the cow. They got so into character, he even licked her in the manner the bull does. He'd heard the Frenchmen talk of this knowing it was one of their highly revered love secrets. Her body and soul became nothing but burning desire. She forgot herself, and felt no shame for letting him commit this act of taboo, knowing she had never experienced what happened next—there was rush, she tried to explain later to her love mate. She finally told him that the feeling was as if there were thousands of buffalo running over a cliff at the same time. This made Adam leap up, hold his hand to his ear, look in all directions at the steep sheer rock wall of their box canyon, and then look down at the nude girl to ask her where she thinks she heard them fall.

He then was horrified to see blood on his member. He fell down on his knees, forgetting all about the falling buffalo. He started to examine her up close. His fears were right—they had played way too rough. He'd damaged her. She hadn't noticed the change in his expression. Adam was showing outward panic, thinking in some of his lunges he'd gone too deep. He remembered how, in their heat of passion, he had been crazed; how he felt his manhood lift her up completely off the ground, and bottoming out. He feared he had killed, or at least injured severely, what he loved the most.

She rose to embrace him, wanting to play more, always knowing he'd be more than willing. She still never noticed it was her time of the moon. All Adam could do was point at the blood flowing down her leg. She saw the panic this natural occurrence caused her white husband. She looked puzzled, thinking he was in fear of breaking this taboo, saying to him, "Why are you so in fear of this one when we have broken so many already? Is one taboo greater than the other?"

Adam tried to explain to her she was injured deep inside. Then she would try to convince him it was natural, saying, "All women, unless old, does this each change of the moon, sometimes at full light, or half. Even when there is no moon. Still, if it is your time, it will flow, usually the days of the fingers on one hand. When my flow stops for two moons, I will bear you a child. If it never stops, you will never have a son or daughter."

Adam never even dressed. He told her he had to go think on this alone. He was gone till the sun made its arc to its zenith on the edge of the western wall of the box canyon. When he returned, he peeked into their lodge, which was quite warm. She lay naked on a hairless thin tanned skin of the doe deer. He started feeling bullwashie again and slipped through the lodge's entry, which had its bottom rolled up and tied to let the evening breeze blow through. It was blowing gently but with enough force to rustle the dry grass and leaves. She never heard his approach till he was astride her with his legs between hers, already erect, and was making his penetration. To his surprise, she rolled and, using her elbow, flipped him off, then sat up and demanded to know what his conclusions were.

Adam started explaining, as much to himself as to her. He had been several years with men of great and far advanced knowledge, had lived with them, and heard their talk for hours on end each day. Women were always their main topic. He told her he'd always listened with great interest, knowing one day his greatest desire was to own one.

When he said "own one," she asked abruptly, "Any ONE of these womens, Strange Eyes?"

Adam saw the jealous daggers flying from her eyes and was quick to change his freshly made statement to, "I always knew I wanted to be yours, Mississippi, be owned only by this Cheyenne girl." Pointing through the entry flap of their lodge, he added, "The most beautiful maiden to ever be born under the sun."

This last statement appeased his god. He hoped by now she'd forgotten about what they started to discuss, and tried once more to get friendly.

She held up both her hands and made the sign by crossing them across her thighs letting him know that for now, the fun was over.

Adam started telling her all that he'd ever heard. The Frenchmen knew most on the subject, and also spoke of the "act" as far as the woman's role, explaining each movement, even with their mouth and teeth. The girl look puzzled and said, "Mississippi doesn't understand," making Adam go over the details fully, explaining it to the best of his recollection.

Finally, she would be satisfied. He continued, weighing even the most insignificant word before he spoke. Then, it came to him. He knew this time it wouldn't backfire like the pipe had. It was all so clear now. This time of the moon was something Indian girls were cursed with. She wanted to know immediately why he had said "curse." He explained it must be a curse because the Indian's holy men had made it forbidden for the Indian man to penetrate the Indian woman during that time. "That is why the French, Irish, and English trappers never mentioned or knew anything about the times of the moon," Adam explained. He was damned careful never to mention the trappers who were or had been married one time or another to an Indian. Evidently, the trappers just never mentioned the curse in the presence of the lad.

"Now listen close, my wife, for it has been just now been revealed to me."

She wanted to know immediately, "How?"

He looked around like a cornered rat. Seeing the shadows cast by the sun on the far eastern wall of the box canyon, he whispered and pointed. "It has been revealed."

Seeing the reflection, she was satisfied. Now she would believe in his all-powerful wisdom and understanding about sacred things and taboos. Confident that he had her convinced, his mind started racing, trying to choose the right word to ensure this statement would be accepted as the final word on this sensitive but crucial topic. He was looking at her high hard small breasts, knowing the feel of fire they brought to him. The sunset was softly lighting her perfectly formed body as he spoke. He knew the wrong word now would end what little chance he had left for fun this night.

He could tell by the flare of her slender nostrils that she was thinking also on some deep concern of her own, so he hurriedly spoke what was on his mind. "Now, since French, English, Irish, and even Mexican women don't have this curse, there is no taboo placed on the women or men. And since I'm of English descent, doesn't that mean you and I can penetrate when you have your time? The taboo has no power over our lovemaking."

Adam was about to find out that she was not worried about the taboos. She led him over to their bed, wanting to experiment and practice the strange techniques she had just heard about. She'd gone over and over them in her mind as her husband labored to convince her of the fallacy of her people's taboos. Now it was his turn to feel the strange fire that built till it swept thousands of buffalo off the sheer drop of their canyon's high stone walls.

The young pair got so caught up in their carnal pursuits, the end of their third month found them still in their original campsite. The buffalo, elk, and deer had migrated on to the high mountains and meadows to seek out the tender grass that draws its sweetness and strength from the cool, high altitude. They started feeling the full heat of the noonday sun that was now lasting till way past dark.

Adam awoke in the early hours of morning, at least two hours before first light. He was still half asleep, so it took a few minutes before it dawned on him she was trying to prepare him for a buffalo run. When he awakened to the fact, he pretended to be in a deep sleep and faked a slight snoring sound. He could hear her breathing deeper as she brought him closer to the cliff's edge. Then he reached out in the tent's darkness, grabbed her and pulled her up to his chest. Kissing and stroking her, he told her over and over the love he felt for her, convinced they were the only couple to ever feel this way.

That is when she whispered in his ear so low he had to say, "Hmm?"

She repeated her soft-spoken message. "I have not had my time, have you not noticed? For two moons the curse has not been."

By this time the morning light had eaten its way into their lodge. Adam cuddled his young wife, holding and petting her as a little Indian girl would a cornhusk doll. Mississippi wanted to stay in their little safe camp and wallow in loving affection forever, but they both knew it was time for them to leave. Later in the day, Adam went to fetch in their horses along with his pack mules. This would be the start of their long journey in life. They assured one another this would never end. They would not let it end.

They started out the same morning Adam learned about her pregnancy—or, as Mississippi would have said, "his pregnancy." As he lay tenderly embracing her, he stroked her stomach, then took his thumb to "bump" her, being careful not to put too much pressure, but enough to feel in the same manner as one does a mare to check whether she is with foal. When the girl realized what he was trying to do, she twisted, sprang up, giggled and wrestled him down. She wanted to make one more buffalo run before they left their honeymoon camp by this little spring they had named Ice Wells, here in their little box canyon.

Adam knew less about a woman with child than he did about the curse that had been placed upon the women of her people. In short, he knew nothing at all. And, he had no time to be alone and decipher it out as he'd done with her "time." Here she was now, once again wild for the act. He allowed in too many thoughts, all of which called for immediate attention, and they were taxing his memory. He held back, not wanting to take the lead as he usually did in their games.

After pushing him back on the pallet, she employed the French technique that she'd become so masterly skilled in as Strange Eyes lay there being brought to his peak. He tried to remember what he had done to so inflame her appetite. He couldn't think of anything that would cause this. All he did was lay there in a half doze stroking her hair, kissing the nape of her neck and shoulders while stroking her flat stomach and breasts. He thought hard on this as she grew more passionate. He looked up at her, studying the naked beauty, thinking, *I wonder if all women are such strange thinking as my own Mississippi. What should make her ready for the act will put her into jealous rage, taking hours of double-talking and explanations. Then, here I done nothing at all, and she turns fiery and full of desire.*

After their last buffalo run at their honeymoon lodge, they started to break camp. Adam was everywhere at once, not wanting her to lift, carry, or do anything. Finally, Mississippi could take no more. She leaped in front of his fast rushes from teepee covering to lodge poles demanding why he didn't want her help. This was her job. This was women's work.

Adam looked puzzled. "You know why. You're with child, you're pregnant."

This refreshed her love for this man. Her man. She remembered the stories and complaints of her childhood girlfriends about how their Indian mates treated them, which made her appreciate and love him all the more. If this was all it took to make Strange Eyes happy, then so be it. She was always doing special little things just for his enjoyment and comfort, which he never took for granted. He openly expressed his appreciation, making her know she was his whole world.

A slight chill gripped her young body at the thought she could have been purchased with a bride price like her friend Na-Kai. They had left the main camp also, staying out during the season. The ponies became fat. When they returned at leaf falling time, her friend came to her, having to sneak over under the cover of darkness. Her husband would not allow her to talk to anyone, not even her mother, saying this is what the Great Spirit had given to him in a vision and that she must obey. If she broke this rule, her penalty would be death.

Mississippi remembered clearly their meeting. They stood in pitch-black darkness. Na-Kai told Mississippi that she told her husband she had to go relieve herself. Even for this, he usually went with her, even when they were miles from the nearest lodge. But this night, he had his only friend visiting him on his return. This gave Na-Kai a rare opportunity for the first and only contact with another human since her marriage. Crooked Nose, the man she was sold to, did not count. He was not human; she thought him more a demon.

Na-kai talked low and fast in the darkness. Mississippi held her ear close trying to hear and remember all that was said. But it brought such fear to her, being yet unwed. She knew it would be anytime now that someone would be leading ponies to her own mother's lodge to be accepted or rejected by her brother, Witch-ka, and was afraid this could be her plight also.

Adam had everything packed and they were on their way toward the high country, which should have alleviated her melancholy. But she couldn't shake the feeling of profound sadness she felt for her friend, especially since all had turned out so outstanding for her. She turned to Strange Eyes, her dearest friend, her most trusted companion, and told him about Na-kai, about what Na-Kai's mate would do before they made the act. Even on their wedding night, he boasted about how he raped women, even little girls of Adam's race, saying he would take his knife and stick it into their neck, and all other sorts of horrible tortures he would describe. He never tried making the act without first telling story after terrible story, going into explicit detail. His own tales of rape and maiming would work him into such a rage, he would literally tear her clothes off. Taking her garments, he would strike out at her with them, hitting and kicking all the while until she either fell or cowed down on the ground. Then he would leap on top, plunging his knees into her stomach, causing her such severe pain she couldn't move. She was too scared to fight back. She would just lay there naked, scratched and bleeding, afraid to move even just to gain a more comfortable position off the stone she'd landed on. It might put him into another fit of rage, especially now since his knees were between her legs and he was playing with himself and having no results. This, Na-Kai knew, is what brought on his next move; he would withdraw his knife, hold it to the side of her throat, and stick it in enough to draw blood. This inspired his member to just enough life to make the act somewhat. Soon as it became too lifeless to perform, this coming after a few seconds, he became violent once again, slapping, kicking, and hitting her, making her life a living hell.

Adam explained to Mississippi that her friend had been released; Crooked Nose had lost her along with all his horses and most of his lodge. He had gambled away everything, and told her his friend Charbonne had swapped him one of his own horses, a horse that had fistulas, for the pipe.

Adam spotted a flock of sage hens and went racing toward them. The birds would make a tasty treat and a nice change from their red meat diet. They looked forward that evening to this meal as they made camp by the little brook they had planned in advance to camp on. They would follow this brook up to the higher meadows, pitch their lodge at each new camp, stay for a few days, then move on. Summer was in its mid-season and they needed to keep bearing toward the south.

From the time Strange Eyes found out she was with child, he hunted and gathered with zeal. One evening at their hearth, she told him how proud she was to have him as their provider. However, he had provided so well, there was no more room to store the pemmican and jerky, not to mention the assortment of stores he'd brought in for the coming winter. They should soon be heading due south to her people's winter camp. When Mississippi's mother and sister-in-law helped set up her honeymoon lodge, they told her she and Strange Eyes could find them at one or the other old camping areas her people had used for ages.

Adam and Mississippi had originally planned to stay out for over a year, making contact the following leaf falling time. He didn't understand why she wanted to return to her people so soon and asked Mississippi what was wrong. "Are you lonesome? Sad to see your mother, nephew, and little niece?" He knew she loved the two children to the point of near worship.

She laughed and pointed at her belly, knowing it must have slipped his mind for a second. Since he had found out, he fussed over her like a mother hen with but a single chick, not letting her lift or tote anything. She even teased him about it, saying, "Soon you will feed me in fear of the weight of my horn spoon being too heavy, since I am the first woman to ever bear a child."

"Bear a child" was all that registered. He hadn't thought this far into the future—that it would actually grow into a little human since she was barely showing at present. It was growing as he sat there thinking. He wanted to relieve her mind and tell her not to worry. He'd helped mares, even fillies way too young to be bred much less have a colt, and he'd never lost a single one.

Mississippi, appearing very serious as she spoke, told Adam he must never, under any circumstances, come into her birthing lodge. This was one taboo that even he couldn't break. If he did, and the child was a boy, it would keep its male body and fixtures, but live with the soul of a female.

"I will tell you as the story was told to me by my mother. She was told by her mother, whose own mother told her. The story began way back before my people had ever seen the horse. This is how long ago it happened.

"There was a young couple. She was with child. Their love for each other was as ours. He, too, would fuss and pamper his bride. Their love grew; they were inseparable. He knew the law that he couldn't enter the birthing tent unless he was a holy man, which he was not. When her labor pains began, all was well. Then the old women noticed it was coming into the world feet first. They tried to turn it, but to no avail. It kept coming. In her agony, she screamed so loud and frightening, he rushed up, tore the entry flap open and entered the same moment his son slipped out into the world. The mother and baby lived, both doing quite well.

"The mother bore more children. Her firstborn son grew tall and strong, but never had the actions of a boy. His actions were more feminine than a girl's. As he matured to the age of marriage, he became overly fond of one young warrior, professing his love. When the warrior took for himself a very plain bride, the young man who thought he was a girl climbed high up on the needle-looking rock that lays to the south where we will have our winter camp. Here he stood, at its very top. He hollered out, cursing the gods for playing such a cruel trick on him by making his body male and soul female. He threw himself off, plunging to his death among the giant boulders that lay at its base, the gods shouting out it was not their fault but his own father's for breaking their sacred law.

"No, Strange Eyes, you must never break this sacred law. We could not possibly live with ourselves knowing in our love for each other we had destroyed what our bodies created."

Adam, seeing her seriousness, spoke of the matter no more, but began heading toward their winter camp far to the south, where their cousins, the Apache, lived.

Mississippi grew larger with each passing camp as they traveled slowly toward their southern destination. He would watch over her as though she carried a thin-shelled egg. She was now in her fifth month at the start of leaf falling time; it wouldn't be long now till the time of the deep snows.

They traveled steadily, wanting to find one of the main camps. Mississippi knew what areas to cover to pick up sign. They would travel for seven days, then stay for three, letting their horses and mules rest and replenish their strength, not wanting their animals to enter winter in a lean condition. Keeping a reserve of fat on them now would be wise insurance for later on.

Traveling in this manner, they made good time eating up the distance and were now in the vicinity of her people, far away from Green River. It was a relief to them since the girl was getting close now, in the top of her eighth month. She loved and enjoyed the ceaseless fussing that her husband bestowed on her. In the night when she grew restless, he would massage her, rubbing her back and shoulders, stroking her head and neck till she fell asleep.

One late night, while he was making his usual commotion over her, she told him he couldn't do all the tasks that he does everyday when they reached the other lodges, even though she was well into her pregnancy. The warriors would make a mockery of him, giving him the name of "old squaw" who was scared of his woman, and all sorts of shameful names that their sons would have to live with and their sons for generations to come.

Adam was massaging the cramps in her calves as she told him of her name-calling fears. She knew how this was going to worry him, and make her man go for a long solitary walk to think on it, like he had on all the other taboos.

Adam laughed and continued to massage, speaking some words in his own language. It sounded so foreign to her ears she thought it must be a prayer to his gods. Mississippi knew even Strange Eyes would have more respect than to laugh aloud while praying to his high deity.

Finally, she could take it no longer and asked what was said that was so hilarious. Adam spoke the little jingle he'd said in English: "Sticks and stones can break my bones, but words can never hurt me."

Mississippi reached for her husband, pulling him close to her, and had him repeat it several times, all the while stroking him, kissing him in special places, telling him how many times she thanked the gods each day for letting her be married to him and how he never wanted any other young girl, only her, like his people's black holy book said.

Adam smiled to himself in the dark of their lodge, knowing it was time once again to console her.

"Yes, my wife, I love only this girl—"

He never finished because she brought him to his peak and his buffalos were eager to leap off the cliff. It had been several days since they'd made their runs and they were really built up for the charge.

They broke camp to move the short distance to her people's winter camp. Adam worried winter weather was on the way, even this far south. Mississippi kept trying to convince him there was no worry about snow for it never fell in the southern country of her cousins the Apache, Navaho, and Comanche. This was the territory of the Comanche further to the east. That is why there were still bison.

She drew on the fresh-swept earth of their lodge, making a detailed map showing all the larger water tributaries, prominent rock outcroppings, mountain ranges, and where water was located in prairie and desert alike. This made the young white man sit back on his heels, seeing his wife in a whole new light. He told her to leave the map in its place; he was getting a tanned doeskin and asked her to bring him his bottle of blue water.

Choosing one of her feathers she used for fans and decoration, he made a quill, and started tracing the map she had drawn—a region that reached north into Canada, south to Mexico, west into the edge of California, and east to the Mississippi. As he drew, he conclusively determined what his lodge would do for the rest of their days. They would spend their time here on this earth exploring, looking, tasting this vast region she had drawn here on their lodge floor.

Adam would point to an area he'd drawn and ask her what it looked like. Her answers made him respect her even more. She'd never been there and had only heard raiding party's descriptions of the terrain, but was able to hold it all in her head and transmit her memories so plainly and precisely. He knew a small portion of the country of this map, and knew it was exact to the smallest detail.

As he drew his map in his neat artistic style, it was Mississippi's turn to be awed, especially when he made an ink sketch of her face, head, and hair on the map's back side, writing her name underneath. He started to include the date, but didn't know what day, month, or even year it was. *No*, he thought, *I am no longer tied to this civilization. I want to break all bonds with it.* He drew next to her picture a pony standing in a winter camp reaching high on a cottonwood tree, stripping a piece of bark off with its teeth, to represent the season when the cold north wind sweeps through the lodges.

When he was through with his drawing, he let the ink dry, then smoked the tan leather map till it turned light amber. Taking bear fat and tallow of the deer and elk, Adam had his woman (no longer would he think of her as a "girl" for she was wise beyond her years) mix portions of the grease with beeswax he had left from his trapping supplies from the previous year. Then she oiled the map, making it waterproof which kept the ink from fading and running together.

Once this was all done, he told her he'd ride out the next morning and scout the area where she said their people's lodges would be.

The light rain had forced them to pitch their camp two days early. She had argued that they didn't need to stop. But she also knew by now that her husband feared their baby, protruding out like it was, resting on her pony's saddle as she rode, would melt and disappear if she got wet from the rain. Looking up with love in her eyes for this strange foreigner, she kissed him, and as he turned to leave she sang her new song, the song she made him sing with her several times a day to break the monotony as they rode the long miles.

He stood outside their entry flap knowing she wanted him to harmonize this new chant with her. He did, singing, "Sticks and stones can break my bones, but words can never hurt me." As he rode away, he listened to all the other lyrics she'd composed to try to convince him not to do women's work in front of their soon-to-be winter camp.

The rain had let up during the night, making a clear pleasant ride for him. He traveled southwest from their lodge, knowing he would hit the tributary, which still flowed no larger than a big creek. This country lay more rolling with three large outcroppings rising in the distance. There were no others in sight. This made them appear as mountain peaks, even being referred to by her people as mountains.

This is why Mississippi knew exactly where her mother's people would be. This was the year that several different tribes would congregate, it being a holy year for them. There would be her people the Cheyenne, then the Apache, Arapaho, Comanche, even some of the southern Sioux that lived still a few weeks riding due north. Some would make the long trek from over 1,800 miles away for this special occasion, his wife had told him, so he knew it wouldn't be hard to locate one of the many camps strung out for miles along this small clear river that was fed by numerous large springs.

His travel was short; he hadn't expected to find them so soon. He'd traveled less than ten miles, he estimated, all on easy rolling ground. He was glad the trip wouldn't be hard on his pregnant wife. He rode to the top of one of the taller rises, wanting to look in all directions and take a bearing on the Three Sisters, the name her people had given the tall, lone outcroppings.

Even before he ascended to the top of the rise, he spotted the smoke coming from the lodges. He rode cautiously so as not to expose himself on the hill's crest, knowing it wouldn't be a good idea to be seen alone since he was obviously white and couldn't tell which tribe they were or what dialect they might speak. He would go back and bring in Mississippi and their horses and mules loaded down with their lodge and winter provisions. A woman in the party signified it was not a warring party. This would make a clear show that they were coming in peace, letting the warriors of any band see they had only come to join up with their own people.

Adam figured he would ride the short distance back, strike camp, and return. Thus would end their trek, giving his wife time to settle in before she gave birth. He knew she would stress over every detail, worrying herself sick in fear some "great renowned warrior," too lazy to get off his ass to help his overworked wife or wives if he could afford them, might try to insult her. *NO, to hell with the little lazy bastards wanting to snoop around my lodge to make my wife feel bad with their childish name calling. I'll knock the hell right out of them. I'll box 'em right in the friggin' mouth.*

When he said "friggin'," he realized he'd gotten so carried away with the different punishments he intended doling out that he was thinking and talking aloud in English. He hadn't heard his native language spoken for months. He'd forced himself to speak and think only in Cheyenne, except for the one jingle his wife had made into a holy chant.

He laughed to himself, saying, "Now since you've whipped the whole tribe, let's get back. Damn, I'm not going to leave her side again for any reason till our baby's born." He was thinking about the taboo, and about how he'd have liked to bust the chicken-livered "brave warrior" or "chief" who made up that ridiculous story of the boy that turned girl just so they'd have an excuse to keep out of the birthing lodge.

Still thinking about what he'd do if anyone hurt Mississippi's feelings, he drew his rifle from its scabbard, never letting his movements of raising, aiming at a buffalo, and firing his weapon break his vengeful train of thought. He rode the short distance to where the young bison lay. He wanted to have one pack animal loaded down with fresh meat for the big feast, another custom of his wife's people. This custom was his favorite.

Arriving at his fresh kill, he tied his horse. He planned to skin the bison and pack it in on his mount, leading the horse and walking the short distance between the kill and their lodge. Drawing his knife, he turned to his chore of removing its hide, then stepped back in shock. The young buffalo bull was a true albino, white as fresh fallen snow, with pink eyes and nose. His first impulse was to ride off and leave it, but he turned around and went back, saying to himself, "Hell, a white bison will eat just as good as a brown or red one." Being highly skilled in the art of skinning and packing, he had it on his horse in less than an hour and was on his way.

When he arrived at camp, Mississippi was out anxiously waiting for him. She'd heard his rifle shot in the distance and could now hear his horse. She knew he'd be bringing in fresh meat, something they hadn't had for a couple of weeks since they tried to make their destination without creating any more chores than necessary. Adam had used the fresh skinned hide as a crude pack, and the meat once again met with its lifelong covering.

Mississippi gazed at the snow-white hide, the few red bloodstains making it appear all the more sacred to her mind. She fell upon her knees chanting, weeping, praying, taking handfuls of dirt, throwing them into the air, and letting them rain back down on her head and body.

Seeing this behavior, Adam dropped his horse's reins and rushed to her, certain that she had miscarried while he was gone. He watched her grief stricken poses and chants: raising, walking around the horse, putting her hands out toward the albino hide, talking to it, praying to it, making promises of sacrifices their lodge would perform if only it would let them have safe conduct.

By now, Adam could see she still was big with child and there was no flow of blood on her or the ground where she had knelt or walked. A flush of relief overcame his own frightened body. He walked slowly toward her, afraid the least wrong movement could send her back into her anguish. He had to circle his horse to get to her. When he was within arm's length, she turned toward him and gave him orders in a completely calm manner as if she was telling him to massage a little lower down on her back.

Adam cautiously unpacked the meat being extra careful not to let the now sacred hide or white hair ever touch the ground. If it did, they would all be cursed to the tenth generation. Adam finally got her calmed down enough to let her know her people were camped less than two hours away. He would help her get comfortable, then he would strike camp. They would arrive with plenty of time before dark and have everything back in its place.

She looked at him like he'd gone mad, shaking her head "no" and pointing at the white buffalo hide, explaining that there was no way they would or could move until it was tanned in the most sacred manner. This great task they were about to embark on would be the most crucial one in their lives. Everything had to be followed according to the law. One thing left undone or done wrong would spell the end for them all. He saw how scared and serious she was about this one custom, so he went along with her every wish.

Before she had the white hide tanned, he was wishing he'd ridden off, leaving the hide to the wolves, bears, coyotes, and buzzards like he first intended. With her so heavy with child, she could only work for short spells, then had to rest before resuming her most holy sacred task.

Adam wasn't allowed to look upon it, much less help out, and so was thankful at least it was a young yearling bull. Its hide was still small and skin lighter in weight than the brown or red buffalo yearlings. It took her a full seven days. Oddly, her back and legs quit cramping. She had an overabundance of strength and stamina at the end of the sacred process. She would now work all day if he had let her. Even he thought, *this was strange all right*. At first, thirty minutes wore her out. He would give it a couple days, then he'd have to break the big taboo. Never in his wildest imagination did he think she'd be able to carry it off and become a picture of health, flowing with energy.

As they broke camp, it had turned cold and fine snow was spitting in the air. He thought, but never mentioned, that she had told him just a few days prior it never snowed this far south. As they rode the short distance toward her people, the girl became so full of excitement she couldn't contain her emotions like she'd planned on doing because they were delivering the most blessed and revered white buffalo hide, so beautifully tanned and adorned.

The party reached the first village that Adam had seen from the high ridge overlooking the little river and the long, winding valley it meandered through. Her folks were camped several miles up on a tributary that flowed into this main one. They had camped out farther from most of the clans, but Adam and Mississippi were more than glad to make the extra effort it took to reach her mother's people. It was worth it for they had chosen a very sensible and protected location to weather the coming winter.

Strange Eyes and Mississippi chose their own camping spot a quarter mile from the nearest lodge, leaving plenty of room for any more late arrivals. Adam learned from Mississippi's cousin, Afraid of His Horses, to be careful of one of the late stragglers who had just pitched his lodge; he was always mean, but doubly so now since he lost his wife and horses at the last rendezvous—the same one where Strange Eyes had married Mississippi. His name was Crooked Nose and he hated everyone. He never smiled or spoke now.

Adam thanked him and kept on working at his task—women's work. He thought if he hadn't given the pipe and tobacco to Mississippi's brother, Witch-ka, he would definitely have given it back to its original owner, Crooked Nose. Mississippi had taken the white hide to her brother so he could, in turn, go through the proper, most sacred channels, making sure not to offend any one of the chief's medicine men or some hidden high deity. Witch-ka must have done one hell of a job on this most holy matter because it put him into position to go with a pack of chiefs a few years later to Washington D.C. to meet with the big man himself . . .

chapter
SIX

Adam Does Women's Work

. . . the top bullshitter of my whole race. For the next few days, I was quite busy with my "women's work." Mississippi was so large now that her sister-in-law would hug her and giggle, patting her stomach. The two girls were very close. Moon Child already had two children, the nephew and little niece, but she was only 3 to 4 years older than Mississippi. Witch-ka didn't marry until his late twenties. Moon Child was a Comanche of 15 summers at their wedding. This marriage created a strong bond between Witch-ka's lodge and the Comanche band.

So, not only did I have the Cheyenne, but the mighty Comanche, the great horsemen of the plains, roaming around staring at me doing my women's work. But word must have got around that I'd sock 'em in the nose if they laughed and made my Mississippi feel bad, because no one uttered a harsh sound in my direction.

Soon, I saw crowds gather in the distance. The warriors never came in close like their women and children did. I would go get Mississippi and take her to our outside sitting robe. There, I would cuddle her like the little girls of the tribes did their hair dolls, stroking, kissing her tenderly, singing her lullabies in my own tongue. I figured this would put a stop to it all. Soon as I started singing the simple lyrics, this really put fuel to the flame. Even the prominent chiefs, subchiefs, and the highest advisors of them, the most holy supreme medicine men, came to gawk. This really got my dander up. So not only did I make a larger show of my women's work and open display of the affection and love I felt for my Mississippi, I now turned to the ever-present children, or rather, the children turned to me.

It had been too cold for a couple days to enjoy being outside. The "always warm weather this far south" had turned bitter cold, driving everyone to the interiors of their warm lodges. Once it had blown itself out, it turned spring-like for over a week. I was sitting outside wearing only a loincloth. I had become fond of this dress of her deep southwest cousins—the Apache's summer attire. The warm sun made me doze off. I'd gotten so used to the onlookers, I even forgot to be angry. My women's work drew a few each day, even when it was too cold for me to be outside attending to my chores.

There were several thousand camped here for this sacred year, so there had been no shortage of gawkers in front of our lodge. When I'd try to slip out the back of our teepee, there they would be. But this exceptionally warm winter day had put me to sleep with its deep, soothing warmth radiating on my scantily clad body.

All of the sudden, I was awakened by a child in my arms. I found out later two boys had dared each other into slipping up to touch me. I still hadn't figured out how or exactly why the constant crowd had never laughed once; not even so much as a smile entered their stone-like expressions.

Now, a dozen or so elders stood in the distance looking in amazement at me as I held this little girl-child. One of the bigger boy's little sisters had tagged along on their innocent coup excursion. They lost their nerve when it came time to administer their touch of bravery. I stirred in my sleep-sitting position, bringing fear into their once brave little hearts. They pushed their little sister into my arms, hoping this would help them make their retreat from this peculiar demigod sitting here in the sun.

Jarred awake by the blow of her little body, I instinctively clutched her in my arms and looked down into the child's petrified face. She was too scared to move or scream. I saw the fear I inspired in this little girl and wanted to reassure her, thinking any day now I'll have my own similar creature. I'd been thinking how I'd hold it and kiss its precious face for hours. I started singing her the old lullaby of "The Cradle Will Rock," stroking her long black hair and every so often kissing her forehead and cheeks. These constituted the most open displays of affection she'd ever experienced in her life. In no time, her fear left, and she was patting my pale face and long sun-bleached blond hair wanting to see whether her hand would go through it as it would a shadow, and told me this is what she had heard her elders say.

While she sat on my lap playing with my hair, we visited for a good hour as my observers stood staring as though they had turned to pillars of stone. I was curious now to find out what this was all about. My new little friend told me all. She had an exceptionally sharp little memory, bringing out all the particulars as only a child can do, having not yet acquired the reserve that is cultivated with adulthood.

I found out from her that my daily crowd had nothing to do with my women's work. I grew even more curious to gain some insight into why I commanded a continuous audience, even after dark at times. So, I let her talk, knowing this would help to calm her. Her name, translated into English, was a sweet one. It meant "Button Nose." She did have a little cute, turned-up nose. Her name couldn't have been more fitting. Over the next few short years, I would come to love her as my own.

She first asked me if I'd seen her uncle, telling me she loved and missed him since he had always played with her and brought her little gifts. "Is he up there, now?" she asked, pointing at the sky.

This really lost me. So, I answered quickly. "There are so many, I'm not for sure." I didn't even understand my own answer, and meant to say in her tongue, "You've asked so many questions, I'm not sure now what you are wanting to know."

She said, "Oh, you would remember him if you saw him before you came down to sacrifice the holy white bison."

This comment really brought me to attention. I became fully alert, wanting to know what in the world was being said in the thousands of other lodges strung out for miles in every direction. Button Nose explained that her uncle was never scalped of his thick, beautiful auburn hair. Her father said the Crow, their enemy, after slaying her uncle, his brother, became afraid of the hair's power, since it was of a strange color and extra heavy thickness.

chapter
SEVEN

Adam Becomes a God and Gains a Winged Horse

Adam began to realize now what was being rumored, but why? He shut his eyes and turned his face toward the heavens. The child ceased her breathing as she watched her deity concentrate. He figured, *What the hell harm would it do to ease a child's fears and grief?* So, he whispered his answer into her ear to make it all the more sacred and mysterious.

"Yes, he is there, and he wants you to be happy—to laugh, play, and sing. Grieve no more for his going. All is well, go in peace."

Now Button Nose was ready to clarify all that had been going on in camp. Even before she finished, Adam already guessed what had happened.

When Mississippi had transferred the white buffalo robe to her brother, together with the red pipe and tobacco (the pipe as a gift to him), Witch-ka was to deliver it to the proper holy man to be used for this sacred year since they hadn't obtained one for several sacred sessions in the past. This robe made a gigantic stir since Adam had done a thing no warrior could comprehend—skinning and packing the meat himself back to his lodge. This was women's work for certain.

Adam had seen before how easy it was for Witch-ka, or anyone, to tell a truthful, exact story, the way it really happened, and have it come out completely backwards with all truth and accuracy compromised. This is what happened with Witch-ka's explanation to the holy men about the robe. Button Nose described it all in detail to Adam.

Button Nose had heard the story repeated day after day, hour upon hour, by everyone. No wonder they had Strange Eyes again move his lodge, this time several miles into the center of the huge encampment of winter lodges. He thought it was simply so they could see a man toil over the chores of his wife. Now he knew why no one ever even smiled, much less laughed. They spoke seldom to one another—even then only in low whispers audible just to the receiver.

Button Nose told Adam how Mississippi was on her knees in prayer doing all the proper rituals for the preparation of the white buffalo hide, how the god-like Strange Eyes came forward on foot, not even using his fast chestnut-colored charger as a great chief or brave warrior would have done. He, Strange Eyes, first reached out his hand, relieving his lowly wife of her fear and distress, telling her to go hide in the safety of the robes of their lodge while he performed this most sacred holy slaughter to obtain the white robe for this larger gathering of all the nations. While Mississippi was hiding in the safety of her lodge, Strange Eyes knelt upon the earth his wife had torn up in her prayer. She had flung some dirt clear into the heavens, awaking the gods. But when they looked down, they saw their brother Strange Eyes. He looked upon them at the same time, catching their eyes before they had a chance to look away or disappear. Then, Strange Eyes stood up and turned into a blue white flame. His voice was as thunder demanding his brothers return all warriors who had died bravely in battle. They started to make preparations to return them to their different villages, but then the gods changed their minds. Only Strange Eyes knows the reason why, but he can never tell it. And if anyone asks the reason why, they will die instantly on the spot. Instead, the gods sent this white buffalo robe, beautifully adorned with strange blue markings and pictures on its tanned surface. Even the oldest shaman among all the different tribes gathered here had never heard or seen anything like this. It was the first time in the history of the people that found all of the holy men in complete agreement: "You, Strange Eyes, aren't just from the gods, your ARE a god since you have never walked through the villages singing of your honor and bravery. Just the opposite. You labor outside each day doing strange things." (Adam could never get Button Nose to call it women's work.)

The medicine men had held long secret meetings making sacrifices and offerings to the gods. They finally made contact with the "ancient ones" and learned all that Button Nose had just explained.

Finished with her explanation, Button Nose leaped out of Adam's lap, running as fast as her little legs would carry her to her waiting mother and father, who had arrived on the scene. They were fetched there by the boys who'd shoved the little girl into the god's arms.

The next act brought Adam to his feet. He even went to awake his wife, who for the most part remained tired and confined to the interior of their lodge. As Mississippi came forward with Adam's help, Button Nose's parents stood before them. The father, with tears in his eyes and unable to speak, used hand signs as he handed his little daughter over to Strange Eyes. The father and mother then departed with Adam still holding the child. Mississippi, being too close to her time to take the little girl, leaned over crying, petting, and kissing the child. Mississippi looked at Adam and told him to bring their "daughter" into their lodge, using the term that always meant "daughter" in Cheyenne. This is the way Button Nose became the daughter of Adam and Mississippi.

Their newly gained daughter became an immediate treasure to Adam. Her keen little ears were always on the alert for any wants or needs of her new mother. At first, Adam, her father now, would only toss her up in the air and catch her in her descent toward the earth inside their teepee. She became comfortable and confident in this play. Her new father, the 18-year-old young man, enjoyed it just as much.

Soon they were playing the game outside in front of their lodge, drawing the other children like a loadstone does steel.

Adam gave each child a turn. Even the two boys who had shoved Button Nose into his arms finally got their chance to count coup as they flew the short distance skyward toward where this god or demigod had come from. Quizzed later by the shaman, each and every child claimed that they felt his power; some having experienced detailed, elaborate visions on their fast and short flight toward the most sacred heavens. The children's own truthful statements were all it took to drive the last shred of doubt from the minds of everyone.

Two nights before Mississippi went away to the birthing lodge, she, Adam, and Button Nose went to bed early, dark coming so soon in these short winter days. They enjoyed now placing their new daughter between them. Adam was in seventh heaven as he heard the two talk about girl things. He listened to how they planned to comb and braid their hair, adorning it with all sorts of shiny, treasured, glittering adornments.

The next thing he knew, his wife was shaking him awake. He thought it was time to help her travel the short distance to the birthing lodge. She had previously instructed him to awaken her mother, who would bring the other midwives in for the birthing.

He kept waiting to receive his orders, and her voice finally came through the thick black darkness. She told him to go as soon as light crept into the world, even before it entered the lodge. Go to where they had camped when they first arrived and purchase the colt that Crooked Nose was going to slaughter for food.

Adam listened closely now for her to finish her sentence and explain why, which was her nature. Then he heard her deep, peaceful breathing that turned into the little snores she'd started making since she had grown so large, the baby within putting pressure on her lungs. He was still awake trying to decide what to barter for the colt when light started edging into his lodge.

Mississippi and their daughter, who was cuddled up in her arms, were in such a deep sleep under their heavy warm winter robes, with light sleeping skins pulled over their heads, that Adam never disturbed either of them. He went forth without taking his saddle or bridle, retrieved his chestnut runner, and rode the mare with only a hair lariat, Indian fashion. He traveled to where he knew Crooked Nose was camped.

Upon arrival, there stood the evil-natured man with a little dirty, straggly colt. The poor animal was starved, filthy, and sick. Its fever had given it diarrhea. The odor of the yellow thin dung smear and rotten flesh came to his nostrils. Adam thought, *Did I hear her right?* then went over everything she told him again. By this time, he was within 10 feet of the ill-tempered Indian.

Crooked Nose, recognizing Adam, remembered him as the new owner of his last valuable possession, the beautiful red pipe, which he treasured more than any of the other things he'd gambled away. He had gotten up at the crack of dawn to butcher this sick worthless colt to keep anyone from seeing how destitute he'd become. Now the one he hated and dreaded most had arrived here to make sport of him. He was still thinking how he would kill Strange Eyes if only he could, knowing it would be impossible since he was considered to be some type of god who could never be killed by mortal man.

Glowering and sneering at Adam, Crooked Nose held his knife in hand to deliver the death plunge into the colt's neck. It had been given to him for food the day before because it was worthless and almost dead. He said to Adam, "State your business and go. I have no fear of you, even though you are a god."

Being called a god stunned Adam. All he could do was point toward the sick colt, making hand signs indicating he wanted to buy it. Strange Eyes had momentarily forgotten how to form his wife's language into the proper phrases and sentences. He swapped his mare, the fastest racer that had won so many times, no more young or old warriors wanted to pit their steeds against her. Now he was leading a sick colt away, leaving his beautiful sleek chestnut-colored racer in the hands of Crooked Nose.

The shitty sick colt limped along behind him as he walked back to his lodge. He felt dizzy, trying to remember how it all had taken place, hoping the colt would quit following him and stray off to die.

As Adam entered his lodge, he saw his wife and daughter still sleeping and realized he'd been gone no longer than an hour. He was staring at his wife's sleeping face, trying to figure out why she wanted this sick, scrawny, miserable looking colt.

At this time she awoke and saw her husband staring at her with a bewildered expression. She sat up, put her hand out to him and asked him what was wrong. He told her he had gone at the break of day, just as she'd told him to do, and swapped for the colt of Crooked Nose. She looked baffled and didn't know what he was talking about. She eased out of bed to keep from waking their daughter, and asked him to show her. Adam opened the entry flap. There sat the colt, sitting as a dog sits when they sit sideways.

This looked so funny—the colt sitting like a large puppy—it made Mississippi laugh, waking up their daughter. She bounded over and peered out to see what her mother was laughing at. Seeing the colt, Button Nose looked at Adam and said, "Yes, his eyes are same as yours, father. His mane and tail will be the color of your hair. Also, as soon as he sheds his colt hair, the color of his body will be so unusual, no one will ever be able to say what color he actually is."

At this time, Adam didn't know whether the colt was a stud colt, nor did he care. He let his daughter speak whatever was in her head, not paying much attention to the child's chattering, till she said, "Oh, yes, he has a large stick in his right front hoof's rind."

Adam stepped through the entry flap, picked up the hoof, and sure enough found a thin piece of wood that had worked its way to the top. He removed it and turned toward the creek to wash his hands. However, Button Nose called him back, pointed to the hoof, and said that it was still there. Adam located the sliver he'd just pulled out and discarded, showing her he had taken care of it already. The little girl came out, squatted down by the sitting colt, and pointed to a large piece of wood. The piece was so large Adam had mistaken it for part of the colt's hoof and had only removed a sliver from the chunk of wood that was crippling the colt.

Then Button Nose said, "Mother will make a poultice of her herbs that she gathered last summer. This must be done now to make the hoof sound."

Strange Eyes wanted to know how she knew all this.

"Don't you remember, Father? You told me all this last night before you took your horse and traded it for the colt you called . . ." She tried to say the word she claimed he had told her over and over. ". . . Pegasus."

Finally, Adam understood she was talking about the winged horse in a mythical tale he had heard as a boy. This made goose bumps stand out on his arms when he remembered who had told him the story, especially considering his daughter had dreamed all this.

As Mississippi was making her herb poultice for the colt's hoof, her husband told her all that had happened. While he explained how she'd told him to go purchase the colt, which she didn't remember, it dawned on Adam that she had spoken to him in English. He'd gotten so used to hearing English again when singing to his daughter the old song lyrics because they didn't rhyme in Cheyenne, that it didn't strike him at the time.

Adam never mentioned to Mississippi about speaking English. His fast charger was gone and he had a scrubby, sick-looking colt in her place. He thought it might be wiser to never bring any of this up again. His wife and daughter never mentioned it, to his relief. Both were soon too busy with their newborn baby boy to care much about the colt, a colt now growing and gaining strength as fast as his daughter and son.

Yes, these were the best of times.

chapter
EIGHT

Two Crow Killers

Adam wished he had someone to ask. Why was it all right for the eight-year-old girl, Button Nose, to go into the birthing lodge? She was the one who named the infant son as soon as he was born. Mississippi, seeing the newborn was all right, pulled her daughter to her. The little girl was looking down at her bare feet, her bottom lip trembling. Mississippi was stroking her head and kissing her face while she nursed her newborn brother. Button Nose whispered that he looked "just like red clay." Mississippi looked at the nursing baby, agreed, and named him Red Clay.

Red Clay was born toward the end of January. At the end of March or first week of April, the bands held their great holy shindig. It went on for days and nights—one hell of a hoedown.

Adam and Mississippi were wishing they could just slip away and start their long journey that Adam had drawn out on the doeskin map, but they had to stay for all the ceremonies. Strange Eyes couldn't believe his eyes—and not about the holy time. What he couldn't believe was how fast Mississippi regained the body of her former tall, slim-waisted self. The only difference was her breasts. They stayed somewhat larger, being always full of milk. Red Clay quickly doubled and tripled his weight and size. All the old squaws were amazed at how long the baby boy was, saying he would tower over the teepees when grown. This made the young pair proud.

Button Nose was the perfect big sister. Strange Eyes nicknamed her Little Mama, pronouncing the name in English. She loved the name and attention her new family gave her.

Finally, the sacred year came to a close. The white robe, along with a mountain of sacrificial offerings, was given up to the gods. Several gifts were bestowed upon Adam. He felt self-conscious, knowing the real truth behind the white robe, and was relieved to no end when he had his lodge and new family far to the north.

As he rode, he thought, *I have a daughter!* and leaned over to kiss her. She had her own horse and rode each day by herself, but Button Nose enjoyed and craved her father's affection, and rode a little way each day with him. She would carry the glassy-eyed pup the shaman had put a spell on and forced on the young god since its eyes were the same as their colt, Pegasus, and his master, Strange Eyes. Adam chuckled, slapped his knee, and wondered why and how he had started that habit of slapping his knee. He promised himself he would break the silly habit before it became too engrained.

Pegasus turned into the spirit horse his daughter had prophesized at the time it followed him to their lodge. He was more human than horse, and soon was considered a member of the family. Even Adam finally had to admit to himself that the colt seemed to understand every word that was spoken. Slapping his leg as he laughed, he thought, *Even some words NOT spoken*, for sometimes the colt seemed to know what the three others were thinking. When the baby fussed and cried too long or loud, Pegasus would come and get one of the three and tug at their clothing. He clearly wanted them to follow him to wherever the infant had its swaddling board and soothe Red Clay until the infant quieted down.

This had Adam recalling every detail of the colt's purchasing and his arrival back at his lodge. He was extra careful never to mention again to Mississippi and Button Nose what had occurred. Maybe it was better just to forget how it all happened last year, the sacred year. The colt was turning into a great stud, strongly built and breathtakingly beautiful: one glass eye, reddish mane and tail, and odd yellow spots on a golden blond coat. He truly looked the part of a "spirit horse."

Being a stud, Pegasus should not have been trusted around women and children. Generally, studs have to be ruled with an iron hand. Pegasus was not only gentle but protective of the children, acting as though they were his wards and it was his sworn duty to watch over them night and day till at times it got nerve-wrecking and they wanted him to go away. Then, the big beautiful stud would sulk off, going a short distance where he'd sit on his rump like a dog and continue his vigil over the children.

Red Clay was now past two years old. His sister was going on ten years and their mother Mississippi was pregnant again. Both Adam and Button Nose finally convinced Mississippi that if the baby she was carrying was a boy, it wouldn't turn girl if Adam came into the birthing lodge. He reminded Mississippi that the shaman said he was part god.

Button Nose pointed to where Pegasus sat playing with her little brother, Red Clay. He was just past two and already as tall as a five-year-old. All he had on his mind was wrestling. Even Pegasus would try to slip off at times when the boy got too wild. Mississippi, looking at Strange Eyes' spirit horse, was convinced. She'd let him help her deliver the baby, knowing it would be a girl anyway, because she was carrying it in a completely different way and never gained great size. She was in the last month and was no larger than she was with Red Clay in her sixth, and had never experienced any morning sickness or evening cramps.

They moved camp only when they grew tired of their old one. They were in the heart of buffalo country, with lots of grass and water and plenty of sheltered canyons for a winter lodge.

Their daughter had grown into such a thoughtful and helpful young lady. Adam and Mississippi would look at her with loving pride as she tended to her brother Red Clay, who was growing so tall and contemplative in the past few weeks. He would sit still for a few minutes, ponder over then attempt some task, wanting to help, which made all three of his family clap their hands and praise him. This would make him so proud he'd run to his sister, throw his arms around her, and wait for a kiss.

A month later, Mississippi gave birth to another boy. It weighed just as much as her first. She realized that she had mistaken the water she held with her first child as being all baby. It was a month old now and she still hadn't a name for it yet.

It was late April or early May judging from the vegetation. Button Nose and Red Clay were gathering young greens and wild onions— actually a little flat-bladed leek. Their whole family was hungry for something green. Button Nose, Red Clay, Pegasus, and the worthless glassy-eyed dog that the medicine man had bestowed upon their father when he was a god, were walking down the little brook they'd camped on since before their mother had given birth. The large wolf-looking dog trotted along with its tail between its legs, keeping a close eye on Pegasus, his archenemy. Pegasus hated the dog because the horse was so jealous over the children. If and when the dog got too close to his wards, Pegasus would run in, baring his teeth with hooves flying. The only thing that saved the mutt, so far, was that it was quick and never took his eyes off Pegasus.

The yellow blossoms of dandelions dotted the creek banks, but weren't thick enough to halt the march of the two gatherers along with the worthless mascot and their strong, well-muscled guardian Pegasus. They kept going with the flow of the creek, looking for a large cluster where they could stop and fill both woven willow baskets. Just around the bend, ahead of their steady march, their green treasures would be found in abundance. The pretty little disks of yellow sunshine had been blooming for centuries on this piece of rich earth. Turning into puffballs, the wind would catch the little umbrellas sending them skyward, only to float back down and seed the field that spread out in all directions to build and array a vast carpet just for this day.

As soon as the two little hunter-and-gatherers rounded the bend, the vastness of their sought after treasure brought them to a sudden halt—so sudden that Mutt (their father had given the dog a fitting English name) took his eyes off Pegasus for a fleeting second. Pegasus, seeing this rare opportunity, charged in with great zeal and vigor and caught the dog's shaggy neck hair, which was matted and thick. But Pegasus missed his target. He had aimed for flesh and bone, wanting to break Mutt's neck in his strong jaws. The dog let out howls of fright more than pain, startling the children.

Button Nose, seeing what had taken place, grew angry, especially since the brutality that Pegasus was administering to the squalling, howling, Mutt had frightened her little brother. Now he was crying so loud she feared it would wake her father and mother. They had told her to take her time, giving her two large baskets to fill instead of the small one they normally had her fill. Before Button Nose and Red Clay left, they again reminded the pair to take their time, even if there weren't enough greens to fill both large baskets, and said they'd probably still be in bed when the children returned. *They had sure grown tired very suddenly*, Button Nose had thought. *Must be all the wrestling and playing together they were doing when they got to craving a mess of fresh greens.*

Now she had let all this uproar happen. The noise would surely disturb her parents if they heard it. She edged in, carefully weighing and judging each movement. Pegasus still had Mutt airborne, shaking him furiously, but realized this was not going to accomplish his mission against this sneaky dog that drew the attention and affection of his little god and goddess. Mutt knew, or should have known, this was reserved only for him, their most beloved spirit horse. Pegasus brought the filthy canine down fast. The ground was a blur to Mutt's eyes as he came earthward. Pegasus intended to end it forever with his hard, deadly front hooves.

The sharp slap on his tender nose stung the nerve endings of his powerful jaw muscles, causing him to release his most hated opponent immediately. Pegasus shook his head, snorted, and blew through his large nostrils, spraying the hot clear liquids into the air that the sharp stinging slap had brought on, taking the fight out of the mighty steed.

He hung his head in dog-like fashion and slunk off to the far edge of the dandelion field, peering back at the most hated dog. Mutt was now laying on the ground pretending he was hurt by crawling on his belly, rolling on his side, patting his long wooly tail, and letting the piss fly with each of his high-pitched whines.

The children paid no attention to Mutt, knowing if they did, it would bring Pegasus back down from his lofty sitting position he'd taken upon the crest of the hill. This time there'd be no saving Mutt since the stud would run off with the dog dangling from his jaws like a large cat with a doomed rat.

Big sister had given her little brother one of the baskets and made a big fuss over him gathering the leaves, flowers, sticks, and stones that entered into his container. His little strong fat hands worked like blades on a windmill, throwing everything in his path into the tall woven basket. Button Nose, taking her time, carefully harvested each leaf and young flower so as to keep silt, sand, and any foreign matter out and away from her gathered vegetation.

Red Clay, now tired of this game of the basket, was rolling and tumbling a short distance away toward the creek bank. It was only a foot or two high, and so brought no concern to his sister, who knew the worst he would get was wet if he rolled down the bank.

Mutt was craving to edge in and romp with the boy, and looked up to see what position his old enemy held at this moment. Mutt saw that the coast was clear; the vile horse that had taken his place as the dog of the family was off grazing somewhere. The dog knew the horse's every habit, and saw this as his rare chance to sniff and lick the boy's hands and face, making him laugh, then run and play together. All he had to do was keep an eye out for that big, dumb, hoofed beast.

In fact, Pegasus hadn't gone off grazing like the dog thought. Instead, he'd wandered just over the crest of the knoll he'd been sitting on, keeping his head eyeball-level with the ground swell to make sure the dog didn't get out of hand. As soon as the dog ran to lick and sniff the boy, the great horse charged down the hill from his hiding place. The girl, seeing all this, ran for her brother.

The same instant, a Crow warrior, who had been concealed under the small embankment, let his arrow fly into the Mutt's ribcage. In Mutt's dying throws, he staggered toward the young brave. The warrior took this as a threat, thinking the dog was making an attack. He was stringing another arrow when he became airborne, life leaving his body forever.

Pegasus did a thing not a single old chief, warrior, brave, or shaman had ever heard of in legend or song before or since.

He caught the Crow youth by the back of his neck, literally breaking it before his strong jaws and teeth ripped away the flesh and muscle, exposing the dead warrior's vertebrae. Pegasus didn't stop there. He then took his hooves and worked the warrior and dog over, with some sense it must have been the dog's fault also.

While Pegasus waged war, Button Nose grabbed Red Clay's hand and ran blindly, first to his basket. She emptied the contents of leaves, sticks, and stones, and filled it from the large store pile she'd picked after she had filled her own basket. She was still careful, even in her panic, not to get any sand or dust mixed in with the greens. Clutching both baskets and Red Clay, Button Nose and their bloody protector raced back up the creek.

It was in this manner her new brother came to be called "Crow Killer" when the family returned, infant and all, to the creek bank. Adam saw that Mutt was no more and was relieved. He never liked the dog, thinking it may have been Mutt's nightly barking that signaled in the lone young warrior that Pegasus had dispatched.

Mississippi nursed Crow Killer until he refused to suck and turned his infant head away from her breast with sleep creeping into his eyes. She handed the swaddling board to Button Nose, leaving her with the two boys and a small Derringer.

Mississippi and Adam, both armed, went in opposite directions. They made a thorough sweep by walking in a large half circle, ending up where they'd started. They wanted to see from what direction the young Crow had come. Because he was still a boy of maybe 14 or 15 years, they figured he wouldn't be wise or experienced enough to cover his tracks. After traveling less than a mile of his five-mile half, Adam found where the Crow boy had camped the night before. The young Crow had four head of horses, all top quality, runner or war ponies, and no other gear. Reading these signs, Adam gained more respect for the dead youth, realizing now this boy had gone single-handedly and stolen four great horses.

The young dead warrior was a Crow whose country lay north to northwest hundreds of miles away. Adam couldn't keep from being sad. He knew there was no way to tell Mississippi his feelings, since the Crow were her people's mortal enemy. Adam took the horses, riding one and leading the three others, and made his circle larger. Shooting out in a star pattern, he found where the boy had ridden to his last camp. But he still was not satisfied. Judging from the quality of these horses, he worried that there must have been more in the Crow party. Adam made it back a good half hour sooner than his wife, covering four times the distance since he was mounted on a fast runner and she was on foot.

Adam took the children back to the lodge, telling Button Nose what he planned to do. He took the shovel back with him. While he waited for Mississippi to return, he buried the young boy and told her when she arrived it was better to leave no sign. By the time he replaced the sod he'd kept separate and a few well-placed sticks, leaves, and stones, no one would ever know there was a corpse buried there.

Adam started to walk back with his wife, telling her he wanted to ride out and look around. She, too, was worried, thinking there could be a large raiding party within a few miles that the boy had spawned from. Pegasus, hearing their approach, left the children and lodge and came prancing. Adam chuckled at this, thinking, *I'll just ride the winged horse.* He'd been training him for several weeks to be a runner, never using bridle or bits, just body signals. This way, he could have both arms and hands free to administer the bullets or arrows into the bison. He wanted Pegasus to be comfortable with both projectiles and know what was expected out of him in the chase and kill whether he was using the rifle or the bow and arrow, each of which required a different style.

This would be the first long ride for Pegasus. Adam knew where the boy had last camped and the direction of his travel. This would save

time. But because Adam wanted to backtrack about 30 miles, he knew
there'd be no way to make it back before dark since Pegasus would have
to travel 60 miles to do so. Even with the full moon, he knew this be
too much for even his chestnut racing mare, the one he swapped to
Crooked Nose, and she was legendary among the tribes.

Pegasus wasn't only just distinctive in color and eyes. His traveling
gait was smooth as though he floated on a cushion of air. Adam's first
impression was that he wasn't very fast, for Pegasus seemed slow; his
gait was so smooth and flowing that the strong, quick horse never tired
or lathered like a normal animal.

Then suddenly, there was the river! Adam couldn't believe his eyes.
He knew this spot well. This is where he'd planned on reaching, hoping to make it before dark. The sun was still several hands high! He cut
for sign, riding up one riverbank then down the other side, and left for
home.

Pegasus, missing his lodge and children, took his master for the ride
of a lifetime. Adam now realized the smoothness of Pegasus's gait had
fooled him into thinking he was slow. Chills went up his spine as he
recalled the circumstances that led up to his ownership of this "spirit
horse." When he arrived back at the teepee, he never elaborated on his
trip, especially as to how far he rode.

chapter
NINE

The Fort

The life they had was good. They were never in any hurry, never bound for any particular destination. The nomad family was at home wherever their lodge was pitched. They had been north for two years and had made contact only once with another human.

The boys were now 4 and 2, with Button Nose going on 12. She was more of a mother to the boys than a big sister, which was fortunate for Adam and his wife since Mississippi was pregnant again. This is one of the reasons they decided to head south, but not the main reason. The more important one was to obtain a sausage mill.

Their sole human contact was an old prospector, Harry Mosier, who was alone with his three burros. He had pointed to the area where he was heading on Adam's doeskin map and indicated he wanted Adam to go also. He told of rumors that gold had been found in the Black Hill country and that he was going to check it out—though not for the promise of wealth, for at his age wealth held no meaning. "If I get my scalp lifted, it won't speed the future up much at my age!" he told Adam.

Adam was not interested in building his wealth. Now in his early twenties, he thought, he *knew*, his world would never change. He planned on leading this nomadic lifestyle until the Grim Reaper laid the big sickle to his carcass, though the little handheld meat grinder was another story. His whole clan was clamoring for one of their own after spending that winter camp with Harry Mosier.

Adam and Mr. Mosier would trap beaver. This time Adam trapped not for pelts, but for meat. After skinning and boning out the animal, they would run it through the old prospector's sausage grinder. Harry had spices to mix with the ground meat: crushed cayenne hot dried peppers, sages tame and wild, thyme, even garlic power and hard rock salt. After heating bear fat in their Dutch oven kettle until it was half full of smoking hot oil, they would ladle platter after platter of the small oval balls into the bubbling hot bear grease till they formed a golden brown, crispy fried crust on the outside, leaving the spiced meat inside steaming hot; so moist and with just the right hint of flavor from whatever wild and tame spices they had in their possession.

Mr. Mosier told Adam several things he didn't immediately interpret to his wife. He would mull over, wrestle with, and try to put this information out of his mind and convince himself, as they traveled due west, that everything was going to stay the same. He wished he'd asked the older man certain questions that at the winter camp never occurred to him.

He couldn't withhold his worries from his life partner any longer. He didn't want to stress her, being pregnant and all, but he felt she needed to know, along with Button Nose. Their daughter was only 12 but was not looked upon as a child. She attended to any chore that needed doing. The boys looked to her for most of their wants, and she had patience with her two brothers that was lacking at times in the rest, including Pegasus.

They'd been settled in on the banks of a fast flowing mountain stream for the past week. They were cooking the last of their beaver sausages in the kettle of hot bear fat. As Strange Eyes ladled the steaming hot, golden brown, tasty meat treats out to the always-hungry boys, he smiled, reaching out to physically adore his three children. Love entered his eyes and expression as he watched them eat off the huge bone platter. The sausages vanished as though they'd inhaled them.

Adam said, out of the blue, "We'll start in the morning toward the south. Mr. Mosier told me the government has an outpost, they call it a 'fort,' close to the 'ancient ones.' (This was the Indian's winter camp where Red Clay was born.) There has been a conflict between the soldiers and our people." Adam didn't consider himself white. "There's a trading post and general store. This store is where Harry bought his meat grinder."

He told them they would purchase their own grinder and an ample supply of spices, then stay the winter with Mississippi's people since she was due to give birth at the first of winter or late fall. This stirred much excitement and anticipation in the two females. Even Red Clay and Crow Killer got fired up, running, yelling, and wrestling till Button Nose swatted their little rears to settle them down before they fell into the fire and still hot grease. They in turn squalled loud for a few minutes, then fell off into a deep, peaceful sleep with their little brown pooched bellies full of beaver sausage. Their eyes were too heavy to shed tears for very long.

Adam was in deep thought, knowing the only way to put his new worries to rest was to go south and see for himself. Mississippi could have their baby born with the help of her mother and the older women, who were the midwives of the tribe.

They worked their way slowly southward. The bison, they noticed, weren't migrating in large numbers as they had expected. But with their fleet-hoofed runner, Pegasus, Adam had secured plenty of hides and meat that they turned into jerky and pemmican and stored in long, heavy rolls. The green hides were turned into soft robes. They had planned on selling or bartering most of these goods at the fort since winter was still distant. There was more than enough time to replenish. This way they would go into the late season with fresh jerky and pemmican. Otherwise, both would eventually turn rancid from the heat of the hot summer.

They had been on the plains for about a month from the time they'd left the last mountain range when suddenly, there stood the fort on the banks of the large river—the same river that was one of the main tributaries Mississippi had drawn on the lodge floor and Adam had transferred to the doe hide a few years before. This fort took the little party by complete surprise. It was a good 800 to 1000 miles farther north than the one the old prospector had told them about—actually warned the young squaw man about. Later, Adam found out that Harry Mosier had been correct—the wagon trains, mostly made up of immigrants, were starting to swarm across the plains heading mostly for California, Oregon, and the state due north of Oregon now called Washington. Many, though, had started to settle in every direction in between.

Strange Eyes and Mississippi chose a camp spot five miles or so north of the fort up a small spring-fed creek. Adam wanted to spend at least one week there, maybe even two, to have plenty of time to gather all the information he could. Then, his fears would either be put to rest or there would be more coals heaped upon the flame.

The old prospector had warned him that night about the fort that lay 800 plus miles south of this one. It was clear now that Harry Mosier didn't know of the existence of this fort. Adam found out why this was so on his first of many trips. The fort had just been built the previous winter. It was now in full swing with saloons, a general store, boarding house, and even a barbershop. The fort bragged it had everything one could find back east.

Adam was astonished by the array of dry goods and equipment found in the large store. He bought two sausage mills, each having two interchangeable plates for either a course or fine grind. He then made a deal with the proprietor to take his surplus jerked bison, pemmican, tanned hides, and robes. The storekeeper told him he could do well if he wanted to by supplying his store with such high quality products as Adam had just sold and bartered to his establishment.

Samuel Thomas Blackburn, the owner of the general store, and Adam sensed an immediate kinship. As soon as he laid eyes on Adam, "S.T.," as Mr. Blackburn was known to all, felt a deep connection, one that brought tears—tears he hid by pretending he had to go into the back storeroom. Once he composed himself, he returned. His easy manner of conversation had a calming effect on Adam. He hadn't felt this relaxed from the time Mr. Mosier told him about the U.S. Army building forts and the rumors as to why they were being constructed.

After visiting for the better part of an hour, S.T. asked Adam, flat out, if he had fought in the War Between the States. When Adam related his short life history up to the present, the strange-eyed youth saw the look of disappointment and despair on S.T.'s face. The old storeowner had his hopes built up so high that he collapsed into a chair, put his head in his hands, and wept.

S.T. told Adam that his eyes were the same as those of his son, his only child. He had hoped, however desperately, that he'd found his boy and he hadn't been killed in the Battle of Chancelorsville. With S.T.'s monumental hopes dashed, tears were the only thing that could balance the scales of his utter dismay.

The storekeeper went over to his large rolled top desk, opened a drawer, and withdrew a small, engraved box. He told Adam in advance he didn't want him to say anything. He placed the box in Adam's pile of purchased goods, saying this was his son's last possession in his keep. Neither of them said a word.

The gold watch and compass, built back to back, would be a treasured possession throughout Adam's life.

S.T. then told Adam to come back after six. There were matters of the utmost importance and urgency—much needed answers to Adam's questions. He told Adam not to discuss the subject with anyone until they had their evening meeting.

S.T. was a man who didn't believe in beating around the bush. He got right down to the business at hand as soon as Adam arrived that evening. S.T. explained all that Adam had wondered about, which consisted of the accuracy of what he'd heard from the old prospector. Adam soon realized Harry Mosier's every word had been the truth, plus a heap more that had and was currently taking place as the two spoke. There had been several Indian massacres in the past year. The soldiers would raid a village and the Indians would retaliate. It all looked so noble on the surface. The soldiers were sent by an act of U.S. Congress to protect the citizens and immigrants on the new land recently taken from the natives. Since the Indians weren't considered U.S. citizens, they came in under no law of protection. Otherwise, it was no more illegal to kill Indians than it was to exterminate a prairie dog village.

Rumors ran rampant of mountains of gold in the Black Hill country to the far north. Even if there wasn't a speck of gold dust, the Union government realized the immense value of this vast land they'd thought to be worthless. Historians and mapmakers since the time of the Corps of Discovery—Lewis and Clark expedition—had drawn and stamped it as a worthless barren desert with no water or life. "This was why our leaders were so willing to give it to their red brothers. Now, the land's worth has been brought to their attention." Some of the more wise among them, using hindsight and foresight, had seen the mistake of placing the eastern and southern tribes on this once believed wasteland. It was better to have them all exterminated like Abraham Lincoln did the Peoria Indians. Lincoln declared straightfor-wardly that this rich farmland was too valuable to the citizens of the U.S. to leave even one Indian man, woman, or child alive and thus risk having to contend with land disputes in the future.

The government was now aware of its mistake—driving and relocat-ing the Indians until they were centrally located smack atop the bulk of the country's natural resources. The Federal government had destroyed their southern neighbors in the first part of this decade. Now came an exodus from the south due to the war and a great influx of immigrants of every nationality all descending on this once-believed "desolate wasteland." They had put the eastern Indian tribes, as the settlers encroached on the native's land, into a position where it would be difficult if not impossible to disperse them again.

Then fashion trends stepped in by sheer accident, showing them the way, their chance, once and for all, to completely conquer the savage and finish the war mother England had started centuries before. This fad was the buffalo robe—popular not just in the U.S., but in Europe and the rest of the northern world they traded with. By exterminating the buffalo, the Indian could be defeated. But, it had leaked out that Washington D.C. didn't want to simply "conquer." It had dispatched its armies of soldiers under their generals—the top brass—with direct orders from the Washington leaders to kill as many as they could, to fight campaigns one after another to diminish their numbers till one small territory they had set up in the south, called Indian Territory, would hold every tribe known.

The two men talked, reasoned, and discussed every last piece of information S.T. had gathered in from officers, non-commissioned regulars, buffalo hunters, immigrants, and government officials. Government officials, high and low, are no different than anyone else. Give them an audience, or an attentive listener such as S.T., and they eventually will leak everything. S.T. wasn't one to feign interest in the knowledge they held. His interest was genuine. He'd lost not only a fortune, but also a way of life. And, life itself he had lost to the Union bluecoats.

If Adam could see through S.T.'s eyes, and both could have seen into the future two short decades, they would have lacked the spirit and will to go on.

They were still conversing as morning sunlight started to creep in. Mississippi had expected Adam's return before the moon had traveled far in the night sky. She'd dozed off and slept only an hour or so. When she awoke, she dressed, went out into the warm summer night, looking, listening for the sound of Pegasus' hooves. At first, she was worried. Then, as the night grew toward morning, her worries turned into jealousy.

She remembered the beauty of the white women; their dresses of showy cloth with odd colors that Strange Eyes told her were made back east where he came from. The lace and ruffled cloth were made on large machines called looms. The only thing the tall, slender, brown Indian girl understood was that they were beautiful, and she was only wearing a handmade doeskin dress that only came down halfway to her knees. Strange Eyes always said, "Look at those long, slender hard legs." Thinking this, the tears start flowing from her large black eyes, the eyes that were set in her thin, pretty brown face that was held up by the long, graceful neck. Yes, Strange Eyes had surely found himself a white woman. She remembered some of the girls had warned her this would happen. She'd laughed at them. Now she felt small, knowing the shame this would bring to her and the children.

Mississippi's sadness soon turned to jealous rage, then to a pure, black hatred toward those beautiful white women in their fancy laced dresses. She recalled the fullness of their white powdered faces. Most appeared to lack a chin. Their beautiful fat, round, chinless heads sat square atop their large, supple shoulders, never exposing a bit of their necks out of their wide lace collars. Their colorful cloth dresses had to be held slightly aloft as they walked in their short, waddling steps as though they were imitating a duck. Oh, how graceful the walk of those short, plump-legged, wide-bodied women. Their beauty and grace had enticed her man to stay away from his lodge. Seeing the light grow toward the east, she knew now she'd never see him again. And if he did return, he'd surely have one of these white beauties in tow, and she would without doubt become the most important woman in their lodge.

Her thoughts got no further. Her ears had picked up the sound of Pegasus' hooves. Hearing the sound made the hate and anger flee from her instantly. They were immediately replaced by feelings of dread and anxiety about the unknown "what if?" Dozens of "what ifs" crowded her mind.

Then she saw, by the early dawn light, Strange Eyes—the one who signed the white man's holy book professing to all the earth's living that he was and would be *mine, Mississippi's, this Indian girl's, forever, including the forever that comes after death*. She saw that he rode along with his head and shoulders bowed forward as if he carried a heavy weight that had sapped the strength of his spirit. She knew for certain now that he'd been with the women of his own tribe. These white wonders of beauty. Then she thought of their short waddling steps. She decided, here where she stood in the warm morning sun's dim rays, she would pay extra careful attention to the way she carried herself. And stop, or at least try to stop, walking in long strides with her shoulders, neck, and head held so straight and high as her long, lean, strong legs ate up mile after mile, never tiring as she walked, even with a child strapped to her back.

Seeing for certain now that Adam rode alone and no other followed after him, she walked toward her "used to be" husband. Then remembering her private vow, she quit her long strides and tried to make the short waddling steps.

Adam noticed her walk immediately. He leaped off of Pegasus' back and ran toward her thinking she had twisted an ankle. As he reached out toward her, he saw the daggers flying out of her cold black eyes. Mistaking this anger for a look of pain, he automatically gripped her tunic to take the pressure off her injured ankle.

Mississippi retreated a few steps backwards where she began to fall, purposefully. She now had Adam where she wanted him. She grabbed his shirt and had her strong little hands full of his buckskin tunic. She made herself into a tight ball and placed her feet into the middle of his stomach, which had him so unbalanced he stumbled, falling forward.

When the girl felt her shoulders starting to touch the soft grass, she kicked, straightening her legs out, and let her built up emotions of jealous hate become a reservoir of energy and strength. Adam flew through the air and hit hard on a protruding rock which connected at the base of his skull. He lay stunned with the wind knocked out of him. As his head started to clear, he realized there were small hard fists hitting, beating and slapping him across the face.

When the punches and slaps subsided, he felt his hair being pulled. Through a foggy haze he saw the hurt and the tears of his Mississippi, and heard her sobs of grief as she spoke on some topic he had no insight on—something about "white . . . no chins . . . waddling steps . . . all being pretty and how her old plain tanned skinny body her man thought was so ugly, and she didn't blame him for looking and desiring one of his own race that was so pleasing to the eye to look upon."

Adam held her in his arms and tried to get her to stop crying long enough so she could tell him what had so enraged her.

After consoling his hurt, mad, little Indian wife, he was able to convince her that Mississippi was the most beautiful, smartest woman who had ever been born to mortals or immortals of heaven or earth and was the only woman, girl, female of any race who his eyes would ever look upon with desire.

Here, Mississippi butted in. Adam saw a small dagger or two entering back into her eyes as she spoke.

"The white women are beautiful. Don't you think the white women are beautiful, Strange Eyes?"

Adam knew here, where he sat on the warm ground of the summer morning, the right answer was next to impossible. Just because his face had lost the sting of her slaps, the wrong answer, even a wrong word in the right answer, would land him in even more trouble. He would fall deeper into the pit he thought he'd just crawled out of.

Adam dreaded to have to tell her all that S.T. and he had talked about through the night. He knew this would devastate her till her spirit would break. But seeing no way out, he told her word for word, as much as his memory could recall.

Adam was still trying to explain the magnitude of the troubles at hand when the girl slipped out of her short summer dress, then helped him off with his buckskins. She made their old style long pallet so perfect for their buffalo run—both desiring the leap far out into space, to escape for a moment, before descending to the rock's below.

chapter
TEN

Sarsaparilla Shootout and the Great White Chief

The two adults and three children began their journey south away from the fort. Twenty-six horses and mules bore their riders and lodge, along with the packed kettles, pots and pans, and the two new meat-grinding mills. These mills brought high anticipation of the mountains of sausage they would cook in the coming decades all throughout this vast land, the great land his wife had drawn on their lodge floor years before.

Their first several days of travel were no different than the preceding ones before arriving at the fort. Even the bison was running similar. There was one noticeable difference, however. The small herds, which never numbered more than a dozen, were so spooked that they bolted into a dead run at the first sight of a rider and horse.

Adam saw one large old bull with his head lowered to the ground, never offering to move. As soon as Adam drew near, he saw the old bison had been wounded in the gut area. The flies had laid piles of yellow blows. Thousands had made their way in and now were spilling out of the large, greenish hole as maggots and flies.

Adam had been warned and expected this a long time before he began seeing the hundreds of fresh-skinned swollen carcasses. The hide hunters, for the most part, had removed only the tongue and hide. In some areas, the red, swollen flesh had been rotting for quite some time. The stench from the mountains of rotting animals actually penetrated their clothing and lodge. There were so many slaughtered, there seemed to be no route around the carnage.

Mississippi could now understand her husband's worries. They were beginning to despair, growing certain the rest of S.T.'s prophecy would come true also.

They quit making their "long camps," and started to travel for several days, allowing only enough lodge time to rest their horses and gather in enough bison meat to be smoked and dried for the coming winter. At times, they worried there wouldn't be enough kills. The bison on the route they'd chosen were so scarce that Adam took to slaying old cows and bulls, fearing if he waited for the prime young ones, they would enter the month of falling leaves that led to the long months of cold hunger with no meat at all.

By leaf falling season, the small party had made its way south to the vicinity of the fort that Harry Mosier, the old prospector, had told Adam about in their last winter's camp.

Adam first started to swing wide to circle it and keep going south. But when they came to one of their original campsites where Mississippi and Adam had so enjoyed their first time together in this land of the ancient ones, she wanted to rest a week before making what was left of their short journey to her people's winter camp.

Two winters before, they had been here on the banks of this little clear brook that flowed into the main tributary on which this new fort had been built. Adam went over for the hundredth time what Mr. Mosier had told him, but his curiosity was beginning to get the best of him. He rested for a couple days, then mounted Pegasus and headed back north. He knew the fort would be easily found, but not THIS easily.

He hadn't traveled but four hours when he came to a deep-rutted, well-traveled road, the first he'd ever seen in this vast land. He knew by the ruts it was heavily traveled year around. He followed the road and came back to the river. At one of its major bends, there stood the fort. It was tenfold the size of the one where he'd made the acquaintance of S.T.

The young man experienced a strange apprehension: he felt small, actually intimidated by the strength this fort held for he understood the reason for its existence. He wished he could find fault with S.T.'s words of warning. This is what made Strange Eyes ride Pegasus into this large government dwelling that had been built for the sole purpose of bringing ruin to his way of life.

It was some type of holiday which gave the rider of the spirit horse a false impression of the fort's population. Every walk of life had gathered here. Some had ridden for days to make this year's rendezvous of dances, shoots, and horse races, even sponsoring a boxing match with bare fisticuffs.

Adam could have chosen no better or worse time to go gather information. He saw the large wagons with tall, wide, iron-rimmed, wooden-spoked wheels that were specially designed and built to stand up under the burden of giant piles of heavy green buffalo hides. Some of the larger wagons were drawn by three spans. These represented thousands of once-live buffalo. Millions of pounds of good red meat now lay on the plains. Their carcasses filled the gullies with their bones and flesh, so thick they eventually created dams of the dead that held water for the living beasts and fowl that knew no monetary gain from the eastern markets.

Adam drew Pegasus up to a walk so he could study the awesome slaughter, the willful waste of this madness that his race's government had ordained. They did not encourage, but demanded this policy be carried out, all for the purpose of exterminating an obstacle that lay in the way of what they called civilization.

There were wagons in every street and more that had been pulled to the rear of the stores and saloons. Many were laden so high that if their loads hadn't been secured with ropes, the hides would have slid to the earth as the wagon jarred along the deep, rough, rutted trail the hide hunters now called the "Fort Road."

Samuel Thomas Blackburn's words of caution and Adam's own uneasiness at the first sight of the fort now left his mind and body. The incoming tide, the unchangeable future, brought only waves of disgust and resentment. By the time he pulled up in front of the general store, he was downright belligerent. He dismounted, started toward the store's door, then changed his mind.

Adam went back to his horse, untied his saddlebags, and took out his belt guns. These were the same pistols he'd practiced with for hours on end as a young trapper when the springs and summers seemed to drag on forever. He'd made holster after holster. By accident, he cut one down till it almost exposed the trigger guard, causing it to take a quarter twist away from his body due to the unequal pressure of the miscut leather. Out of boredom, he strapped the miscut holster on his holster belt that normally was worn high around the waist, not only for convenience, but for comfort. It, too, should have been notched so it would stay secure high on his waist. But his fell low, riding more on his leg. Adam, being a boy, had started to goof off. As he played with the one pistol, he realized his hand and the pistol's butt lined up perfectly. The boy practiced for over a month. He perfected his draw till his hand was quicker than the eye. He shot pounds of lead until he learned the art of eye-hand contact. The other older trappers would come to watch and bet on Adam's marksmanship and speed. He only shot and practiced the art of quick drawing to beat the boredom of the long idle spells between trapping. Now that he had acquired a wife, this pastime never entered his thoughts since pistols were fairly worthless as hunting instruments.

As he strapped on the matching pistols, he had to admit to himself the reason he'd packed them in his saddlebags. He left Pegasus hitched in front of the general store and walked slowly toward the saloon, an establishment he'd always made it a point to steer clear of.

He walked through the saloon's short half-door. The main one had been propped open to let out the cloud of tobacco smoke and stench of unwashed bodies mixed with the aroma of whiskey and the cheap perfume of the "soiled doves" who worked the crowd of men sitting at the tables drinking and playing cards.

Adam approached the bar feeling an aggressive contempt for every living soul that sat or stood, not only in this saloon but on this spot of earth the U.S. called their fort. He disliked this new feeling and was wrestling with it, trying to figure out what had brought it on.

He then heard some soldiers talking, bragging, laughing about their great deeds of bravery. Each in the rowdy, raucous crowd was trying to shout his story over those sitting at the surrounding tables—tales about first-hand escapades of murder, rape, and pillage in the different Indian campaigns they'd fought in since arriving and about what they'd heard was in store for the coming winter.

To hear them tell it, they comprised a special chosen force, considering the great natural ability their company alone displayed with rifle and pistol. They were going to make winter campaigns against the savage heathens where and when they would be most vulnerable: when their ponies were too weak, too starved down by winter to be ridden in battle. Their special chosen company would single-handedly eradicate the heathen lice. Their courage in battle is what had won them all this rest and recreation.

A stocky, muscular, bulldog-faced man entered through the half doors causing laughter and jeering from the loudmouth speaking soldier, making him holler out the man's name, saying his company would be the ones who killed the lice. Then "Reb" would take the nits by their heals, knocking their little dark heathen brains out like he'd done on their last battle just two weeks before.

The bartender finally made it to Adam, asking if he wanted a shot or a bottle. Adam experienced the same gut-felt fear of long ago in the Taos saloon where he'd witnessed the "act." However, here all eyes weren't glued to the spectacle spread-eagled on the tabletop. There would be no way for him to make an escape without anybody seeing him. He started for the half doors, hoping to avoid drawing any attention.

Reb, the bulldog-faced sturdy man, had been standing and talking to the sitting soldiers, but had taken to looking at Adam's pistols and the strange way he carried his holsters. They swung so low they looked as if they'd drop from his hips if he tried walking. And walking he was, straight for the half doors that would lead him away from this madness and back to his world.

As his long stride carried him past the soldier's tables, the one they called Reb stuck out his foot, tripping Adam.

But Adam never fell the way Reb expected this tall, lean, buckskin clad man to do. Instead, Adam righted himself as a gymnast would have done. Turning toward the soldier's table, he made the sounds and motions of a quick apology for he thought he'd bumped their table accidentally.

Reb took Adam's apologetic manner for fear which only fed his hostile nature. He strutted back and forth in front of Adam in the manner of a tom turkey challenging a new arrival for a fight. Adam knew what was coming down and apologized again, figuring this is all it would take. Then he could make his exit and be on his swift horse, alive and gone from this fort, forever safe and sound.

But there was never a bully born under the sun that let one he thought was weaker or intimidated off without at least a good thrashing, if not more. And when it came to bullying, few could outdo Reb.

Adam noticed everyone was clearing out, vacating the space where Reb and he stood. Reb told Adam he was going to buy him a drink. This puzzled Adam. He thought the man was spoiling for a fight. Reb's offer brought a sigh of relief to Adam, but he could see that the rest of the saloon's crowd did not feel the same. They moved again, making even more room between Reb and Adam, some even going through the half doors, making their way out into the dirt street.

Adam walked back to the long polished bar. Reb told the bartender to give Adam a sarsaparilla. The barkeep, in a low tone, pleaded for Reb not to make Adam drink one of them. "At least let the man's last drink be a whiskey."

Adam knew the taste of whiskey and could never see what people saw in it. Its flavor and taste were awfully hard to choke down. He remembered how he'd gagged on his first and only encounter with this expensive liquid. He figured sarsaparilla must be pure skunk essence. It was so horrible, even the bartender had spoken up on his behalf.

The barkeep noticed the look on Reb's face. He poured Reb a double shot of whiskey out of his special canister, then set a long-necked corked bottle before Adam and pulled the cork out slowly. Adam heard the fizz for the first time in his life coming from the bottle of amber liquid with foam rising slightly on its surface. He smelled the sweet fragrance of the bottle's contents. He picked up the long-necked bottle of soda pop and placed its open end gingerly to his lips as if the bottle might turn into a timber rattler. Taking a small sip, he realized immediately that this was the drink of the gods. He emptied his bottle and ordered another one for himself, telling the barkeep to also give one to Reb explaining that there was no reason for anyone to try to choke down that god-awful whiskey when there was a drink such as this available.

Adam's innocent comment was taken by the patrons of the establishment as an open challenge to Reb for a gunfight, which was the new fad. It could even be classed as a new sport that was catching on to settle differences quickly. Usually no justice was meted out for either the loser or winner.

Adam was still waiting for the bartender to fetch the sarsaparillas when Reb walked to the center of the saloon's floor and released his pistol's tie-down loop from its hammer. Standing with his legs apart, he wiggled his fingers, relaxing his hand for the last time here on the face of old mother earth.

Adam, seeing what was happening, put out his left hand to indicate, "Wait, no, stop." The spectators discussed among themselves later the performance they witnessed, the likes of which they had never seen.

Truthfully, no one SAW anything because not one could remember ever seeing the strange-eyed man draw or his gun "barking" in his hand.

Three shots rang out so fast that before the cloud of black-powder smoke lifted, there lay Reb. The first two bullets had entered his chest cavity, throwing him backwards. This made the third rapid-fired shot enter where his chest would have been, which at that point was Reb's head as his body was being hurled backwards. The bullet entered between his eyes and came out through the top of his head. Skull fragments and bits of white brain mixed with his red blood were matted and hanging in his hair.

Adam now had his second low-hanging revolver in his left hand. He motioned for the bartender, telling him to get four more bottles of sarsaparilla and come with him. The bartender didn't let grass grow under his feet. He'd never seen anything like what he just witnessed. He had the clearest view in the house and knew this man could and would kill as many as he had bullets left.

When they made their way through the half doors, there stood Pegasus. The spirit horse had untied his reins and was standing waiting for his master. Adam had the bartender put the four sodas in his saddlebags along with the revolver he held in his right hand.

The bartender spoke telling Adam to ride fast, but cover his tracks by going the wrong direction first, then zigzag using water, rocks, or heavily traveled trails around the fort to throw off the army for they were just a bunch of bored bastards under a general with the mind of a child. This George Custer might just be bored enough to come and hunt him down for sport. He'd made his brags, this general had, just the night before. He had his pack of dogs in O'Leary's bar, saying he would lay wagers, and even gave odds that his hounds would track a man on foot or horse, just as they would a beast. "So, use water travel every chance you get till you've made distance. Sure it was self-defense," explained the barkeep, "but that don't hold beans with the Army."

Adam never spoke. He just nodded his head, turned Pegasus the opposite way of his arrival, and held him in till he was at the edge of the new settlement. Then he let his winged horse out.

His wife and children tasted their first and only soda late that night. They broke camp before first light and were on their way. Adam told Mississippi what had happened, leaving nothing out. He wanted her to understand the enormity of what was taking place. He knew as soon as spring came, they too would have to start north to make as much distance as possible between them and the bluecoats. Then, he thought maybe they could travel toward the "great waters" he'd heard the Frenchmen talk about years before. They called it an ocean. Surely the bluecoats wouldn't make it that far in their lifetime. With this new idea, there formed a spark of hope once again.

They had traveled for a week and were a couple days from the Three Sisters. They decided to stay until they had the three bison worked up as fresh meat or jerked, which would give them sufficient stores and plenty of overrun if Mississippi's people were short. They were planning for the worst since they'd seen the rotten carcasses of the massive slaughter on their way south.

Their arrival held several surprises in store for Strange Eyes and especially for his wife. Mississippi gave birth to a healthy little girl. She had figured her "time" and thought she still had at least another month. She initially mistook her labor pains for bowel cramps. The birth of their daughter was so fast and painless compared to the births of their two sons, Mississippi named her immediately, even before the cord had been tied to be cut.

"Morning Joy" was truly the joy of Mississippi's heart. Adam knew his two sons needed him more than ever since their mother made no bones about the extra special feelings she held for her daughters, Button Nose, and now Morning Joy.

Button Nose was almost 13, and far as the two boys were concerned, she was godlike. If Button Nose didn't know of something, that something simply didn't exist. Now there was this special little pale creature with yellow hair and different colored eyes who so fascinated their mother, she didn't ever want to put it down. As soon as she did, Button Nose was there waiting for the chance. She would kiss its little pale face and pet its father's odd-colored hair. Button Nose had already made up several songs about how Morning Joy would become legendary with her beauty and wisdom. Even her rowdy brothers would become quiet and disciplined when Button Nose would let them hold their baby sister. Each would kiss her cheeks as gently and softly as though they were fragile china.

Adam, seeing the happiness and enjoyment this baby had brought to his lodge, was all the more anxious for the arrival of spring, the "month of the green grass shoots that make the ponies fat." There was an ill wind a-blowin', and it wasn't the weather. Since they'd last seen his in-laws, their world had changed irrevocably. There had been several battles with the U.S. Cavalry. On a few occasions these had lasted long enough for the bluecoats to bring in their foot soldiers—wagonloads of them reaching into great numbers.

Witch-ka, Adam's brother-in-law, told him he had fought with the Comanche, his wife's people, for they had been with them the summer before. This is how Witch-ka was chosen, along with the chiefs and sub-chiefs, to go to Washington D.C. to obtain the peace treaty and peace medals. It was because of the power of the sacred white buffalo robe.

Witch-ka told Strange Eyes every detail of the journey of the 2 ½ dozen chiefs, sub-chiefs, and shamans, their names, what each said, and what was said in return to each, and what each of the party said during the trip there, the stay, and their return. What amazed Adam the most was Witch-ka's memory for the smallest detail, not to mention the word for word narration. Witch-ka even remembered little fragments of paper or different colored threads that lay on the floors of the Great White Chief's house.

There were many things that disturbed his brother-in-law about the whites, but the main one was their Great Chief. He'd learned that this chief was neither born from the lineage nor had to prove himself in battle after battle. The most baffling thing was that he was chief only a short while before another would take his place, even if he was young and healthy. Why? Strange Eyes told Witch-ka he knew nothing about his people and hoped he'd never see another one in his lifetime. He, Strange Eyes, was Cheyenne.

Mississippi's people were low on meat and staples because Witch-ka had just returned from the peacekeeping mission. This important mission had come at a time when the band should have been farther north where the bison were plentiful. The massive slaughter of the bison in this southern region had also begun to take its toll on this small band that Strange Eyes was united with through his wife's people. Although Adam and Mississippi had plenty of meat and staples to last them through the winter, Adam saw clearly that S.T.'s warnings were proving true.

Being young and unworldly, Adam knew nothing yet of his own people's government. Witch-ka seemed so zealous and confident about his part in obtaining the peace treaty, even though this had greatly increased his people's risk of hunger or perhaps starvation.

One of the federal government's stipulations was that while the chosen chiefs of the different bands were meeting in Washington D.C., their remaining tribesmen had to dwell in the area that the Great Father had designated in advance. These locations were too far south from the prime hunting grounds of the Cheyenne and Comanche.

When Strange Eyes questioned his brother-in-law about this matter of prior stipulations that would surely jeopardize the tribes' food situation, Witch-ka held up for the Big White Boss, saying, "Yes, the Great White Father was very, very concerned also about this oversight of making the different tribes stay so far from their prime summer hunting grounds. He wanted to know, very specifically, from each individual chief and even the sub-chiefs, how this would affect us. After the chiefs told of the hardships that would come, this Kind Father, the Great White Chief, bestowed on us wagonload after wagonload of commodities."

These commodities had to be picked up at a fort even farther south of the bison's range. The several tribes that were eligible for the government handouts picked up their green moldy bacon, and corn meal and flour crawling with weevils. The only cloth sacks that weren't full of weevils were the ones that had turned hard and green with mold. The weevils that called these sacks home had died years earlier. The coffee beans had never grown any farther south than Missouri. They were scorched and burned regular dried beans. The sugar was slightly mixed, this meaning a slight amount of low-grade sugar had been added to 50-pound sacks of sand.

Witch-ka told Adam the hungry camp dogs, when thrown a side of the bacon, would turn up their noses and trot away. Nothing would touch it, not even crows or buzzards. They hoped their horses would at least eat the sugar and get some nourishment from the mountains of mixed sand, but this turned out the same as the flour and meal. Their mounts would starve to death before any of the staples would ever be considered as food. Not one sack of the wagon train loads of staples was ever consumed by man or beast.

"Winter has caught us with the lowest stores anyone can ever remember at the winter camp of the 'ancient ones,'" said Witch-ka. "We will surely have to break out into smaller bands. These bands will have to send out their warriors and young men on long hunting trips or the occupants of their lodges will not survive the winter. The hunting and packing will have to be done on the backs of ponies too weak to carry themselves."

These forced hunts and moves would take a great death toll on their best mounts. All this left the winter camps vulnerable to marauders. But the worst enemy was the long days and cold nights with the hunger that would first drive them to madness, then to weakness and eventually death—death being the only release from their miserable predicament.

Adam asked Witch-ka if the inevitable hardships had been explained to the "top bullshitter." His brother-in-law told him that, yes, this was one of the reasons the Great Kind Leader, with tears in his eyes, had appropriated the wagonloads of commodities far, far, to the south. All to help out his red brothers in this lean time.

The Great White Chief told them not to worry about hunting and gathering stores for the coming winter, but to stay where it had been designated. Then take the long journey to the south, get their food draw, and be sure to return to their treaty vicinity. This way they would remain protected under this peace treaty and peace medals. Witch-ka always wore his large medallion hanging from its red, white, and blue ribbon. The bronze medal was the size of a small saucer and he displayed it with pride as he spoke. Witch-ka drew inner strength from it and felt very proud of his newly designated rank.

Adam now knew the fear of starvation. The ruse of the far south trek to pick up the moldy filth sealed their fate. They were only days away from the worst starvation they had ever known.

Still, there was no way for Adam to make Witch-ka comprehend that the Great White Chief's kindness consisted of putting these tribes into a position so his armies could destroy them like Abraham Lincoln had annihilated another tribe.

Samuel Thomas Blackburn's message to Adam was now striking home each day as his brother-in-law remembered other discussions that occurred at the chief's peace conference. Adam had been forewarned by S.T. about what the U.S. would try to pull. They would make their adversary put their guard down so they could make their killing blow quickly and easily. They would launch winter campaigns when the tribe's ponies were weak from starvation. This year, the people and the warriors were just as weak as their war ponies.

Adam wished he had his lodge and family with Harry Mosier to the far north, away from this vulnerable southern camp in case S.T. was right about the cavalry's winter campaigns. There was no way to make Witch-ka understand that the peace treaty paper was just another rotten moldy trick to make it easier for the U.S. Cavalry to carry out its mission of extermination more efficiently with fewer casualties. This exalted and honored the generals in charge. The medals and peace papers were bestowed to give the chiefs and their subjects a false sense of security.

chapter
ELEVEN

Major Elliot Under the Command of General Custer

There had been over a foot of snowfall. It had turned clear and cold on the full moonlit night.

The Cavalry struck.

Pegasus awoke Adam by striking his hoof at the base of a lodge pole. It made a hollow muffled knocking sound because the snow had accumulated deeper there than the rest of the teepee's circle. Adam had scolded Pegasus for doing this and his reprimand always worked before. But this time, the spirit horse had worked his strong jaws and teeth around and under the tied entry flap and was shaking and pulling at the lodge.

Adam now knew there was something amiss. He hurriedly dressed, reached toward his arsenal of weapons and came up with his knife, axe, bow, and quiver of arrows. He untied the entry flap and as he exited he heard, then thought he heard, hooves running through the frozen snow.

As he cupped his hand to his ear to draw in the sound, the sound of the bugle charge was upon the village. It was too late for him to even go back in for his rifle and pistols. The cavalry horses' hooves came bearing down on the sleeping village of old men, women, and children. The warriors left on a hunt two days before the snow came. The weather had turned mild, being southerly drawn by the cold front that had dumped the foot of snow. But it was now bitter cold.

Adam saw the 20 cavalry horses and riders in full charge. The horses were throwing up clouds of frozen top ice, turning the powdery snow beneath into a white whirlwind. The fast moving horses with the full moon to their rear cast the swirling powder into a spectrum of colors with sparkling diamonds of winking yellow and blue lights.

The charging troops held a close compact square of four abreast. The lodges were formed in an oval circle with the creek running through the middle the long way. This caused the cavalry to split in half as soon as it entered the village. Only the flag bearer rode on through to the opposite end.

Adam realized the cavalryman wasn't bearing a flag, but a long torch. He was throwing something from a container, then lighting it with the torch's flame. It immediately burst into fire and traveled the path of the spilt liquid. The arsonist was making his way back through the circle of lodges while the other cavalrymen were slaughtering the women, children, and elderly who tried to flee from this encampment of horror.

The well-lit drama of flame and moon played out against the once-white snow. This white garment was now being adorned with red sashes as the slain bodies emptied their blood upon the mother earth's fresh frozen blanket.

Adam had never moved. His legs became too weak to hold up the massive lead form his body had become. He even lacked the voice to shout out a warning or plea of mercy for the little ones he was seeing slaughtered by the U.S. Cavalry.

He spotted his sister-in-law, Witch-ka's wife, so heavy with child she could hardly walk. Strange Eyes watched her as she staggered toward the insane killing men in blue. Even their horses had taken on diabolical features: their nostrils dilated out of proportion, their eyes bulging and rolling back into their heads till only the whites shown. His sister-in-law was making her way headlong toward this demonic scene.

She held the peace treaty's paper high over her head as a truce, an offering. It was, to her, the most Holy Arc of the Covenant. She knew as soon as the murdering, raping, pillaging U.S. Cavalrymen saw the peace treaty paper that she held aloft, along with her husband's peace medal hanging from the red, white, and blue ribbon that represented the glorious and honorable colors of their flag, they would see the horrible mistake they had made.

Her two children were apprehending her movements even more. The little boy and his toddling sister clutched her soft doeskin garments and were hanging on with the strength that extreme fear gives to a child. Their little brown fingers became vice grips of steel, their hands turned into claws of terror as the cavalryman on the tall, black gelding charged their mother. He slashed his blood-soaked dripping sword through his commander-in-chief's own handwritten signature of peace.

The white paper was now turning a crimson red: the precise color of the peace desired and planned hundreds of miles to the east where the Great Noble White Father lived.

The rider on the black gelding wheeled his steed around once again toward the helpless, pregnant mother and her two little ones. He knew their only protection had been the paper that he'd successfully slain on his first brave and triumphant charge. So, the black horse and bloody rider came walking slowly toward the three motionless forms.

The woman and the young boy started singing their death song, setting the stage for the next blood-bathed scene.

The U.S. Cavalryman, a major, was the officer-in-charge and an "officer and gentlemen" by an act of the U.S. Congress. This time he took his sword and plunged it with a hard downstroke, driving it through the squaw's large protruding pregnant belly. The long blade went in at an angle behind the unborn child to her pelvic bone. Then he bore down hard on the razor sharp blade.

Most all cavalry swords were used in the same manner—as a lance— and so tended to be on the dull side. But for the owner of this long sword, its razor sharpness was his pride. He would boast that his blade would decapitate his adversary's head with the ease of halving an apple.

The heads of the two children rolled away from their bodies, leaving a long spewing trail of blood on the trampled white snow.

Mississippi had slashed their lodge at its rear, which faced the standing trees. The entry flap was toward the brook. Her mind went completely blank, devoid of thought or emotion. Running toward the cover of brush and timber with her children was simply a reaction to her most base instincts of motherly animalistic preservation. Mississippi ran with the two boys and Button Nose fled carrying the infant baby girl.

Morning Joy was strapped to her swaddling board which Button Nose had slung on her back, leaving her hands free to fight. She had a Green River trade knife in one hand and the small two-shot derringer in the other. Her mother had no weapons, only her two sons. Her only thought was of escape, of getting the four children to the safety of the standing timber.

The frostbiting cold night offered the only warmth of life left. Their lodge had been pitched in the crook of the small stream's bend, placing them not only out of the cavalry's initial charge, but also at a vantage point that gave them a larger panoramic view of the cavalry's slaughter.

Adam saw Mississippi and the children at the rear of the tent scrambling for the timber, snapping him out of his hypnotic trance. His body was moving, but his mind was vacant. He couldn't break the spell. He wasn't scared. He felt nothing. His body and mind were not unified. They could not even be considered separate for neither existed at this moment.

Then all hell broke loose in their little corner of this cruel night. There were screams of women, crying of children, death songs sung in the cold, crisp night air. There were moans of the injured and dying mixed with the laughter and curses of the blue coats as they galloped their beasts of destruction back and forth through the burning village.

Some cavalrymen spotted the lone teepee, the only lodge that hadn't been put to the torch. It sat at an angle from its neighboring lodges, which had kept it out of harm's way. If only the lodge's occupants made a break when the cavalry first charged, there would have been hope. With the snow so trampled, the troopers wouldn't have thought to scout for tracks out of the perimeter. They would have been too busy with looting and raping after the heat of their charge and slaughter wore down.

The screams and wails of the dying along with the flames and smoke from the blazing teepees putting off the scent of burning, smoldering leather had gripped Pegasus's brave heart with fear. He also had crept to the edge of the woods and concealed himself among some scrub red cedar trees, sitting as was his custom when he became nervous or unsure as to what was expected from him. He watched his family as they moved one direction, then another. They trampled back and forth in the snow, trying to use their lodge as a shield from the half dozen soldiers who had grouped around Moon Child and her beheaded little son and daughter. They were laughing as the tall, redheaded private took the girl child's head and placed it on her brother's headless shoulders. Next, he positioned her little blood-drenched head along with that of her brother on her headless form to create a two-headed body and pretended to be a barker at a carnival telling all to come pay a thin dime to see the wonder of the world.

The U.S. Cavalry, under the command of General George Armstrong Custer, had created, by the noble act of Major Elliot, officer-in-charge, an unbridled orgy of savage butchery.

There were a couple other fellow troopers hearing Red's loud shrill voice and the laughter, hoots, and hollers that accompanied his "barking." They left the young girl they'd been raping, took their sheath knife, counted to three, and plunged their weapons into her rib cage. One of the soldiers got his blade hung between her ribs while the soldier with the free knife laughed. The other kicked and cursed the naked dead girl. He yanked her little limp dead body into the air with the hilt of his knife while his raping buddy took his booted foot and stomped down hard by the blade.

With the knife free and their sexual urges satisfied for the moment, they were curious to see what Red was doing to attract and hold so many in audience. They found their officer-in-charge astride his tall, black horse. Major Elliot raised his sword while two other soldiers held the squaw's dead body out, thus providing the major the perfect swing to prove his skill of beheading with his special blade he had imported from the Orient. It was very doubtful that any there, except the major, even knew the meaning of the word "Orient."

He had righted himself for the swing when Adam's family made their break for the safety of the moonlit tree line. The two young murdering rapists remounted, making their way to see Major Elliot's beheading exhibition. Mississippi and Adam kept their eyes and ears toward the mutilating party. They never saw the two mounted soldiers approach because the six horses and the remaining mounted cavalrymen blocked their view.

When they were halfway to their destination, they saw the two incoming demons. At the same instant, these two murdering rapists spotted them.

The shouts of the soldiers to alert the rest of troops about the fleeing family stopped the major's sword swing. He spurred his black horse so violently that it lunged forward, knocking down the two noncoms who held the dead woman about to be guillotined. They were hit with such force that the living and dead became intertwined. The sudden, hard blow that the tall, strong, horse delivered to the two men left them temporarily out of commission as their leader charged his new target.

The mounted and dismounted soldiers remained in the dark as to what was going on. They still sat or stood unmoved as their comrades rode up. The two whistle blowers were still too interested in Red's performance to inform the remaining party about the escaping Indians. This left Major Elliot with all the glory of the slaughter for himself. Realizing this, he spurred his steed to a full run.

The black horse was running out of control when he made his first contact. His sword swing went wild. The horse bounded in giant leaps as it tried to turn to make the next and final killing charge. The major, feeling its iron-shod hooves slip in the snow, had to give it more rein before he could bring it up.

Seeing this, Adam snatched the baby from Button Nose's back, hoping to help the girl by relieving her of her burden. As the straps cleared her shoulders, traveling down and off her arms, they caught the hand that held the Green River knife, yanking it from her grip. She bent momentarily to retrieve it.

This gave Major Elliot the few seconds he needed. As she rose, he was in position. She pointed and fired the small Derringer. The bullets lodged in the wooden tree of his army saddle as he swung his heavy blade, cleaving her head from the top down toward her jaw.

Her body lay on the ground making wild jerks, throwing itself up into the air, then pawing and kicking violently in the snow, spilling her brains, which mixed with the squirting blood as her strong little heart pumped its last beats before death claimed her.

Adam saw all of this through the strange fog that swirled before his eyes. He saw Mississippi and his sons entering into the woods' edge.

Suddenly, Pegasus charged out from the small cedar trees, his mouth open producing screams that Adam had never heard before or since from a horse or any animal. It still felt like a dream. Surely he would awaken from this horrible nightmare. In an almost unconscious daze, Adam turned and walked back toward the blood-bathed body of his eldest, Button Nose.

The major had worked his black horse into a frenzy. It was reined short and rough and was being spurred unmercifully with the rows of his tied down spurs. The horse either slipped or shied away as its rider swung the killing blade. It missed its mark of Adam's neck, connecting low. The angle of the blade struck the head of the infant, who was tied to its swaddling board for protection. The blade cleaved Morning Joy's head in half at a 45-degree angle, starting at the top of her right ear and ending at the left of her little mouth.

Pegasus hit the black horse high in his mid-air leap for Major Elliott and caught the officer as he'd done the Crow youth years before. The hot salty taste of human blood and the sight of his dead goddess Button Nose had turned him into a spirit horse of the demons.

Adam remembered neither mounting his winged horse Pegasus, nor his battle of kill after kill. The soldiers thought their massacre was over since there was no one to contend with except the helpless. This over-sight gave the insane man and his mad spirit horse the advantage needed to succeed in their vengeance. The horse needed no guidance into the battle; he chose the course of their slaughter. He carried the man to where the need was greatest, then helped him subdue their enemy unto death.

Strange Eyes and Pegasus killed riders and horses in a running battle. The kill was easy—child's play compared to a buffalo hunt. The winged horse would rear and strike with his front hooves, pulling the living mounted off with his strong teeth—crushing bones, tearing flesh—while Strange Eyes swung his double-bitted war axe, cleaving the enemy's horses and riders.

Three soldiers at the far end were watching this. They figured a great force of warriors had overrun the village from the surrounding miles of Indian encampments. They left unnoticed on foot, leading their horses as Adam swung his axe into the skull of a struggling soldier who'd been cleaved earlier. His collarbone and shoulder hung limp. This was Red, the "barker." Adam's axe handle was so slick with blood from his many kills, it slipped from his grip as Red's body flopped out of control, thrashing in his death throes.

Pegasus then took Adam through the village, his speed double that of the poor quality horses the three regulars were mounted on. Pegasus followed their tracks and fresh moist scent like a hound tracking game. He overtook the fleeing soldiers in less than a mile. They had mis-placed their weapons while they were plundering and raping, never fig-uring on having to make such a hasty departure from their domination over the helpless. The momentary pleasure and lust toward the young daughter of man would bring all three to ruin.

Major Elliot, who Pegasus had first injured, was alive. He now stood and staggered like a drunk. He pointed his pistol skyward, then fired it off into the snow at his feet. He was again raising it heavenward as Adam's large Bowie-type knife entered into his soft stomach. The blade opened the major up, traveling upward through his sternum and hanging in his ribcage. Pegasus was carrying his master while Adam was carrying his dead foe skewered to the hilt of his knife's large blade. Pegasus turned sharp when the dead soldier's spur hit his front leg. This sudden outward force freed the dead body from the weapon of its impaler. The body slipped from the knife blade and rolled into a small cut of a ravine. The gully had been dredged three feet deep but was narrow—no more than eighteen inches wide. This concealed the officer's body from the mutilation the crazed man delivered to the remainder of the dead soldiers.

In the bitter cold and illuminated by the first rays of the morning sun, Witch-ka and his hunting party rode upon the scene of his once standing village. The wind that comes with the morning's light produced little trails of smoke wherever small amounts of hide or wood had been smoldering. The slight breeze would bring it to life for a few seconds. But being too feeble to sustain its newfound energy, it would again extinguish itself into the stench of acid smoke and the smell of burning flesh, hair, and dried animal hides.

There, in the oval hub of the once thriving village, labored a madman. Upon returning to camp, he had retrieved his blood soaked double-bitted war axe he'd used astride his warhorse. As Pegasus dragged the dead soldiers' bodies into the center where the original slaughter took place, Strange Eyes hacked and chopped the carcasses beyond recognition. Only the hidden body of Major Elliot and the Indian scout of the Sioux tribe were never mutilated. Witch-ka scalped the Sioux, but because the Sioux were the Cheyenne's cousins, his scalp was left by his body and his body was unharmed. He'd been killed mistakenly by his own blue coat comrades in the heat of the first charge.

They did not bury the bodies in the Cheyenne custom, knowing the soldiers would return to claim their own the coming spring. They were taken to a cave in one of the Three Sisters. This was Adam's introduction to the natural caverns that would become his true passion the rest of his life.

There had been several hundred cavalrymen and foot soldiers—1,800 according to military record—involved in this first winter campaign of the U.S. government's annihilation of the savages to open the country for the God-fearing civilized human population.

Yes, the red man, woman, and child would be placed on reservations, but not with the ease the West Pointers and government officials had predicted. The motto at West Point was that one officer could whip and kill ten Indian warriors single-handedly. They would eventually be forced to establish reservations across the U.S. to pacify these easily whipped nomads.

chapter
TWELVE

The Final Wedge

After his daughter's were laid to rest, Strange Eye's mind started to mend. He couldn't stay in this state for the sake of his sons, especially since their mother refused food and water. It was clear the shaman was of little help to his wife's mental collapse since they'd moved camp with the help of Moon Child's Comanche relatives.

The weather had turned mild; the snow had been melted off for days. The sap had started rising in the maples, making them put out their red buds—the first sign of spring. By noon, the sun felt hot to the small party. Adam, Mississippi, the two boys, and their grandmother, the old Mandan squaw, were heading north. Not for the exploration journey of the doeskin map, but to put as many miles as possible between them and the murderous armies of the U.S.A.

Adam remembered the Frenchman telling about the country of Canada that lay to the north where the U.S. had no jurisdiction. Even some of the chiefs were talking of this "grandmother"—the name they used when speaking about this far northern land where the winters came early. The hunting was good but the winters would be very hard on their ponies.

Adam's least concern was the winter's hardship on his horses and pack mule herd, with the cavalry massacring village after village under the false pretense of punishing wrong-doers. There indeed was a group of redskins raping, torturing, and looting on the frontier. However, they were always miles away and most generally didn't belong to the tribe that was receiving the retaliation and punishment that the U.S. Cavalry and foot soldiers were so enthusiastically doling out.

So, Adam put as many miles between them and his family as they could stand to travel that spring and summer. By fall, they'd reached their old territory where they first met Mr. Mosier. They were now into the country of their cousin, the Sioux. Their enemies the Crow and Blackfoot lay a little ways farther to the north. The bison were plentiful once again.

Mississippi had started to mend through the kindness and help of her mother. She was returning to her old self, at times even laughing and playing with her sons. It seemed too good to be true. As winter drew closer, the days began to shorten fast. They had plenty laid in for the coming winter and even looked forward to the beaver sausage cooked in bear fat that the cold winter days would bring.

They'd used their animals' reserves of fat and strength gained that spring to make the far travel that summer. As the days shortened, they decided to go into the Green River country and winter up with the help of Mississippi's mother, Mandan Woman.

The winter was a pleasant one. Strange Eyes learned many new things from Mandan Woman, a full-blooded Mandan, about survival and life in general. She was a young girl when the first whites came to their village. The whites were all young men. There was one among them who was a "black" white man. His hair was black, thick, and coarse as the bull buffalo's. "My people felt he had power at the time of the 'blanket dance of becoming a maiden.' He was chosen twice and each of the girls bore a daughter by him. Then the men left, taking a Shoshone girl who'd been captured a few years before and traded to our people. Then she was bought or lost in a gambling game to a half

Frenchman. This Frenchman went with them, also taking the Shoshone girl and her newborn son to the great waters far to the west, the same great waters you want to go to. This place you asked me about, I will tell you how far. Now I remember what my mother told to me. It took these young men so long, the newborn infant boy was walking and talking when they made their return. Many moons had passed. We would have forgotten about them if it hadn't been for the medals they gave the chiefs.

"But what stood out about their visit the most was the two daughters of the 'black-white' man. They too were walking upon their father's return. The black-white man then went east with his chiefs, but not all of the whites left our village on this return trip. Some stayed with our people for a spell. Then, the black-white man returned when the seasons had changed twice. He came with many gifts to purchase the maidens who had bore him his daughters. Years later, he became a chief."

Adam had heard an ancient white trapper at his first winter's camp, when he was 12, talk about the "black chief" who'd been a slave to one of the captains. This captain was in charge of the expedition that went to the Pacific Ocean and was from the same people's government, six decades later, that now wanted to destroy the Indian. Adam desired to go to this same ocean to exile his remaining family.

As Mandan Woman told her stories, Adam wished they could've been alive in those early days. Mississippi and his dead children would've lived out their days in the way they had originally planned. But now, the country was too settled, so overrun there wasn't room left for a man to breathe. As he stared into the dying embers of the coals while everyone else had retired to their teepees, he realized how fire and life were symbolically the same. Each held and gave off the energy of warmth, light, and life for a short time. Then it was extinguished forever. He shut his eyes, trying to hold the mental picture of his Button Nose and Morning Joy, but they too were as the dying embers. They made their last feeble attempt to glow, then cast the lodge in complete darkness, the same darkness that tainted his thoughts as he lay with his mind racing. Sleep would not come. He was haunted by the same question over and over—why?

The winter ended at Green River and so did his hopes of recapturing the happiness and contentment of the past. As they arrived on the plains, they encountered signs of buffalo hunting. Slaughtered carcasses were everywhere. Adam now knew S.T. was right—the hide hunters were like locusts. They wouldn't stop until the last bison was exterminated for its $2 to $3 hide and tongue. The hide hunters had not only caught up with their trek north; they were miles ahead of them and it was only early spring.

As summer grew, so did the number of hide hunters. The mad slaughter was at its height. Back east, they couldn't get enough to satisfy the demand for home and export. At first, it seemed there would be no end to the bison. Some of the knowledgeable, higher educated mathematicians in the east claimed the bison would multiply faster than they could be slaughtered. Despite their self-assured statement, the majority didn't care one way or the other. Since it didn't happen on their doorstep, it was no concern of theirs.

Adam's only concern was to get farther north in hopes of outrunning this invasion of white and black hunters. The War Between the States had given the black man in the far west hopes for a new life also. Not a better life, not a worse life, but life, just life itself. Here the opportunity turned out to be the slaughter of millions of bison, stripping them of their outer coat and leaving to rot the millions of tons of life-giving red meat that the nomad's depended on for food, clothing, and shelter, wasting nothing down to the tools they made from their bones.

Seeing their dead brothers laying and rotting on the plains as far as one could travel in any given direction, the Indian sang not only the bison's death song, but also their own.

Adam's small band had been traveling north following the dry bed of a once-prehistoric river. This was the same river his wife's people had told stories about around the winter lodge fires, stories of bones found there that belonged to the giants. Some were so large and heavy, the strongest pony couldn't pack them. There was only one watering hole in this drier area, it laying to the east of their morning journey.

As they climbed out of the flatter terrain of the dry streambed, the land became rolling. The slopes were gentle and sweeping. Suddenly, they could see in the distance that they were approaching a hide hunter's outfit consisting of two large wagons pulled by four mules, each with an extra span lead-hitched to the rear of the wagon by their halters. Two hunters were mounted on Indian ponies.

Adam and his mother-in-law, who were riding several yards ahead of their beasts of burden pulling their own travois of lodge poles and livelihood equipment, knew there was no use in trying to outrun or evade this meeting. Each party stayed on course, advancing toward the other. Both slowed the pace of their animal's march, trying not to be too obvious to the other in performing this reconnaissance move to obtain the adversary's number and strength.

Adam saw the two muleskinners. One was a white man and the other black. Each rose from their wagon's springboard seat with their weapons in hand. Then the two mounted hunters drew back, keeping in step close to their wagons in case they needed the protection the heavy wooden wagon boxes would provide for them as breast works— immediately if called for.

It wasn't needed this day. Adam recognized the little Frenchman who was mounted on the paint pony. Still, he made no sudden move showing the joy he felt, knowing how easily it could be taken wrong. This could cause the firing of several well-placed lead balls, sending him and the remainder of his family to their graves.

He sat, turned Pegasus to a 45-degree angle to their approach and lifted both arms, extending his open hands outward in the sign of peace. The wagon's remaining youth, who was riding the bay, huddled close to the two teamsters as Charbonne, the Frenchman, approached the rider of the spirit horse. Still, Adam did not voice his recognition, not wanting to excite or agitate the little Frenchman until the rest of his group's nerves relaxed.

When Adam saw that the giant white teamster was no other than Sybane, Adam laughed and hollered out.

"Sybane, are you going to set there all day and—"

Adam never finished his question. The two old ex-trappers recognized Adam—the man who was, to both, the son they never had. The old men ran to embrace him in the Frenchmen's custom of encountering long lost relatives. Mississippi, seeing who it was, could not keep her Cheyenne dignity any longer. She wept bitterly as she told Charbonne about the massacre of her two daughters. This made Charbonne cry as hard and long as she. He looked up through his tears and saw the others' uneasiness. The rest kept their eyes cast down, studying imaginary things that lay at their feet.

As he hugged the grieving girl, Charbonne spoke again. "When a man is young, he has to pretend to be strong. Hard like the iron, cold like the rocks of the high country. When you're old, there is nothing, or was nothing, ever to prove." He took the girl's little trembling hands and they walked a short distance to a rock outcropping that had formed a natural table and chairs. It became, for a time, their wailing wall.

Adam didn't realize until it was too late that Mississippi's quietness was not something to be relieved about. She'd drawn deeper into a depressed dark void that was on the verge of swallowing her. He felt helpless with no knowledge of what to do. So, he started to stay away longer on hunting trips as he scouted out new territory for the hunting party.

Adam had let himself be convinced it would make no difference in the bison's extermination whether he participated in the slaughter or not. Wouldn't it be better for those like himself to kill the great herds of the mighty bison—those who loved and appreciated the way of the nomadic man and animal—than the lowly eastern hide hunters who were just a "Johnny Come Lately" to this vast, once untamed land of theirs? The trapper eventually either vanished or turned hide hunter.

The wicked current had now drawn Adam into its swirling edges, the dangerous eddies where one can be quietly sucked in and held forever.

Mississippi seldom spoke or ate and had grown skeletal thin by fall.

Autumn found the party of bison hunters far to the east of the Platte. The direction was as contrary to the course of their original plan as the about-face of Adam's personality. He'd become short to the extent that when Red Clay saw or heard his father ride in, he would take his younger brother Crow Killer and vanish among the piles of green hides. That is, if they didn't have immediate chores to keep them busy and out of his way. Even old Mandan Woman, who worked from first light to way after dark, felt Strange Eye's wrath. She not only skinned hundreds of bison, she also dried loads of meat and made pemmican. She filled gut after gut full with the help of her two small grandsons and failing daughter, but none of this ever brought a kind word or even a gesture of recognition from Adam.

The days had become short and the weather cold enough to keep the hides from spoiling. They were now able to stay out longer and make the journeys to the different forts and outposts that were set up for the sole purpose of buying the green hides and tongues that had been salted down.

The Frenchmen and Adam were making more money than they'd ever made in their lives. They paid the black man $20 and the mute and deaf boy $15 per month. Each got room and board free as long as they were able to pitch the tent they shared. What was odd to the rest was, with all the tons of fresh red meat and the choicest cuts, the old black man and mute and deaf boy ate salt pork every meal till it ran out. They'd have to wait until the pile of salted hides grew till the wagons couldn't hold one more and it took all three spans of mules to pull the grades to the different trading posts. Then, on the empty wagon's return, the salt pork barrel was full for the two hired hands.

The whiskey barrel was also full for the Frenchmen, Adam, and Mississippi.

Strange Eyes and his Cheyenne wife had turned to the spirits. At first, the alcohol was soothing and calming. They thought it was the answer; a cure-all for their overwhelming guilt and crushing grief. But the swirling and spinning gave them a false comfort. Soon, their anguish and distorted sense of reality led to pointing fingers. The wedge was now being driven, making the first gap.

It started as a small fissure, not even large enough to be called a crack in the foundation. Now it had grown proportionally to the size of a great canyon. The jagged walls were too numerous to attempt a repair, much less completely mend. With each try, where it looked smooth enough on the surface that a bridge might have a foothold, the gap would become a wider. At the slightest attempt by either of them, the canyon walls crumbled and caved in worse. By winter, the man and woman seldom spoke.

If it hadn't been for the two boys' grandmother, Red Clay and Crow Killer could have died of malnutrition. Even with both of their parents alive and living in the same lodge, little to no attention ever came their way from the self-blaming, self-pitying drunken pair they called mother and father. Grandma was their world, their life. As long as she lived, they lived.

Hard working, kind, thoughtful, self-sacrificing, the old Mandan Woman now lay dying under a pile of buffalo robes that she had stretched, fleshed, and tanned to a soft amber yellow. The long, hot summer gave way to a mild fall that would prove the perfect autumn for their massive buffalo slaughter. But this also put long, cruel, slave toiling hours on the faithful woman until it actually bowed her old bony back. She lost the ability to walk straight and proud as she had at the start of the journey at the dry riverbed of the bones of the ancient ones.

She'd worked herself to her death as the mild fall turned into the harsh cold rain, sleet, and snow of winter. The bison kills were strung out seemingly for miles for her to skin. The buffalo skinning was a grueling chore in favorable weather. Now, the skin was frozen to their dead carcasses. She would plod out alone with her aged old body, back bowed under her load of skinning equipment made from the dead beast's bones. She used their ribs as implements to gain leverage between the frozen skin and the once warm, live flesh. The deaf and mute white boy and old black man refused to leave the warmth of their worn patched cavalry tent to give her any assistance in skinning these massive forms that had become impregnated blocks of ice.

Old Mandan Woman worked long days outside in the freezing, drizzling rain. She wouldn't take the time to eat except for the occasional bites of raw meat she'd chew as she worked. But as winter turned severe, the small bites of hard frozen flesh would drain the last reserves of warmth from her frail, overworked body and end up taking more energy away from her than she could gain.

The chills eventually shook her bony frame until it made the hair of her buffalo robes seem to come to life as they quivered in response to the constant trembling of her feverish sick body. As her fever rose higher, her companions and family became drunker.

Finally, someone thought they'd heard back east about a method of curing the ague. Packing the ailing one in ice or submerging them in cold water could bring down the fever. Snow was the handiest since nature had supplied several feet of this white medicinal miracle powder with a couple of inches of ice thrown in to boot. The idea may have worked if only they had remembered to bring her back in.

After packing the old Indian woman down, doing the utmost job, they returned to the warmth of the lodge's fire and to the more important matter at hand—each trying to talk louder and faster to make their point to whomever had run out of breath or speech or had become so drunk their tongues rebelled, hanging limp. Some tongues hung out of their slobbering mouths, their owners making dry heaves and sounds as if trying to call in a hog herd. This only added fuel to the speaker's speech. His story of grandeur, bravery beyond doubt by his own blaring words, always winning, always cinching the whole thing down pat, all accompanied by the music of the mute and deaf boy's dry heaves. They came to the listener's ears with long, whistling, whining grunts as he clapped as if applauding . . . swirling . . . spinning . . .

The speaker staggered and weaved as he held on to each side of the lodge's entry flap, making his long yellow stream out upon the fresh, white falling snow that was turning the world into a whiteout. If his stream of urine could have penetrated deep enough, it would've been all the warmth the old Mandan woman received that night as she lay freezing stiff under the snow where the big Frenchman's piss was falling.

As he lay under the pile of buffalo robes, Adam sensed, more than knew, that the six-mule team and heavy hide-laden wagon were being whipped toward the half frozen river. The frozen ice of the river would support the heavy wagon until it made it to the middle where the current flowed fast. There the ice would hold a man easily, even a man and single horse if the rider dismounted and led his animal, keeping some distance to displace the weight. But this large heavy wagon, six mules, and two small boys asleep under tons of green frozen wet hides, was doomed.

The old silver-headed man could see her face. He kicked violently toward the small hole she and the boys disappeared into. He became enraged, then wild with a fear that grew into absolute madness as each lunge through this small opening would stop his progress. Each time he started to give up and die with his Mississippi and his sons, either she, or Red Clay, or little Crow Killer would bob up in front of his face. This gave Strange Eyes a new reservoir of strength to kick and struggle through this small crack that had fingers of cold stone blocking his way to the lives he was trying so desperately to grasp . . .

part
THREE

TO TOUCH
THE SKY

chapter
ONE

Ma Terrill's Command Post

The Terrill boys had gotten up early that morning to go squirrel hunting. They went every chance they got, which was quite often now that it was late August. Bill and his little brother Roscoe left their yard gate with their old yellow shepherd, Mack, and the little terrier gyp, Judy.

Mack was just as good a hog dog as he was a squirreller. His only drawback, however, was that he caught the wild hogs by the ear like all the shepherd breeds do and had many deep, long scars to prove his valor in battle with his enemy, the swine. Little Judy was young and quick. She proved her worth by being able to keep one hog or half a dozen at bay, leaving the catching and holding to Mack. The pair knew what to expect from each other and so did their masters. Bill and Roscoe knew as soon as they heard the terrier's high-pitched yelping barks of bay, they'd soon be hearing the squealing of a hog that Mack had seized by the ear. There wasn't a second to lose, more for the sake of their old yeller shepherd than the hog he was fastened to. His teeth would have to be pried open because his jaw muscles would lose the ability to relax on their own if he had to hold on for very long.

The boys and dogs had made about three miles, half of the round they usually hunted, when they heard little Judy's high-pitched baying. They mistook it, at first, for a tree bark, since Mack was baying also, a thing that had never before happened. With hogs—or any other beast with four legs and hair—Mack would already have a hold of it.

Bill broke into a hard run even before he grasped the full meaning of the message his ears had relayed. Roscoe's shorter legs were churnin' butter to keep up. Bill would have arrived first if his foot hadn't caught the forked root of a gnarled burr oak sending him flying headlong. The barrel of his single shot Steven's .22 came in contact with the rocky ridge, making his other hand give up possession of the three red fox squirrels and two young grays that he'd strung on a fresh-peeled dog-wood stick.

The dogs were at bay directly under him, no more than 100 feet away at the bottom of the hollow. Bill could hear his younger brother Roscoe hollering. His voice was full of panic and fright. Bill looked for his .22. He found the squirrels and was racing back and forth for his gun when he heard his kid brother's screams of absolute terror.

Bill walked toward the sound of the screams, his knees and body trembling, weak with fear. He was not afraid of the old gray-headed nasty man who the dogs had found. He was weak because he knew if he'd found his .22 before he ran off the ridge to his screaming little brother, he would've shot the old crazy man shore as a cat covers its shit.

Bill tried to get a clearer picture of all that happened as he walked back toward home, leaving Roscoe with the old helpless man. The old man had been too feeble to stand. Bill went over the whole scene, slowing down his mind so he could take in everything that happened, trying to convince himself that he wouldn't have shot the old man if he hadn't lost his gun.

He had pushed his way through the thick, growing, red brush toward the dog's baying and his brother's piercing screams. He thought *shore as hell Rosco was bein' et up the way his little lungs was a-screechin' out and Mack jest standin' thar all bristled up a-bayin'*. Every time this thing moved or wiggled, it made crazy sounds, inhuman noises that came from under the long hair that was as filthy as his clothes.

The earth's dirt had him so well camouflaged that as Adam sang his death song in Cheyenne, Bill knew what he saw and heard was not from this earth. The dirt had become alive and was makin' every animal sound of the ones who lived, present and past.

Damn, I'm glad I lost that .22. I shore as hell'd shot that old helpless sick man. By now, Bill had recovered enough to get his bearings. He hit a short lope, a mountain-man gait that would eat up miles fast. It was but a short time till he was entering through the same yard gate he and Roscoe had begun their hunt from four hours before. He handed the squirrels to his mom while trying to explain why Roscoe wasn't with him. The longer he talked, the louder she became in her demands.

"Whor's Roscoe? Don' je remember Roscoe?" she was yelling. "Yer kid brother! Whor's Roscoe?!"

She was still hollering when his pa ran toward the house, leaping over the rail yard fence, not wanting to waste the extra second it would take to enter through the gate. He knew before anyone spoke that his baby boy Roscoe lay dead. He grabbed Bill, shaking him, hollering, "Whor's Roscoe? Whor does he lay dead?"

Finally, Bill, the calmest of the Terrill clan, (if you don't include the terrier gyp, Judy), got his chance to explain. Judy had stayed with Roscoe. Mack still had his hackles up, but little Judy had crawled up into the old man's lap. This act had calmed the man till Roscoe and Mack were just settin' side by side when Bill and his pa returned with their mule to fetch the old crazy man who had babbled to Bill earlier he had fallen out of a cave full of Indians.

When Ma Terrill heard the statement about the cave full of Indians, she had it all figured that the old man was the runaway from the county farm at Eminence. There was an old man that had been missing since spring. She remembered the women talking about it at Booker's meeting place. She lost no time sending her man and son on their way with "Godspeed" saying, "One can never tell 'bout a crazy person. Heared tell when they go into one of them thar fits, a lil' ol' frail woman has the strength of ten strong men and this ol' man's a-ravin' 'bout a cave fulla Injuns. He's probably ready to bust. Calm folk like us jest don' know what goes on in thar heads so ye'd better light a shuck and get them feet to poundin'! Boy, yer pa can ride the mule. This way he can keep up."

If Bill had trotted, he would have outdistanced the old mollie mule by a country mile. Soon as they got out of sight of Ma standing on the porch, Pa slid off her old white bony back. Her hipbones stuck out till you could've hung your hat on them. Pa and Bill knew to conserve the mule's strength for packing the insane man back. Trotting her wouldn't do either one of the aged gray ones any favor.

They tried lifting the tall, thin, stooped silver-headed man onto the tired, gray and white mollie mule. The old man was lifeless as the old mule till she caught the scent of the musky damp cave emanating from Adam. Then her old tired skeletal frame became alive, shooting adrenaline through her sinews and leaders. There wasn't enough flesh left under the matted mite-eaten hide to be called muscle to absorb this sudden rush. She rolled her eyes, snorted, and sprung sideways. With her long ears forward and her front legs stiff and locked at the knee, she reached her thin sunken neck forward, breathing so hard her breath made shrill whistling noises that set the old man into another chant of the Cheyenne. This spooked the old beast into a small sapling. Her energy had already played out. She leaned against the small tree, head down and legs trembling—not from fear, but exhaustion.

The old crazed man wouldn't turn loose of little Judy. He petted, stroked, and spoke to her, making strange guttural sounds. The words were so strange to their ears they just knew it was the babbling of a madman.

The old mule was too weak now to fend off the loading of this filthy live varmint upon her protruding backbone. With the familiar scent of the terrier dog to her nostrils and Roscoe holding her halter strap, the mule began leading the party on its one-mile-an-hour trip homeward.

If the old man hadn't been as poor as the beast that was packing him, she probably wouldn't have ever seen her barn lot again. As the old mule trembled the last few feet to the cabin's front porch to be relieved of her burden, Ma Terrill had already assumed her command post. She stood with her legs apart, her wide squat body almost crouched as if she was getting ready to spring forward. As the old man was dragged from the back of the plumb tuckered out mule, he kept a death grip on little Judy, who was actually enjoying the affection.

Ma came out of her wrestler-like crouch, placed her short fat arms with fists on her well proportioned hips and stomped her feet together, making the dust fly from the porch's rough-sawed lumber floor. She drew her five-foot-two inch frame as high as the 375 pounds it was wrapped in would allow. She'd slicked back her hair for this occasion, even put on a dress with less morning gravy and tomato canning stains. She saw right off the bat it had all been folly. The old man was worse off than she had reckoned. She wasn't willing to help with anything except advice. The family was well accustomed to this.

"Yep, he's a dead 'un all right. I coulda tol' je fer ye ever loaded 'im. It war a waste of time." She spit a long stream of tobacco juice and scratched her greasy head where the tight little knot of gray and black hair rested. She then inspected the dark goo she raked from under her nails for any sign of lice or nits, and saw this time she was in the clear.

She returned to her men, who were struggling with their burden. The old man released his grip on little Judy, then folded up and passed out on the dirt of the front yard a few steps away from the front porch.

"See, I tol' je. Roscoe, ye go down to Aunt Sarah's. This is mail day. Ye tell her what I tol' je."

The boy kept standing, staring down at what they all thought was a corpse.

"Why ain't ye gone yet, boy?" Ma bellered.

The boy looked up blank and said, "Ye ain't told me nary thing yet, Ma."

"Hell, boy, he's dead! That's all ye need to know! Now, get to scootin' fer ye miss the mail carrier. We need the High Sheriff. Now remember that, we need the hi'en. The others won't work, only the High Sheriff can move a dead man."

Roscoe then proceeded to ask about a dead woman. Ma, taking the boy's question as a jab, set to waddling toward him with one of her many well-placed switches she kept handy since them missionaries read her out of the Holy Bible: "Ye have got to take the rod of discipline to the foolishness that's tied up in the heart of a boy."

Watching Roscoe go, playing all the way, she thought, *What did I ever do to be punished with these boys? Yes, my sister's girls, them daughters, woulda been a blessing to me here in my ol' days. I bet that boy clean fergets what he went fer, and this darned ol' crazy man them Shannon County folks down there at the ol' county farm ain't got enough sense to keep an eye on, jes lettin' them up and run off when they feel like it. Lay here, he will, and rot in my front yard.* This made her purse her lips and nod her head up and down as she thought of another fitting scripture description of herself. "They will choose you out and persecute you for you have been chosen. You are my holy ones." She looked at the old man's corpse and thought, *Yep, and here it is layin' damn nigh on my front porch. I don't reckon it takes a heap o' words to paint it out, but I'm gonna make damn shore it's printed in the Current Wave newspaper, jest so folks will know what I've been through. I reckon I've had my share of Armageddon this morning and I think it'd be right fer some I know to read 'er.*

Then she remembered that the folks she mostly wanted to hear of it couldn't read or write. Here she was, having "the whip of the Lord" scourge her again. Yes, she surely was the one the missionaries had read her about. "I reckon if the shoe fits you have to wear it." She turned and waddled back into the cool of the cabin. The summer's heat was going to be terrible today. As the sagging patched screen door slammed behind her, she thought, *I wonder whor that sheriff is, no how.*

She returned to her central command post—the huge white oak rocker lined with two overstuffed pillows. There she dozed as the old white-haired man made slight moans. His ailing body would tremble slightly as the hot sun penetrated through the cave's dried mud, bringing back life as the sun does to all its cold-blooded reptiles.

Adam had been in the cave for 28 days.

chapter
TWO

MISTER Troop, Professor and Famous Explorer

Roscoe made it to Aunt Sarah's in plenty of time. The only drawback was that there were uncles, aunts, nephews, and nieces as well as grandpappies, grandmas and cousins all eating watermelons and cantaloupes. There were a half dozen boys, all Roscoe's age, all kin in some way. There were so many people, Roscoe would've been overlooked completely and probably forgotten his mission. Maybe he'd have remembered before dark when he'd have to head for home after all the melon feasters said their goodbyes and praised Jesus since the reverend was present also.

The reverend had head-saved a couple, baptizing them in the pond. This would've gone fairly well had the girl kept her mouth closed and not got strangled on the green frog moss scum that had grown two inches thick on the pond's surface. She was still hacking and coughing, trying to clear her throat and lungs, when she noticed the knife Roscoe was slipping out of his overalls to show to her kid brother and several other mixed cousins. She told her cousin Roscoe she'd like to see it also, being still young enough to have some tomboy left in her and a fascination for Bowie-type sheath knives. Roscoe, having an older girl's full attention, started to strut, talking louder than normal about the old bone-handled Bowie knife and the strange Indian-fashioned sheath. The bead and quillwork had worn off decades before. He was telling his older girl cousin how its original owner fought a cave full of Indians with it, even "cuttin' one open clean to his gizzard."

Before Roscoe could become louder and longer with the narration of his firsthand exploits, there stood the mail carrier, looking down at the knife eating a large red slice of watermelon. Then Roscoe started remembering what his mission was all about. It wasn't to eat melon and show his new prized possession. But if not, *what was it?* Then it came to him as the mailman studied the knife and its sheath. He blurted out to the carrier, "Mr. Smith, Ma wants ye to tell the High Sheriff to come and git this ol' dead man that's a-layin' in our yard."

Now, little Roscoe's presence was known. Everyone stopped their visiting; even the most holy reverend drew no cards. All eyes and ears were tuned in on Roscoe as the mail carrier asked him to relay all he could remember about the dead man. Roscoe told everything. Well, almost everything. He didn't figure anyone would be interested anymore in the old worn-down Bowie knife and slick leather scabbard.

The High Sheriff decided to go late that evening to investigate the death of the old man the rural route mail carrier had told him about. He took his time so as to arrive before dark for two good reasons. He laughed, tried singing, but since he could never carry a tune, turned to whistling that came out even worse. He gave up on both while he was still ahead.

Nothing could dampen his joyful spirit except a gully washing rain since he was driving his new bucket T model, feeling pretty slick about getting away by himself. He thought about how he'd wrecked his first automobile a month ago. A thunderstorm came in and he'd had to get "her" back to the brush arbor meeting place before her uncle and aunt missed her, especially since she was only 16. Damn, the rain came out of nowhere. It had been sunny, then the wind came up. By the time he got up and pulled up his pants, there that friggin' black cloud was on him. He'd never heard the distant thunder due to their own lightning bolts they were putting off. They jumped in his rig as the first fat drops of rain started drumming on the Chevrolet's black metal top. It was a downpour by the time they arrived at Mockingbird Hill. It was gravel on the south pulling side. But as soon as he topped over its summit, the trouble began.

First, he was going too fast for the slick red clay mud. Added to this was the fact he'd been driving for only eight months. Also, the road was steep as a horse's face with a curve halfway down. Even if the curve had been banked to the inside, it wouldn't have helped. In addition, he got terribly excited thinking he'd have to downshift to a lower gear. They were traveling very fast by now and the sheriff had a bad habit of looking down at the stick shift knob when he changed gears.

When the car quit rolling over and came to rest on its side at the bottom of the hollow, the sheriff and his young love were lucky to have only one broken arm between them. He finally got the county to pay her doctor bill. He convinced the board but not his wife, who put her foot down hard and said he could only buy a bucket T. This made him laugh even harder, remembering the look on his wife's face and her comment of, "Hope you and your next little floozy rolls this one to the bottom of some hollow, too!"

It had been hard on the High Sheriff lately. He'd ordered those new mail-order uniforms and ever since he'd started wearing them, his wife wouldn't let him out of her sight. She even came to the office in pretense of all sorts of things. Since he never knew when she'd pull check on him, he'd been sending messages to his new girl, letting her know it wouldn't be long now. Finally "now" had arrived. There wasn't going to be anything stand in his way tonight. *Yes, I'm damn slick*, the High Sheriff thought. *Here, I've fell into a crock of shit and come out smelling like a rose. Got a new bucket T. A "ladies man" car, it is.*

Honking his horn, he braked and swerved hard to miss the cows in the road. He started to curse, then caught sight of the young girl who was driving the cows home to be milked. He straightened his new shiny black leather-billed sheriff's hat and glanced in the rear view mirror at his image to check the cock of his hat. He slowed the car to a crawl, gave the girl a slow up and down looking over, smiled, and winked at her. She blushed and hung her head. He drove on knowing he had no time to waste, wanting to spend it all with his new lady tonight.

The High Sheriff bumped up the rough wagon-rutted trail that was now being called a road by Dent County. They'd started taxing the little dirt-poor farmers for their upkeep, which was to come at some point in the future, which forever meant the next election.

The sheriff cursed as his new flivver slid off into a pair of deep ruts that had resulted last winter when the ground froze deep and hard, then thawed fast making the bottom fall out. Wagon traffic pulling heavy loads of logs did the rest. He heard the oil pan hit rock, making a dull thud as he floor-boarded the accelerator. The light-ended bucket T fishtailed in the wide, dry, and dusty hard-packed rut. The left rear tire spun and caught a firm grip just as the nose of the vehicle cleared the rut's end that drained into the hog's wallow in the middle of the road. The wallow was occupied by its evening residents of three large Landrace sows and their offspring that now weighed upwards of 90 pounds each. The shoats broke and ran at the sound of the bucket T's roaring engine and spinning tires. Nothing disturbed the old sows at their evening mud bath, not even the Terrill's dog Mack. They'd put their hackles up and fight before they'd budge an inch.

As the new shiny black bucket T bore down on them, one 600-pound sow rose up into a sitting position. The High Sheriff saw her along with her two mud-covered companions. Had he more driving experience, he might not have swerved so hard.

At least this time he had something to blame for the bent-in bumper and front fender that now stuck out at a right angle from the car. Its headlamp, or rather the smashed glass that had been its headlamp, now lay shattered at the base of the crooked red oak tree. The tree was pistol butted. He never saw it in the evening shadows. The little car struck it full force while its driver was occupied with the swineherd. The old gnarled tree "jumped right out" and caught the new black shiny fender, bringing the "little love boat" to a sudden stop sideways. The new black leather-billed sheriff's hat, and the head that it sat upon half-cocked, all met the windshield at the same instant, all coming to a jolting halt.

The sweet corn-sized, wide-gapped yellow teeth that sat in his perched mouth and appeared somewhat bucked had split his upper and lower lip. This made the blood drip from his red, fresh-shaven, slick chin onto the sheriff's hat with its emblem of the High Sheriff's authority embossed above its patent leather bill that lay between his trembling legs. By the time his head cleared from the jolt and excitement, the blood from the soaked hat had oozed into the crotch of his new, blue, mail-order uniform that had turned so many heads since arriving last week. He'd hung them on his tall, thin, pot-bellied frame, toning his pear shape down to some extent. Now, here he sat in a puddle of blood, uniform ruined, and the right fender of the "ladies man" car sticking out waving at a right angle from the rest of the rig.

The fresh mashed lips turned into two large bloody gizzards that throbbed with each heartbeat. He sat stunned, trying to recall where he was and why. Upon remembering, he started to curse the old dead man. But then he remembered the real reason for this late night outing. He mumbled aloud a string of new curses about the shortcomings of his brother politicians for being so corrupt they didn't have the rural roads maintained as each had faithfully promised to achieve if he was put into office. Taking his rearview mirror in his bloody hands, he positioned it to reflect his image in the dwindling evening light for a last good look before he climbed out and tried to crank the bucket T's engine back to life.

He chugged the last quarter mile to the Terrill's where he was greeted by Ma and Pa Terrill, the boys, and two dogs. Pa slapped him on the back, sending a new volley of pain through his whole being. Ma tried to elbow her way in to get her due recognition for her role of pain and suffering and how she'd sacrificed all as it was her Christian duty since them missionaries "done and told" her she was the chosen one and the good Lord would always persecute the one He loved and what she'd put up with today and "shore drives the peg in the right hole . . ."

Neither of the senior Terrills noticed the High Sheriff's mangled face. This was a relief to the lawman. He didn't want to have to try to explain since everyone in the country knew the Terrills were "tellers" not "listeners." They were now telling him, both at the same time, trying to drown out the other with shouts that beat tom-toms of pain through the injured sheriff's gizzard-sized swollen lips and head.

No one heard little Roscoe scream in terror. He was hollering at the old crazy man who now sat up with the little terrier gyp Judy sitting sideways, half curled in his lap. He was holding Roscoe's arm.

Roscoe shrieked again. "I never took your ol' knife. Hit wuz Judy! She brung it to me! Ye go haint her! I ain't the one ye want to spook! She stole 'er, not me!"

While Roscoe was screaming in mortal terror, the High Sheriff was trying to explain that under the law, he couldn't move the body tonight since he would have to get this other feller, he couldn't remember the name they called it, to come and pronounce the old man dead. That was the law.

Roscoe felt the big bone-handled Bowie knife touch his flesh under his overalls where he'd securely tied it. The knot had loosened, letting the old knife slip several inches down before its sheath caught once again. This was enough to put the fear of God into Roscoe.

He fled right into his Ma's fat waving arms as she argued with the sheriff over his sworn duty to take her persecution away from its place in her front yard claiming she'd bore her cross long enough.

Ma was starting to end her rant for the dozenth time about how no one knows how she had labored, toiled, and sacrificed. She'd just opened her large mouth to inhale enough air to sustain another round of self-sacrifices when her baby boy Roscoe hurled himself through the air, leaping into her outstretched waving arms. Ma Terrill never quit talking. She now pointed at the old dirty man with her fat hand extending a chubby finger in the style of a great commander with his coupe stick and said, "I told ye so. I knowed it all along. The ol' bastard wuz jest playin' possum. I reckon thar ain't no law says ye cain't load and haul a crazy man, Mr. Sheriff, ary it?"

The Terrills, with the help of the High Sheriff, lifted Adam and placed him in the bucket T. The bunged up "ladies man" car now carried the new aromas of cave musk and urine—a far cry from the scents linked to the once fantasized romance this night was to bring to its owner.

The High Sheriff wasted no time. The throbbing in his lips and head grew unbearable as the little car bumped and weaved back along the path it had just rolled over an hour before. With its fender partly torn off, the bucket T took on the appearance of a little injured bird with a broken wing. The pain had made him forget about the spot where it all began. He steered through the hog wallow, around and over the deep ruts, and was back on the main gravel road anxious to be back with his wife and her unconditional sympathy and the kind nursing care she always gave him under these circumstances.

Aunt Effie May ran the Salem Hotel and Boarding House, furnishing rooms and meals by the night or week. On occasion, there were some who stayed a month or longer. She also furnished the two meals a day for the jail's inmates when the county was fortunate enough to ever have one, which was seldom.

The High Sheriff had gone by the boarding house to inform his aunt-by-marriage that he had an inmate who would need her food services. He dreaded to have to make contact with his wife's aunt, even on business. She always made him feel ten years old again—the age he was when she'd been appointed by the state to keep him and his sister. They were two years under her care. He shuddered, even in the summer heat, at the thought of how his sister became so successful, always pleased Aunt Effie, and still did. He detested the letters his sister penned to Aunt Effie, knowing she found great pleasure in bringing them to his office. There, she'd read them slowly, stopping to comment and forcing him to give his opinion before she pursed her lips, arched her brows, and gave that little clucking sound with her tongue. She would then shake her gray head and say, "No, yer still just a simple-minded lying little boy. I don't see on God's green earth what my niece ever seen in ye."

Here again this morning, thought the sheriff, *that old battle-ax had the gall to tell me how to run my jai!* He remembered how she seemed pleased and interested in hearing the story about the old crazy man since every-one remembered the massive search that took place last spring, more out of boredom than concern. When he started to tell her about the old man who'd wandered away from the county farm, she cut him off short. He never even got to tell her about the accident that had knocked his fender off, or how he'd sacrificed his new car and laid his life on the line to save the "two small children" playing in the middle of the road on a blind curve at the bottom of Whiskey Hill.

He pursed his swollen lips, not caring if the pain shot through them. He arched his brows and tried imitating her little sarcastic clicking sounds. He spoke aloud to himself, mimicking her last questions—questions that were none of her damned business. "It's law business, and ain't I the sheriff?" he mumbled to himself. "What the hell do you know about these affairs!" he wanted to shout at her. Here alone, straightening out Aunt Effie was easy. "Why in the hell does that ol' mouthy bag make me feel like a stupid little boy? This time I'll show her!" He then mimicked some of the many questions she had rapid fired at him:

"Leroy, have you called Eminence to verify this? Leroy, is the elderly gentleman's description the same? Leroy, I thought you said he's quite tall. Remember the poor, mentally deranged man was short—five foot, two inches as I recall. Leroy, have you gone through this pack you call hide and sticks? You still afraid of getting your little pink hands dirty? Have you learned to wipe yet, Leroy?" was her last question as he exited the boarding house's long kitchen. He remembered the chicken broth's aroma upon first entering. He cursed again, knowing this scent had caused him to lower his guard, giving the cat its chance to pounce on the helpless mouse. Then she, like all felines, kept him hanging on for the pure pleasure of sport.

Aunt Effie made eggs, grits, and bacon, put them on a platter with two biscuits marinated in butter and honey, and delivered them to the High Sheriff's office. He accepted the large platter without a word, and she the same. Her silence penetrated his now throbbing head deeper than any of her sarcastic recommendations or comments would have done. He slid the platter into the locked cell through its entry port and turned to leave, but realized he'd forgotten to give the insane inmate any water since his lockdown over thirteen hours before.

He walked toward the sink to fill the tin water pitcher, then remembered it had sprung a leak at its bottom seam. He cursed, first at the pitcher, then at the Eminence officials who had this old bastard in their care. Last but not least, he cussed the old, dirty, smelly crazy man who'd brought this all on: the mashed mangled lips that gave him the appearance of a jack-o-lantern, the "ladies man" car that looked like a little helpless bird with a broken wing and, the greatest resentment, the loss of the love night he'd anticipated for so long.

He slammed the pitcher down hard, knocking its bottom out completely. He cursed the old man again, wishing now he'd dumped him like he'd started to last night. The only reason he hadn't was because he knew big-mouthed Ma Terrill was a "teller." She'd spread the word. Since they were kin to half the county, he couldn't afford to lose a single vote in the upcoming election that was only a couple of months away.

Adam's fever had risen. He was speaking in Cheyenne, motioning to "them" in a quiet whisper as the sheriff locked the front door, still cursing as he left through the jail's rear entry.

Aunt Effie served her noon guests and regulars. After their meal, she strolled down to the county jail to retrieve her platter and utensils, a thing she usually did at the evening meal. The jail was locked upon her arrival. She sighed, but gave Leroy the benefit of the doubt. She didn't even call him "Little Lying Leroy" to herself, which had been a long-standing custom of hers that ran back decades to those two miserable years. His lying little vicious mouth lost her his kid sister and caused the long court battle it took to finally get her back.

Aunt Effie decided on a plan as she walked along the boardwalk, nodding at this person then another. All greeted her with affection for she'd helped about everybody at one time or another in time of illness or need. She knew what she would do. *Yes*, she thought, *I'll return each hour till the little liar comes back to our public office.*

Sheriff Leroy finally returned, coming through the rear entry. Aunt Effie was standing, not too patiently, out front holding a large bowl of chicken and dumplings and a glass of cold milk. Sheriff Leroy opened the locked door, looked as stern as possible and said gruffly, "Give 'er to me."

Aunt Effie brushed past the newly pressed blue-uniformed figure, making sure the hard, rolled cloth napkin that held the silverware brushed against those gizzard-sized swollen lips. This put the High Sheriff back to being Little Leroy again as Aunt Effie went through the entry toward the holding cells. There were two. One was the main cell that slept six to eight. Then there was the bullpen that had no light or facilities—only a drain in its middle to accept the water when the place was hosed down.

Leroy got the pain under control that Aunt Effie's utensil roll had brought on. He was now standing by her in the runway that divided the two sections. She demanded to see the old gentleman. Simple Lying Little Leroy tried to become the High Sheriff and order her out of his domain. Aunt Effie, as usual, hit him with so many questions and answers that Leroy was eventually glad to say, "If you love him so, you take the old crazy bastard!" He unlocked the heavy solid metal door, letting in the first rush of light since Adam had been shoved in 20 hours before.

There Adam lay, his willow rawhide pack still strapped on his back. The breakfast platter lay in front of the entry's passage. The grits with the pat of butter had formed a white hard mound with a yellow center. The eggs glistened as the bacon grease they'd been fried in lay cold and hard—cold and hard as Aunt Effie's look and comments to the sheriff.

She first informed him that he had lied, as usual, about being in his office all day. Then she detailed the trouble he would be in if and when she brought this inhumane act to the attention of the press and the authorities. The sheriff knew what she'd done years before and figured she was even more versed in the art of the world now. He didn't completely comprehend about the press or who the authorities actually were. But, if she wanted to relieve him of an old crazy man who didn't have enough sense to eat, much less take care of his bodily needs on his own, more power to her. At least he wouldn't be troubled with the cleaning of his cell.

Aunt Effie was no beginner at the chore she had taken on. Her father had been a senile invalid for three years before the deterioration took its toll. At first, his death was a relief to her. Then it turned to a feeling of guilt that had no rhyme or reason. Just guilt over the sense of relief of not having the extra work she'd become so accustomed to. At least this tall, old, thin man could still walk on his own with a minimum of support from her strong arms as they made their way back to the Salem Boardinghouse.

There, she filled the six-foot iron bathtub that sat in the middle of the bathing room. She then sat Adam down on a drying bench, took off his pack, his coat, and his wool shirt. Seeing the raw areas where the pack's straps had galled his old senile flesh brought tears to her eyes.

She said aloud, "Old feller, you can stay here till you die."

She then crumbled a handful of herbs into his hot bath water, relieved him of the rest of his filthy garments, and settled him into the extra warm water. Seeing he could sit by himself, she went out of the bathroom, returning a few minutes later with a warm flannel nightgown and a quart jar full of hot chicken broth that reflected the dim light off its rich top juices, showing bits of floating fat. She knew if she could possibly ladle a couple of spoons down his weak invalid throat, there was a chance he'd eat something before he died, which would probably be this night. At least he'd be clean for a proper burial.

The first tablespoonful ran out of his mouth, down his dirt-filled beard, and into the hot bath water. His tongue and throat tried to convey the next spoonful to his empty stomach. His lungs received most of it, putting him into a fit of heaving and coughing. Aunt Effie placed the jar of broth on the bath stool next to the tub. She'd been in this situation so often with her own father. It made her feel a strange bond for this old silver-headed man, knowing there was no use trying. He wouldn't be able to swallow.

She turned away, taking his dirty garments and pack into the adjoining laundry room, intending to wash them so he could be at least buried in his own clean clothes. She opened the rawhide pack, revealing its contents. As soon as she saw the carbide lamp, extra carbide, flint and steel, something resembling a small piece of hard dry cheese, and a pack of corn meal that still had a double handful left, she knew he wasn't the old senile man from the Shannon County Farm near Eminence.

She returned to check on him. To her amazement, Adam had the quart jar in his trembling hands and was greedily draining the last of the broth. She knew if she tried moving him now, he'd probably become sick. So, she set to scrubbing his head and body, singing to him as though he was a small child. The sound of her voice was as soothing as the hot broth and bath to the mind of the old mountain man.

By the time she'd finished, he had spoken several words. None made any sense—something about, "Your finger, Jennie, is your gun. You'll eventually have to kill or be killed." Then he started to chant with guttural sounds that sounded at times like a young crow trying out its caw for the first time.

After he was bathed and fed, she bedded him down in the first bed he'd laid on in 30 days. Adam slept short 30 minutes of 24 hours. The 23 hours and 30 minutes of sleep still left his body weak, but his head had cleared. He never remembered leaving the cave or the journey he'd taken to the small exit where the Terrill brothers' dog, Mack, had found him. His last memory was of the fall he'd taken with his watch and compass and the strain it had placed on him to recover firm footing on the cave's floor.

Adam wrote out two notes to be telegraphed simultaneously. This caused one hell of a stir in the small hamlet of Salem as well as the far reaches of the rural areas. The reply to his telegraph spread faster and farther than any telegraph known to mankind could have transmitted. Folks "in the know" grew exponentially in size, bursting out and running wild, the number mushrooming on its own.

He no longer was the old crazy man. He was now MISTER Troop, the professor turned famous explorer. He'd opened up caves right there in the Ozarks, like the caves in Kentucky along with several hundred across the U.S., Canada, and Old Mexico. There were other countries, too, but no one knew where they were or could even pronounce the names.

Adam had Western Union out of Rolla, Missouri, wire for money. His account balance turned out to be $134,235. They would have been impressed with the $235. The $134,000 drove them all over the edge. The Union office couldn't keep it a secret for long. Husbands confided in their wives, wives confided in best friends, best friends confided in any and all who'd listen. If they'd run it in the local paper, fewer would've known.

Adam gained back his strength in the two-week stay at the boarding house. Ma Terrill even came to visit him, letting him know in long and lengthy speeches how he would have "died right thar in my 'own bed' iff'n it hadn't bin fer that good nursin' I give 'im. The rest done and give up on ye, when I started a-prayin' to my Sweet Jesus how ye'd done and went and died when the Lord remembered I wuz one of them 'chosen ones.' Ye know that Lord Jesus has to listen to us folks fer he ain't got many, so he knowed to step 'round lively when we speak and I ast fer ye back. I reckon ye can look in yer mirror and figger out the rest. Now I ain't astin fer money or setch, but ye did ruin my beddin'. This here furniture store right here in Salem has those new fandangled 'intercourse' matteresses that has springs in 'em ye sleep on. I've been a-prayin' to the same Lord I had to deliver ye up. Ye know, ye wouldn't be here iff'n it wuzn't fer me. That all I got to say, Mister Man."

As it turned out, that wasn't all she had to say. She was still talking when Adam had the two new "innerspring" mattresses bought and paid for, plus paying the delivery charge, which was free for everyone else. The storeowner figured an old man with that much money would be dead before he could ever spend it anyway.

In the meantime, there was a surprise for the sheriff also. Adam had the city garage order out a fender and headlamp, plus a new windshield for the bucket T. The "ladies man" car was made whole again.

Ever since Leroy, the High Sheriff, had heard about Mr. Troop's large fortune, he had daydreamed about it being illegally gained by its owner. If so, he'd be able to confiscate it as rightfully as he did the cash that was on the moonshine makers at the time of their arrest. This was the sole reason he fervently hunted down the stills in his county, making it so rough on the liquor makers there were only two operating stills left. Both just happened to be owned by Leroy and operated by his so-called deputies.

The High Sheriff's imagination was beginning to overrule his better sense. He'd always stayed clear of the boarding house unless forced to enter on business. Even then, it was put off as long as possible. But he'd got himself all keyed up with his imaginary cross-questioning. In each fantasized scenario, the old wealthy gentleman broke, confessed all, and pleaded for mercy. Sheriff Leroy even started twice to the local lawyer's office to find out the legal procedures surrounding seizure of bank accounts, trusts, property, etc.

Finally Leroy could take it no longer and took to pacing back and forth in his usually empty jail and office.

When evening mealtime at the hotel and boarding house arrived, he stepped out and locked his office for the night, confident that the old tycoon would slip up at this sly questioning.

He entered the long dining room where the meals were served family style. The guests and regulars were already dining. Luckily, the seat opposite Mr. Adam Troop was vacant, so he sat himself there. Unknown to Sheriff Leroy, the reason for the empty chair was that Aunt Effie, after serving each evening, would eat together with Adam. Afterward, Adam would help her clear the table and clean the kitchen. Then they'd visit. It was their private time. Each enjoyed the other's company, thoughts, and stories of life.

The High Sheriff Leroy had every sneaky trick question all worked out. This was his first eye-to-eye meeting with Mr. Troop since Aunt Effie came and rescued him from the bullpen.

Adam's piercing black and blue eyes, his "strange eyes," stared unblinking at the intruder, more in wonderment of who he might be and what he might want. The old man's hard steady stare made the sheriff feel the same way as old Aunt Effie did when he was caught lying as a little boy.

Everyone quit talking around the long table. All eyes turned to the sheriff, whose own eyes were cast down, peering at the floor under the white and red checkered tablecloth. There was a good minute of silence. The guests could hear the grandfather clock ticking at the far end of the dining hall.

At this time, Aunt Effie entered to take her place. Seeing the sheriff in her seat, she knew Little Lying Leroy was up to no good. His lying pitiful life flashed through her mind and she felt the old hatred boil up. She walked up, approached behind Adam's chair, and looked down at the sitting sheriff. She grinned, speaking softly and kindly to him. The guests and customers who were not enlightened on the history between the two would've mistaken her manner for affectionate warmth. That is, until the end of her short greeting.

"Well, well, look who's here. Little Leroy. What little lie have you come to spread tonight, little lying boy?"

This statement threw the High Sheriff for such a loop, his mind went blank like it always did in her presence. If only Aunt Effie had known this, she would've always made it to every political speech Leroy gave when campaigning for office instead of staying clear out of the sheer contempt she felt for her nephew by marriage.

Leroy looked up, trying to become the High Sheriff just like he'd seen in the movin' picture shows he'd gone to see up at Rolla. He pointed his finger, extended it almost clear across the table in Adam's face and blurted out, "Whor did ye git all that money from?"

"From robbing banks," Adam said calmly. "Everyone knows that."

The room roared with laughter. Some laughed so hard they began to cough, which brought on another barrage of cheers and laughter. Adam then excused the sheriff from Aunt Effie's seat. The skinny, pot-bellied sheriff knocked the chair over when he stood up, bringing more chuckles and heightening his embarrassment. He bent over, grasped the chair's back, and straightened it upon its legs. He then turned and hastily departed.

When everyone had finished their evening meal, Adam and Aunt Effie cleaned the kitchen and mopped the floor. While waiting for it to dry, they sat in the two easy chairs situated by the grandfather clock.

The clock's ticking put a hypnotic spell of serenity on the elderly man and gray-headed woman.

She spoke first. "I relished your comment to Little Lying Leroy." She never called him sheriff unless it was to his face. Even then, the word "sheriff" would be spoken sarcastically. Adam saw the sheriff at the supper meal and knew he was tall. By always calling him "Little Lying Leroy," Aunt Effie made very clear the disdain in her heart. She'd already told Adam the whole history. She also told him how Leroy presently conducted his personal affairs that affected not only his loved ones, but also the public whom he had taken a sworn oath of duty to serve with honor.

She told Adam many personal things from her own life; secret feelings about her own shortcomings that were difficult for her to reminisce on in the privacy of her own mind, much less ever declare aloud to another. There was one that bothered her—haunted her—the most. This was the thought that she was responsible for the death of her husband as much as if she pulled the trigger that sent him to his grave—a grave in a far distant foreign soil.

They had argued. She started her explanation to Adam with these words, then corrected this statement for the first time in the many decades that she'd replayed the events in her mind. No, she had fussed. *Badgered.* Oh, she had wanted a child. She would cry, endlessly inflicting her resentment and pain on her husband John. He'd sit silently when she starting "talking babies." She admitted now to herself for the first time that this was the reason John left the very next day after they'd returned from Rolla. She had John go to the hospital there for the test she'd read about in a medical journal that had just started to be published.

John volunteered for the Army with several others, including Clem Stewart and Charlie Smith. Clem was killed also. Charlie was one of the few who returned. "He married Wave Harrison, my best childhood friend. She is a sister-in-law to Susie Smith, the widow where you have the cabin on the Current River rented."

Aunt Effie thought, but said nothing, about the new comforter she'd sent to the grieving family for Fiddling Jimmy Smith to be buried in.

You do not let your right hand know what your left hand is doing, she thought to herself. *What good is giving if you blow a trumpet before your offering?*

It was silent now except for the squeak and groan of the old rockers as each set their own rhythm on the white oak floor. Then, Adam spoke. His comment broke the silence and the sadness in Aunt Effie's mind.

"You know, Aunt Effie, I didn't lie to Little Leroy." He laughed and slapped his knee, saying," I damn sure didn't!"

He laughed again, reached over, squeezed her hand and said, "I DID get all that money by robbing banks!"

Both rockers stopped rocking. They laughed long and hard. This was "good medicine," the temporary cure they both sorely needed this night.

Effie didn't speak. She knew he would tell his story in due time.

chapter
THREE

Adam and Sam Bass

"Yes, Effie, it all came around strictly by accident. I had drifted from one place to another, not for capital gain or employment, but purely out of boredom. Actually, being 'lost' would be a more accurate description. Pegasus had become lame. I wasn't simply without a horse; when I lost him, I felt I'd lost my last tie with this earth.

"By this time I'd made it north to the Dakota country in the Black Hills. The gold rush there was in its heyday. Tales of riches and grandeur beyond belief brought hoards of treasure seekers of every age and description. From the highly educated to the lowly, all were brothers of the spear united by one hope, one thought: wealth. Wealth beyond one's wildest imagination. Dreamer's dreams. After finally making it to the gold field, it turned into a nightmare for most. The strong and the young would hold out longer. Lucky was the one who gained employment with a mining or placer outfit that had already proven itself and was in full swing.

"I never worked. I never went there to become wealthy or with the hopes of finding a single flake of gold dust. I went in search of Harry

Mosier. I would've been in the same shape as the hoards of gold seekers if it hadn't been for the knowledge of survival I'd learned from old Mandan woman. People will starve to death in a land of plenty without the know-how to hunt and gather.

"Anyway, I had my fill of the Black Hills and the rumors of its mother lodes that drove so many to madness. After their money and short supplies ran out, hunger pushed them over the edge. Even the 'would be' honest sometimes turn bad at such times. Looking back, I figure this may have been the case that led up to one of my unchosen occupations as a bounty hunter.

"I had drifted from gold camp to gold camp looking for Mr. Mosier. Summer had come, and it was hot and dry. I don't know if this had anything to do with the hollow, lonely feeling that engulfed me, but all of the sudden I got a hankering to go south to Taos. I realize now, as an old man, I was homesick. Since I'd never had a family or home in my boyhood, I didn't understand this feeling that had taken over my mind and spirit. All I knew was I wanted to return to Taos. Looking back now, I realize how foolish it was to travel south in the heat of the summer.

"I paid fare to ride the stage lines that were in operation from one point to another and worked my way south. They were crowded at times. I usually rode on top. Even with the sun beating down, the jolting one received from riding on top of the stage was more pleasant than being confined to its interior, which held not only the heat from the dry hot summer sun, but the eight crowded passengers as well. Sardines placed in one of those little tin cans would be a likely comparison. The old and very young had to gasp for air like a goldfish in a bowl too small.

"I would travel for a few days, sometimes as long as a week. When I found a suitable camp with water and fuel, I would rest before paying fare to my next waypoint. I'd made it into the Colorado territory. It was all beautiful high country since I swung west toward Denver instead of holding to its eastern boundary. There was a fort north of Denver. I think it's called Fort Collins.

"At present, the grades ran long. They pulled the coach's three spans of horses down to a walk. One grade in particular was very long. The stage was loaded to the maximum and had a gold shipment aboard. No one knew of its existence. At least, I'm sure the paying passengers had no knowledge of it or most would've done like me, and wouldn't have taken this run.

"A day or a week's difference in one's travel time wasn't desperately important like it is today. The world went at a much slower pace and we were certainly traveling at a slow pace that day. Two of the horses started showing lame halfway out. By the time we made 'killer grade,' the driver had to let them blow out three times and we were still a mile or more from its summit.

"The men passengers got out and walked alongside of the stage. I felt something was amiss. I never was a mentioner, so I held my peace. Looking back, I realize now that my silence cost the life of a young lady passenger. She was heading for the fort to be wed to one of the officers there. I could tell at a glance that each of the lame horse's shoes had been reset that morning before their run. One lame horse, I wouldn't have thought twice. But two, and the fresh reset shoes at that, it just didn't add up.

"This was going through my mind as the stage came to a stop again. I had my eyes cast down trying to peer more closely at the tall bay's hoof that was limping profoundly now. He was actually trying to carry his hoof off the ground with each stride. I was in the process of asking the driver if it wouldn't be wise to unhitch the two lames since it was a downgrade from the summit to the next way station.

"Neither the driver nor the shotgun man looked my way. They had their eyes glued to a dry deep wash. Some call this impression a gully. Its banks dropped so abruptly, they were almost vertical on both sides of the narrow road. Even I looked in the direction that the driver and shotgun guard were staring toward. The guard stood up and stretched his arms up over his head with the pretense of relieving his aches and pains.

"He feigned a stumble and dropped his double-barreled weapon. It hit the spring seat and fell, lodging on one of the lame horse's traces, where it balanced for a second before falling to the ground under the bay's tender elevated hoof. I started to reach under the gelding's traces to retrieve the shotgun. The stage driver intervened between the horse and me saying, 'Leave 'er be. Keep your damn hands off of company property.'

"I turned to walk away. To my surprise, I was looking down the barrel of a .45 Colt, one of those new fangled ones that shot all-in-one brass center-fired cartridges. I never thought much of them. Seems their powder load—well, seemed like no two cartridges were the same. One hull would be way overloaded. The shot's blast would be enough to bust the barrel and make the gun buck with such force, you could never get off the second shot close to even a still target, much less one that was alive and shooting back."

Adam laughed, slapped his knee, and said his least concern at that moment was which powder loads were in the cartridges of this highwayman's gun. "I froze in position pretending to cast my eyes to the ground as though I was inspecting my old worn moccasins. This move automatically relieved the small bandit with the large red handkerchief tied over his huge Roman nose who'd suddenly appeared from out of the gully and aimed his Buntline in my face. This slightly built man wouldn't have tipped the scale at a hundred pounds. If he did, his nose would've been a quarter of his weight. Even there, with his pistol waving to and fro, I couldn't bring myself to take his holdup attempt seriously.

"I glanced around to see what the stage attendants and other passengers were doing. The two male passengers were decked out in suits, but they'd removed their coats when they started walking up the grade to relieve the lame horse's load earlier. They had their coats tied around their waist, using the sleeves as binders. I could see that neither of the two was armed. There were four women and two children still sitting inside. The driver and guard riding shotgun were craning their neck and heads from one gully to the other that lay on either side of the narrow road. There we stood in the boiling, scorching, noonday sun. The horseflies had started to buzz and circle like a pack of hungry, tiny vultures. Still, no one spoke or moved.

"I'd relaxed enough by now to really start to observe. It had become quite humorous. One of the bolder, hungrier hummingbird-sized horseflies had silently lit on the driver's bare neck at the base of his skull. The teamster was either fairly numb or the large old fly was quite the professional for he roosted there, sucking and drawing a good tablespoon of the driver's blood into its abdomen.

"All of the sudden, the driver kicked his heels and pranced around like he was starting up to do an Irish jig, cursing and slapping the air around his head and shoulders. The old horsefly had sucked so hard and deep, he was hung. The man slapped, hollered, and cursed, never hitting even close to the horsefly. His sidekick, the guard, reached over and gave him a mighty wallop. His open palm contacted the now full, soft fly. The blood flew. I don't think his shotgun loaded with double OO steelies could've drawn more blood.

"The driver squalled out, 'What in the hell did you go and do that fer, Slim?'

"Slim, the guard, never got a chance to answer. Here came shuffling upon the scene a huge man who looked as though he'd stuffed an over-sized cushion in front and rear—either that or ingested them. His head was the size of a nail keg. He was the little man's sidekick and the 'brains' of their outfit. He'd made it into the wash with only minor diffi-culty and would've been okay had his tremendous weight not pulled away the bank's sides. Yes, I said 'sides'—not only the front, but the rear also. In his fall, he somehow managed to grasp and bring down both banks simultaneously. Each time he tried to crawl out, more slid off, attempting to bury him along with his lost hat. Now his exposed bald pink head glistened under the sun's hot rays as the sweat beaded, then turned into little rivers of salty water that drained into his shaggy long eyebrows. The brows worked to stop the flow like a beaver dam in a high country's spring thaw, but the brow eventually broke, releasing gush after gush till the portly one's red and black bandanna tied over his nose was saturated. It already had a good coat of adobe on its outer side. Each time the fat bandit gulped for air, his snot rag would bellow in and out like a jib on a sailing vessel that had lost its air, then righted itself on course to bellow out in full once again.

"I had to bite my lip to keep from laughing when the portly bandito reached up, tore his bandana off and exposed the pink, mottled, blotched face beneath. His pint-sized comrade, with the hatchet-sized nose, was busy with a heavy swarm of bloodthirsty horseflies since his over-sized nose worked as a blinder on a workhorse's bridle. He'd wall his eyes the same as a young green colt does at its first encounter—only difference being, theirs can be shed with the slipping off of their bridle whereas the little man's was permanent. And, at this moment it was also proving to be a huge handicap in his war against his opponent—the two dozen biting, sucking flies.

"He had purchased himself one of those long barrel Buntlines that would've hung down past his knees if and when he ever holstered the large 'hog leg.' It was being put to good use at the present to whisk the hungry intruders off between his small shoulders. His sidekick, 'Heavy,' realized he hadn't performed his role in this staged-up robbery. Remembering his important rehearsed part, he headed for the still seated passengers: the four women and two small children. Heavy's hands were sweating profusely on his gun. The once-dry adobe earth that had collected on his clothes and bandit kerchief had become mixed with his sweat until he couldn't stand the slimy feel of his steel peacekeeper.

"He crammed it down in its sweat-mudded holster trying to square his rabbit shoulders. He raised his fat hand, pointed his sausage-sized index finger in the air, and walked back and forth giving silent orders to an invisible audience. This made his runt partner-in-crime momentarily stop the war he'd been waging against his winged enemies.

"'You damn fat-headed idiot! Get your mask back on!' he squeaked.

"Heavy, stopping his performance, bellered back, 'I ain't got no mask! It's a bandanner, smarty pants!'

"This made everyone laugh, even the driver and guard at the rear of the stage. They were trying in vain to break the army's payroll box from its iron-clad straps that were in front of the stage's gold shipment safe. Heavy reached the door's handle and opened it. Seeing the ladies and children, he bowed and reached up to sweep his hat off to complete his macho gesture. He then remembered he'd lost the Stetson he was so proud of. He said, gruffly, 'Y'all get out here where we can cover ye.'

"The large-boned Swedish immigrant bride-to-be didn't understand Heavy's slang of being 'covered.' The older gray-headed lady explained it meant to 'keep an eye.' This lost the young woman, too. They all unloaded. The blond-headed girl followed their example, still ignorant as to what was in progress. She walked a short circle to relieve the cramps in her legs and ended up standing in front of me. This put her between Half Pint and me.

"When Shorty temporarily ceased swatting, waving, and slapping at the swarm of fresh reinforcements on the wing, he noticed he'd forgotten to disarm the passengers. This must have been his role in their slick, well-thought-out hold-up. He only gave a glance my way. He was still waving his long Buntline like an orchestra leader does his baton at the real imminent danger—the hoards of biting, sucking flies. He informed me that I was to take my left hand, cross over, and give my right gun to Heavy. Heavy marched up stiffly like a toy soldier and retrieved one of my old cap-and-ball Navy Colts. He looked at it and laughed, then walked over and showed his little friend the old-fashioned weapon. Half Pint held his long, new Buntline up beside my old black-powder Navy Colt so as to illustrate, 'See what a big, mean man I am' to the ladies. This made Heavy laugh till his 500 pounds of fatty pones quivered in tremors.

"The robbery episode had been so comical from the beginning that no one had taken it seriously. The women had huddled together in order to keep the bloodthirsty little intruders off the children and one another's back. The Swedish immigrant bride-to-be was tough as old nails. She paid little to no attention to the horseflies. Every so often, she'd catch a few when they got too vicious on her white flesh and would pull their heads off or part of their wings. Then she'd grin, watching them kick and buzz in the dust around her feet.

"I was waiting for Heavy to come back to disarm me of my left Colt. I'd been watching the girl torturing, or playing, with the horseflies—I don't know which category to use when speaking of these worthless irritating insects.

"I never saw Heavy leave. He'd gone back to his former hiding place in the gulch to look for his Stetson. I could hear the two employees of the stage line arguing. I stepped backwards slowly, working my way toward the coach to hear what the driver and Slim, the shotgun rider and guard, were saying in their now heated up argument. The driver was telling Slim to go unhitch the sound lead horse. They would use it to jerk the iron-clad strapped box from the stage's rear-end compartment.

"Slim had no more than gotten even with the rear lame horse that was still holding up his sore hoof over Slim's shotgun, still lying on the ground, when Half Pint became overly zealous with his Buntline baton and was swinging it with the hammer fully cocked. One of the old sly bloodsuckers had landed on the red bandana and had a good suction on the largest part of his body—his nose. Most of his nerve endings must have been attached to his well-formed honker as he let out a screech that made the hair stand up on the nape of my neck. Everyone turned and looked toward the little bandit. He struck the side of his nose with the long 'hog leg' of a gun with such power his arm ended up straight out as though he was aiming to take a bead off his front sight.

"His gun went off accidentally. The bullet struck the Swedish immigrant girl square between the eyes. If I hadn't moved to hear the employee's conversation, I would've been dead or at least badly injured.

"I never thought. Automatically, my left hand had drawn the old Navy Colt and three bullets entered the little feller's head. He was dead before he ever hit the ground. Slim saw that his partner-in-crime in this bungled up robbery had been shot dead. Being at the rear of the lame horse, he dove for his shotgun. Slim didn't realize that I didn't give a damn if every stage was robbed on each run. My part in the killing was never premeditated. It was purely an innocent reflex on my part. But since we never had time to sit and discuss our personal stance about the issue at hand, Slim figured he'd better take me out.

"This was the last thing poor ol' Slim would bungle this day and for eternity. As he was trying to grasp his gun, he bumped the gelding's sore hoof. The 1,500 pounds of muscle that was attached to the sore sensitive hoof struck—also reflexively. The bay's move was lightning quick. In the quietness, even the horseflies seemed to quit buzzing. The iron-shod hoof made a dull thud as it connected between Slim's eyes and forehead. His skull was sunk in till I could put both my fists into the cavity that was formed.

"Then, as he struggled for life, the blood started oozing out his ears and the sunken spot started to balloon out, turning blue purple. Slim started jerking, half-rising and flopping around like a chicken does when its head is freshly chopped off. This made the two children cry.

"I figured the women would go to pieces also. But instead, they took command. They put the young ones back in the stage, told the driver to unhitch the two lames and brought the other sound lead horse to take the lame rear horse's position. In ten minutes the stage was off.

"We didn't travel more than a mile. We were within a stone's throw of reaching the summit when one of the horses fell and started coughing up blood. The bullet that had killed the girl had entered into the horse's lungs. No one noticed since there was so much blood already on the steeds from the horseflies. I got down, along with the two easterners in suits, cut the dead horse out of its traces, and rigged up the coach so it could be pulled with the remaining three. The two gentlemen and I decided we'd better walk the remaining distance to the way station, taking no more chances till things were squared away.

"The walk, I figured, would be nothing for us since I'd never been around people who'd never learned to walk. I hadn't thought to look at their footwear until the one in the black and punkin checkered suit started limping. He said his shoes were new. He'd brought them from back east just for this occasion. He broke 'em out and donned them for the first time this very morning. We hadn't walked more than a mile. I'd already heard his whole life story and most of his kinfolks back to the tenth generation. I realize now his steady stream of talking may have stemmed in part from being exposed to all the sudden death by violent killings.

"The older man was mostly silent. Each time the younger newspaper reporter stopped to squeeze and pick at his fifty-cent-piece-size blisters, the older journalist would spit and swipe at the toes of his strange bumpy looking footwear which were clearly made for show, not work. The younger reporter, noticing my curiosity in his friend's queer-looking shoes, never paused, prattling on about his great-grandfather's part in the Revolutionary War of 1700 and something. All I heard was that they were 'gators'—alligators, to be correct, he explained. I took this to be the old war hero's last name. So, to be courteous, and feeling self-conscious about mentally blocking out his continuous rattling as we walked in the 100-degree August sun, I felt I had to at least try to make some sort of comment since this was first pause in his story since we'd started walking.

"I reckon he'd never have paused if it hadn't been for the gopher hole he stepped in and twisted his ankle. While he was holding his leg, making low humming, panting sounds, I said more to the hot air and empty space than my road companions, 'Yes, it must have been pure hell on earth for your old great-grandfather 'Alleygater' to have to fight that olden day war dern near single-handed.'

"No sooner had I finished my comment than the one in the odd-colored bumpy shoes became tickled. He became so limber with laughter, he fell on his knees and pounded the earth of the road. He laughed till tears streamed down from his eyes. Seems he'd get almost back into control, then another spasm would catch and it mounted greater than the one before. Here, the young one in the dainty-made black patent leather shoes was humming and rubbing his injured leg while "bumpy shoes" was laughing and pounding the ground.

"I walked out at a right angle a couple hundred feet, figuring this move would let them get control of whatever was eating at them. Here is where I saw a cloud of dust being stirred up in the hot, still summer air. At a glance, I knew it was several mounted horses coming fast our way and suspected they had something to do with the staged-up, bungled robbery attempt. I went immediately to tell the reporters what I'd seen and that we'd have some sort of 'company' soon.

"The older one impressed me by his comment of, 'If the large party coming this way has anything to do with the attempted robbery, I'd wager giving odds we're in trouble, Mr. Troop. There's no way there could be time for anyone to be informed unless the said approaching party was waiting in anticipation of the reward—the stage's stolen property. The way they're riding, not sparing their mounts, they're coming for one purpose and I'd be obliged to you if you'd spare me one of your pistols.'

"We were too far away from the gulch to make it back. There was no other suitable place to take a stand, so we waited for sure death. We even discussed different plans. The bumpy-shoed reporter laughed, saying, 'Damn, I made it through four years of war! Never got a scratch except a small cut at the Battle of Chancellorsville, and here we'll all die today in the middle of a peace-time country. Damn!'

"He started to say more, then did an odd thing. He stripped off his shirt and was in the process of unlacing his fancy shoes when the younger journalist exclaimed, 'Hell! It's the U.S. Cavalry! I think . . .'

"Sure enough, it was the U.S. Cavalry all right, riding 'hell bent for leather,' bearing right down on us. They were riding four abreast. Only the insignia bearer rode single. He was out front, I guess, to make more of a show. The four abreast, four deep others held formation until they were within two hundred or so feet of us.

"Here, the first two columns went right, the rear two left, holding in their formation till all formed a close tight circle with the three of us as the bull's-eye. When they pulled up their charging horses, there wouldn't have been space enough for a rabbit to run, much less escape.

"The officer-in-charge first addressed the reporters who were now standing in the high heat in their full suits of clothes. They'd even run a comb through their hair and brought out their ties and put them on.

"They introduced themselves. I never caught their names. I had my mind in such deep thought, remembering the older one had called me Mr. Troop and said something about a battle called Chancellorsville. I knew I'd heard of this battle, but where? With the heat, the swarms of horseflies, and everything that was going on, I never noticed that the circle nearest me had their weapons drawn and were standing at the ready.

"Then, I heard one of the reporter's voices. He was in a heated argument with the officer-in-charge. His words went something like, 'You will, sir, have to kill us all. That includes the four lady passengers and two children. I don't think the driver has much gray matter, so him also. No, sir, when you pull your triggers, the bullet's report will be heard clear back in Washington, D.C.'

"Their top dog dismounted without giving an order or signal. Six of the largest regulars approached at the same time in marching formation. Without a spoken word or command from their leader, they split up. There were now two on each side of me, and two that stepped to the rear. I never saw the movements of the two behind me until they had pinned my arms. Then the other four leaped in. One disarmed me of my knife and the one pistol I had left. The same instant, their fearless leader demanded my remaining pistol from the reporter who had already laid it on the ground at his own feet when he'd seen it was the U.S. Cavalry, even before they arrived.

"The officer-in-charge informed me I was under arrest for murder and the attempted robbery of the United States of America's Army's payroll. I started to explain my part in the past drama, but received a backhanded blow from the large sergeant who was standing at his master's side. He stepped in to swing again. I was still pinned by the four company regulars when the tall reporter intervened again on my behalf.

"I was still too confused to understand what was being said and why. The gentlemen in the bumpy shoes and the officer were engaged in a shouting match by this time. The officer was informing the reporter that I was as good as hung. The Army was sure to swing me by the neck till dead. The reporter was informing him that I had better not be mysteriously shot on my trip to the fort or he could discard his uniform forever. His newspaper didn't only carry weight back in Washington D.C., it controlled it. He then added, 'No brag, just fact,' and turned and walked away. His crippled shiny-shoed sidekick went limping after him toward the stage that was stopped in the distance.

"I was shackled and mounted on one of their horses, then was kept to the rear on the ride back to the fort. I would catch heated words between the officer-in-charge, his subordinate, and the sergeant.

"By this time, the puzzle had formed itself together until even a child could see the picture. I was in serious trouble with no way out. I became mad and disgusted with myself. I knew if only I had kept my other pistol and the pack that contained my rifle, ammo, and powder and shot, I could've killed the two officers and sergeant instantly, leaving only the regulars. They would've milled around, putting up a half-hearted battle, if one at all, with their fearless leaders being eliminated. They were so used to being told every move. The majority were immigrants in these far outlying posts. They would've been like oxen left on their own without a goader to attend to them.

"Now, here I was laying on a filthy lice and bedbug-ridden bunk in the fort's brig to be hung for their bungled up robbery. They had obviously staged the robbery to steal their own payroll along with Denver's shipment of gold from the Black Hills. I was going over the past 24 hours, trying to analyze each and everyone involved—even the ladies and children. I knew the damn U.S. government would have not only the last say, but the only say. Whatever wild and crazy lie they concocted would be considered as hard fact just because it was written on paper and signed by the dictator in charge of this precinct.

"The heavy solid iron door was unlocked and thrown open while I was still in deep thought. The light that rushed in blinded me. They again had to act like a pack of fools. Here I lay in shackles and still they fell upon me. I guess they hadn't been informed of my condition. As soon as the six strong men saw my shackled feet and hands with a heavy chain running to and fro connecting them together, they laughed and all babbled in some foreign tongue, and were relieved at the same time.

"I knew by this I was as good as dead. Sure, I could've killed one or even two of these young, unprepared, ill-trained foreign lads. I knew they were no more in control of their own lives than I was my own at the present. I walked along briskly. Even in shackles, I made them six-step right along.

"The orderly took over and unshackled my ankles and wrists outside of the post commander's office door. When I entered into the large quarters, I received the shock of my life. There stood Samuel Thomas Blackburn, the two eastern newspaper reporters, and the top lawyer of the city of Denver. I was later introduced to him after the fort's commander-in-charge shook my hand and congratulated me on my role in saving the fort's payroll and S.T.'s gold shipment. He handed me $250 in gold. The reward was for the little hatchet-nosed bandit. It would've been $2,500 if I'd only killed or caught the 'brains' of this bandit outfit. He called his name, but it never occurred to me he was talking about 'Heavy' until I was at S.T.'s in Denver, Colorado.

"S.T. had migrated to Denver after striking it big in the Black Hills at the first of the gold rush. He opened the Denver Emporium and Opry House, along with a half dozen or so other businesses. If it hadn't been for the two eastern reporters, Bob and James, I wouldn't have kept my life. They coincidentally happened to be on their way to gain employment from S.T. That summer I stayed as a guest until fall. Later, S.T. told me that when he heard their story, he suspected the military all along.

"But what the hell can one do against the warlords? You dethrone one and they'll put a worse thief and murderer in his place knowing they have to—to keep pillaging. This reward money is a bunch of bullshit of theirs. After a robbery or two, they make up a phony character, apply a name or two, and offer a ridiculous sum of gold like $2,500 to even $5,000 if and when one of the so-called highwaymen is ever killed, never captured. The captured bandit is usually only worth $50 to $100.

"'If it hadn't been for Bob and James, they would have hung you, Adam,' S.T. told me, 'instead of doling out the $250. The U.S. military was offering the reward themselves. Now Adam, don't get me wrong. There is plenty of bounty money offered by legitimate companies and individuals.'

"S.T. explained to me the proper procedures of this most hated of trades. Every citizen loathed the hunter, even the ones who desired and advertised for bounty hunter's services.

"This is the way I became the hunter of man—an occupation I enjoyed in a strange, warped way. It wasn't much different than trapping. In fact, I relied on lots of my old trapping methods. When one traps, he has to go into the vicinity where the species lives or travels to make the sets. The bait, or cubbies, are already supplied in the latter case by greed. The majority of humans are not unlike the domesticated beast and fowl. The goose is the best comparison. It will beat its wings, honk and hiss, make more noise than all the rest put together over the problem at hand. But they will never leave the barnyard to correct the matter. The hog, the smartest of all, will lay in its same wallow. The dog, the most vicious, the most trusted, can and will run off. But the swine will return by sundown to wallow once again, over and over.

"I found bounty hunting to be just the same. It didn't take a lot of brains to figure out the highwayman's or the law dog's pattern. Each was as corrupt as the other. Sure, there are good lawmen. Anyway, they started out to be and would've succeeded if they could've been killed or died early enough in the game.

"I found out soon enough S.T. had told the truth of the high-price bounties. Most of them were a front to appease the companies and individuals who had been robbed. So, when the goose squawked too long or loud, the hogs and dogs would nail up posters in their vicinity. Their local artist's sketches were so vague as to fit one and all. Since a large handlebar mustache had become a fad of the day, they'd add one to all the phantom bandit posters. One could call it a trademark of this occupation.

"Now, Aunt Effie, I don't want you to misunderstand me. I'm not saying 100% of the 'big money' posters were fake. No, there were some real ones, like the James's, Daltons', Youngers', Wells', Bart, and Bass. Yes, Sam Bass.

"Sam Bass is the outlaw who turned me away from the straight and narrow. Not only me, but a man by the name of Jim Butler. Sure the name means nothing now, but I remember all too well when his name was spoken in Texas, it put chills down even evildoers' backs. That name is what brought me here to your country. But first, I'll tell you how it all began. Then maybe, just maybe, you can put the finishing touch to a mystery since you know everyone in these hills.

"I'd drifted into Texas. Looking back tonight, I'm afraid it was a 'handlebar' poster. As they say, I was deep into Texas and I don't mean the heart. I was as far south as one can go. The two countries' border ran through the middle of town. I hadn't been there for any more than a week.

"I quit drinking spirits the same night my wife and boys drowned. However, I would've been much healthier if I drank beer instead of their water. Everyone there drank some form of liquid instead of the water unless it had been boiled. I don't understand why and it made no sense at all, Aunt Effie, but if a person boiled the water, he stayed healthy. But the first drink one took that wasn't boiled, you were in trouble. That is, unless you were a Mexican or Indian. The water seemed to have no effect on them, boiled or no. That's what got Caucasians in trouble, especially the younger ones. They would say, 'Anything a Mexican or red man can take, I'll double 'er.' And double I was, doubled up vomiting with dysentery like none has ever seen before in the upper states.

"I was losing it fast. I knew I didn't have but hours. However, between the vomit and the dysentery, I guess even the Grim Reaper decided to back up. I know you've nursed many who are extremely ill. You're one of the few who can appreciate this story.

"Jim Butler was the sheriff on the U.S. side. The Mexican side was lawless to a point of ruthlessness that I learned later to hate and love at the same time. But at this present time, I was too damned sick to care one way or the other. This is where James Butler came into the picture. He was a big, tall, dark man who I first took to be part Mexican. He knew I was a bounty hunter for I had stopped by his office, which was customary in this trade. I had a poster and the man's head encased in red clay mud as proof of capture. He would sign the proper affidavit. Then it was either wired or sent by postal mail back to the city, town, or county that had set up the currency reward."

Adam laughed, slapped his knee, and said, "In some cases, the reward had been lifted or banned, but their 'head sheets' were still out there flying in the breeze, waiting for some trigger-happy greedy person to expel them from among the living.

"I don't know why and sure don't remember when Jim Butler came to my rescue. When my fever broke and I came out of my delirium, I was in such a weakened state, I couldn't hold my own head up. Jim had hired an old Mexican woman who knew her herbal medicine and was renowned for being able to cure every ailment from a broken heart to rabies. I still don't know how she forced it down me, but whatever it was, it worked. I was weak, and I'd lost so much weight I was little more than a skeleton. During my recovery is when I met outlaw Sam Bass.

"While I was at the height of my illness, there had been one hell of a brawl and gunfight between two saloon owners—one on the Mexican side, the other on the U.S. Jim sided with the Mexicans, I later found out. The Mexican cantina was owned and operated by an Irishman by the name of Paddy O'Leary or O'Brien. I'd heard them address Paddy by both names. I never made it to his premises so I couldn't say personally what name or title his saloon went by. I do recall it made quite a ruckus. There was a small army of ex-lawmen, gunfighters, cowboys, and outlaws who came to the aid of Paddy. There was an eastern newspaper reporter present for some other reason. He had photography equipment, so he took a picture of all the ruffians together at Paddy's and sent it back east to illustrate all the romance of the 'Wild West.'"

Adam laughed, saying, "I think this ruckus is where Jim Butler lost favor with the town fathers on the American side. I was still too weak to travel, but knew I wanted to be anywhere there was clear cold water and hopes of a snowflake or two when winter came.

"Jim and I hit it off right off the bat. Being so sick and near death, I opened up and said things I wouldn't have spoken of had I been more healthy. When I talked of my childhood, I could tell it touched him also. I meant it as a jest when I told him that if I 'kicked the bucket,' take and keep my money belt and the reward I was still waiting on to arrive at his 'ex-office.' It was 'ex' now that the good citizens had turned against Jim when he'd sided with the wrong team. He was out of a job.

"I was just about to tell him he could have it all if he'd cart my carcass north to the first snow bank, when the door flew open. There stood a slight-built young man in raggedy overalls, a beat-up flop hat, and clodhopper shoes that were not matched. Their toes turned up at the end till they resembled horse's hooves that had been foundered and grown out for a year or so. He had a pistol in each hand and a long knife clenched between his teeth, looking wild. I first thought the raggedy looking bum had overheard our conversation of the money belt. I never got to play on my thoughts for long. Next thing I knew, Jim had embraced the pistol drawn man, slapping him on the back, calling him son.

"'Damn, son, where in hell have you been? I heard you were dead! I haven't seen a new sheet on you for a spell!'

"The man in rags pulled out a wad of bounty posters and sailed them one at a time through the air. He called off the reward amount for each company, bank, or individual. When we lined them up, all three of us laughed. Not one poster's sketch even came close to resembling Sam.

"Jim turned first to me and introduced outlaw Sam Bass. He then said, 'Sam, this is Adam Troop, bounty hunter.'

"Sam had one hell of a personality. There was a wide, tall mirror on the dresser opposite of us. Here we stood side-by-side—outlaw, law, and bounty hunter. We all had one thing in common—we were all unemployed at this very moment 'through no fault of our own.' Sam had us all laughin' and feeling close.

"'Here, Adam,' said Sam, 'has literally had the shit kicked out of him by a quart of water. You, Jim, sidin' in with ol' Paddy, you'll be damn lucky to ever gain rightful employment to buy grub enough to even make a turd again. Fer as me, I've done and went and squandered all this here stolen loot on my fancy aytire. You know me, always worryin' about appearance and appearel!'

"Sam Bass kept us laughing. So, he took over. He knew exactly what and how to cook to get a body back on its feet. In no time flat, we were ready to head out—I mean head out to rob banks, railroads, and stage lines.

"I never met a finer pair than Sam and Jim. The alleged and infamous Sam Bass gang of 20 or so actually was no more than us three. The rest were just hungry and broke baggage, except for the old camp tender, Mr. Pinky.

"Sam was a natural when it came to figuring out different methods and tactics. We rode north, made camp, and took out time till I'd gained back my strength. We'd go in and case out a job, learn the layout of the streets, then go over it a dozen times.

"Sam gave me an eye patch to wear. Neither Jim nor I would've ever thought of it. I remember when he handed it to me. I looked puzzled. Sam said, 'Hell, Adam, why don't ye go get yerself a snow white horse with a red head and jet black mane and tail with a bright yeller belly?'

"I still didn't understand until Jim got control of his laughter saying, 'Adam, I'll buy you a mirror. Look at your eyes and you'll figure it out.'

"Then it hit me what my comrades in crime were talking about. There seemed nary an hour went by that Sam didn't have us laughing.

Not one of us drank or used tobacco. I think this is what kept us on top of the game. You show me a man with either of these vices and I'll show you a man that can't keep out of town and trouble. Sam would say, 'Give him two shots of old "big mouth" and he'll belly up to the bar tellin' everyone in earshot, and lots of 'em out in the middle of the street, everything he's ever done and gonna do. It'll mess a feller's senses up. Take one that ain't got no nerve at all, too scared to sleep unless he has the covers pulled up over his head. Give him a few belts of old devil's brew. By the time he has half a quart drunk, he'll challenge ol' Jim thar to a shootin' match. I've done and seed it whor Jim would sidestep every way he could and have to end up killin' 'em. Damn, the liquor's what should be against the law. It ruint my—'

"Jim had his own way with people, also. He'd cut in, telling Sam that if he was going to start preaching, he'd have to keep one of his fancy hats instead of discarding them after a heist. We used these items solely for business purposes.

"Yes, Sam was truly an artist of disguise. No wonder the posters of him at our first meeting had all the eyewitnesses' accounts of him so inaccurate. Each was telling the truth of what their eyes had seen of his image.

"Sam would ride along, saying nothing at times for miles. He would study the features of Jim, me, and the rest. Then he'd go to one of the larger cities that was not even close to the town we'd decided to rob. Once there, Jim, me, and the old black camp tender would camp out a few miles. Sam and the rest would go into the city and buy whatever he'd decided on."

Adam couldn't keep from laughing when he started telling about the power of persuasion that Sam had to use on Jim to get him to don a blond wig. "Sam finally said, 'Hell, Jim, look at poor ol' Adam. He was bornt with yeller hair and he don't go around all bulled up about 'er and furthermore, from the looks of things, his pa couldn't even decide what color to make his eyes.' This got us all to laughing. If Jim hadn't worn the blond wig, we'd sure have stretched a rope that day for everything went wrong."

Adam quit talking, looked far off in space, and stopped his slow, even rocking. He reached out, took Aunt Effie's hand and said, "Hell, Effie, I haven't even had a dram of old 'big mouth' and here I've set and ran my mouth about a man I'm wondering if you know or ever heard his name."

Aunt Effie sensed the embarrassment that Adam had started to feel and always had an easy way with words. She smiled and said, "You've already forgot, Mr. Troop, about what I said about my John and our baby problem. I can't remember for my namesake what you were just talking about. Now didn't you say you wanted to inquire about a relative or friend for someone?"

Adam laughed, slapped his leg and said, "Sure did. Aunt Effie, have you ever heard of a gentleman by the name of Jim Self?"

Now, Effie's rocker quit rocking. She closed her eyes and pushed her chair as far back as the rocker would allow. Her breathing was so light, Adam would've thought she'd gone to sleep if it hadn't been for the steady slight drumming of her index fingers on the arms of her rocking chair.

Aunt Effie knew the name, but the fear was so ingrained at such an early age. She was 19 years old that day so many years ago at the molasses making. Even as a grown older woman, each time the "witch girl's" name came to her, it still affected her in an almost demonic way. It didn't matter whether the same was in the paper or someone casually mentioned her. Even here tonight, Adam wasn't inquiring about Lillie May. He was inquiring about her late husband, Jim Self.

This brought on feelings of guilt for Aunt Effie. She'd known about the three or four small children of Jim and Lillie May's and remembered hearing about the old man's death. Normally, she would've done like she always did in times of mourning. But she used excuses like some pious hypocrite. When she read Jim's short obituary, she became their judge and jury. Now her own words came back to haunt her. Why did this young woman marry a man old enough to be her grandfather, let alone have a pack of children by him? Effie had tried over the years to blank out even the memory of what she'd thought.

She gripped her rocker's arms and let it come slowly forward as she recalled her pious statement: "The witch girl had better give herself one of her OWN readings of the future!" she had said. *Why didn't I help this family in grief and need?* She knew and admitted to herself the reason why: FEAR—fear of what she saw at that large black boiling kettle of molasses. What happened that day was not of this earth. She still could not, even this many years later, bring herself to answer Adam's inquiry about the Selfs.

Effie took a long breath, bit her upper lip, and said, "No . . . no . . . I don't recall ever hearing that name here in Dent County."

Aunt Effie wasn't lying. Jim Self was originally from Doniphan, Missouri, which was in Ripley County, two counties away. At the time of his death, he was residing in Shannon County. His widow, Lillie May, was living only a few hours ride, even by horseback, from the cabin that Adam had rented from Susie Smith on the old Bert Bealert farm.

Adam felt faint and short of breath. He thought it was because of the long intense story. Now he wished he'd kept to himself. This tale would've been better buried in the old man's head. Adam felt awkward and foolish. He stood and excused himself by saying, "If I get an early start tomorrow . . ."

Effie stood up. She raised up on her tiptoes and kissed each of Adam's bearded cheeks. Her tears flowed down into the silver white hair leaving two small damp spots. Later, as Adam lay across the bed, still in his clothes, he felt where her tears had saturated. The tears from his own eyes mingled with hers as thousands of images from his past flowed through his mind.

chapter
FOUR

Adam's Last Chance

Just as the sun burnt its first early rays of the new morning, swathing the earth in her light and warmth of life, the old silver-headed mountain man had already been up two hours waiting for Buddy—Cousin Buddy, as he was called by the locals.

Cousin Buddy drove the one and only jitney of Salem. It was an old Star half-ton truck referred to as a pickup that doubled as an ice delivery and soda pop truck. It delivered goods of all sorts: coops of fowl, swine, and even a horse one time. Actually, Cousin Buddy wished everyone would forget about the horse delivery since the poor creature fell through or stomped through the old Star's wooden bed slats. The bed's steel spacers kept the horse's belly held flush while her legs made contact with the road. The 27 miles of friction over rocks and gravel would've been hard on the mare's legs if only there had been any legs left to inspect at the end of her ride home. Her owner had taken her to the county's renowned stud and left her there until she was bred. He'd paid high for the boarding and stud services. He held great anticipation for her foal, until Cousin Buddy pulled up to her waiting family and master's front gate. Then there ensued one hell of a commotion to the rear of the machine that was entrusted to his care.

Cousin Buddy had a one-track mind. When he drove, his eyes never strayed even for a split second from the bull's-eye—his half of the road. This is why the owner of the truck and proprietor of Salem Ice & Pop had created his own bumper, front and rear. He had the city garage and welding works, formerly the village blacksmith and wagonwright, weld extra heavy-duty steel braces fore and aft to the Star's frame. Then he went to the local sawmill and lumber company where he purchased the bumpers: two winter-cut second-growth white oak 7X9 tie cuts that had been sawed from the heart of a butt cut. This way Cousin Buddy could hit range cows, horses, or 400-pound hogs wallerin' in the middle of a back road or city street. All the damage that would ever get done was jar some of the thick green snot off of Cousin Buddy's thick handlebar mustache. The mustache wasn't worn for fad or looks. Its sole purpose was to catch and hold the thick green sheep's leg that ran from the wide flaring nostrils, resembling a chimpanzee's in formation, above the wide mouth and protruding jaw. One couldn't keep from staring at Cousin Buddy. Anthropology scholars would've taken one look and been sorely tempted to claim they'd found the missing link between man and ape.

Cousin Buddy would argue to his dying day he "never kilt the damned ol' mare. Hit wuz her owner. He's the one that shot 'er betwixt the eyes right in the back o' the pickup truck." Cousin Buddy still had yet to figure out that a horse had to have legs to load and unload on the bank that he'd backed up to in front of their yard gate. It took the rest of the daylight hours for the farmer to hoist his dead mare up high enough for Buddy to drive away. The mare then swung from a huge, straight limb of an old post oak that stood in the barnyard. The limb was mainly used at butchering time, either to swing beefs to be skinned or swine to be gutted after they were scalded and scraped.

Cousin Buddy never lifted a hand during this or any procedure. He felt as a great sea captain or latter-day airplane pilot. He only piloted his ship on course to its destination. All manual labor was left up to its owner, even for most of his city deliveries of blocks of ice and cases of different flavored sodas. It was especially true for the fall deliveries of coal when Buddy would develop a series of mysterious seasonal ailments: back, knees, elbows, wrists, and hands, any and all of which were liable to go out, rendering them useless for taking on the large, steel scoop shovel's handle and shaft.

Coal delivering time is when Buddy usually called upon his little brother, who everyone referred to as "Tiny." Buddy could only use Tiny around town. He couldn't haul Tiny up front because there was no possible way the Star's small cab could handle Tiny's large, cumbersome frame. He buckled the leaf springs of the little truck, giving it the appearance of running aground on the passenger side. It made no difference to Tiny since no thoughts and few images were ever transferred through his large bulging black eyes clear through to his brain.

One time Tiny refused to trot along behind the old Star and Cousin Buddy knew he'd have to unload not just one load, but several. He argued with Tiny, even taking a lump of coal and throwing it at least a quarter of the distance toward the port of delivery, Salem's Drug and Soda.

Tiny rebelled. Tiny never spoke in full sentences. He just kept mumbling, "No ride, no shoveler," until his brother Buddy gave in, knowing no harm could come to his boss and master's great ship he was captain over on such a short distance.

Right from the start, the old Star had become to Cousin Buddy the magnificent ship he'd seen at Rolla's moving picture show house that his first cousin, Sheriff Leroy ("Actually, half brother AND first cousin Sheriff Leroy," the good church ladies would have said), had taken him to see. Of course, Buddy supplied the money for gas, movie for two, and meals at the General Café. Buddy also supplied two new tires for Sheriff Leroy's former car since one had blown out and the sheriff's keen eyes had caught sight of the red rubber tube sticking out of the other. He only had Buddy buy them for Buddy's own safety's sake.

Yes, his cousin Sheriff Leroy was only concerned about Buddy's life and limb. That night, they even went several hours early. Buddy was proud to tell everyone he met that he was kinfolk to the High Sheriff.

Sheriff Leroy seemed just the man for this most sought for office since he always put everyone else's life, health, and safety first.

Anyway, Tiny first started mumbling, "No ride, no shoveler," till finally he got to chanting the words at a pitch way above the usual mumble he spoke in. This started to attract a crowd of spectators. Cousin Buddy knew this type of attention would be relayed back to the great ship's owner. So, he decided to simply load Tiny up on the heap of black coal he had in the Star's bed.

Tiny mounted the Star from the left side. The truck was equipped with high sideboards and an end gate that were used only for this type of delivery. He felt the little pickup tilt and sway under his extra poundage. Tiny stood spraddle-legged aloft its already overloaded bed, held on to the sideboards, and drove his huge stump-like legs deep into the hard coal until the coal refused to pack any lower.

Then Tiny, for God knows what reason, began to shift his weight from side to side. The continually gathering audience sent him into a shifting frenzy as they clapped, laughed, and shouted out praise and encouragement.

At times, the left or right side of the overweight vehicle would become airborne, which would propel the crowd to new heights of roaring cheers and squeals, in turn further reinforcing Tiny's enthusiasm. The crowd merely added fuel to the fire and the Star would've finally flopped over on its side, but was saved when the leaf springs snapped on the driver's side. This left no momentum. The show was over. The little Star truck was crippled beyond operational movement. Its load of coal had to be transferred by wheelbarrow by the two brothers to its final destination—the coal shoot at the rear of the store.

What was considered late for Adam was much too early for Cousin Buddy as he cranked the old Star to life. He was mumbling under his breath, taking the back of his hand and swiping at the gray, green goo that had collected in its catcher—the thick, stiff handlebar mustache that now drooped over his lips under the weight of the flowing mucus. Buddy then entered into a fit of coughing and sneezing that brought out long streamers from his nose and mouth till even Adam had to look away.

Finally, when Buddy got control of his flow, he climbed in under the wheel, set spark to gas, and lunged away. The cold engine coughed and spluttered. The cylinders kept firing faithfully under the weight of the turning wheels. They were on their way. Cousin Buddy knew exactly where the old man wanted to go. He'd spent days, sometimes up to a week or two (if his Uncle Riley would permit him to stay), in the same vicinity playing with his second cousins, Osrowl, Cletis, and Clytis. He'd only leave when old man Riley put his foot down and demanded that Buddy chop wood or do any kind of work for his vittles and bed. This always moved Buddy down the road in search of greener pastures that didn't require any mowing, maintenance, or physical effort of any kind.

Adam was always amazed at the ground one of these automobiles could cover in so short a time. By horse, this trip would've taken the better part of a day. By foot, a day and a half, if one stepped out. In an automobile, he could be on the banks of the Current River in three hours. This was as far as a traveler by motor vehicle could go. Adam would then paddle the wooden johnboat across, putting him within a quarter mile from his cabin on the Bert Bealert place.

They had made a little over half the distance to the ford landing when the old man knew there was something bad wrong. Buddy was heavily concentrating on keeping his vessel trained on the bull's-eye, but the truck was swaying and weaving something terrible. Adam knew he was going to have to break the silence soon or be piled up in a man-gled heap of rubber and steel. He could even smell hot rubber. Adam then did the one thing one was supposed to never do when Cousin Buddy drove—*speak*. Buddy couldn't drive and talk or be talked to while he struggled to keep the old Star on course.

"Buddy, you've got to pull 'er over! Hell, man, can't you see there's something wrong?"

Adam had to shout above the engine's roar since Buddy had knocked the muffler off its pipe in one of his last bouts with the road's bar pit. He had just got 'er under control at Adam's shout. The shout brought Buddy's eyes off the bull's-eye. When his head turned toward the speaker, so did his hands that held the Star's steering wheel in a death grip. Buddy automatically steered whichever way his eyes focused, and he was now looking through a partial stand of pine and blackjack oak. The oak was old and gnarly. The pine had seeded among them years later making the pine tall and slick. The smaller pines reached the same height as their older siblings, but were only inches through. This helped Cousin Buddy's ship come to rest. Its strong 7X9 white oak front bumper mowed down the pine until the old rig was brought to a halt. No harm came to either of the two within. And very little harm came to the old Star thanks to the farsightedness of its owner and the oversized bumpers.

The old Star's engine had died on its first encounter with the young pine saplings. This was extremely lucky for Adam. In his excitement, the captain of the great ship had the accelerator pedal pushed flush against the floorboard with his right foot. The left foot had curled backwards and hung under the seat. Both of Buddy's hands were gripping the steering wheel with such force, it took some time before Buddy could relax enough for Adam to pry his fingers open and away.

Adam got out and expected the driver to do the same. Cousin Buddy never budged, even after Adam told him he had a tire slipped on its rim. The tube was ruined beyond repair. He could see a good portion of it hanging out from around the steel rim. Buddy sat staring straight ahead like he was expecting the gravel road to appear again before his eyes at any minute.

Adam had started feeling his old self again. His strength was returning like the morning tide over the last week. This made him anxious to get back to the little rented cabin on the Current River. Then he would pack, say his goodbyes to the fine Smith family, and be on his way to Doniphan, Missouri in search of Jim Self.

As soon as he discovered the pickup's spare tire was flat, he walked around to retrieve his old willow rawhide pack. It had bounced from the tailgate up toward the cab on the driver's side. This put him face to face with Buddy, who was still staring straight ahead. The snot had flown out of his wide nostrils as it always did when things made him nervous.

As Adam looked at him, there was a forgotten memory from long ago that flashed through the old traveler's mind of boxcar loads of sheep he had seen in Arizona. They were from some northern state. The ride had either given them distemper or they'd already been infected and their long ride had given the sickness a chance to really take hold. The sheep looked something like Cousin Buddy—long streamers of gray-green mucus running out of their noses, hanging, dangling in the slight breeze before the goo was pulled by gravity onto the wooden bed of the cattle cars. Buddy simply sat letting it run down the front of his shirt. *Damn*, Adam thought. *Maybe we did spring from apes like that Darwin feller's theory says.* He'd read and laughed about Darwin when he was recuperating. He looked at Buddy again. *Yes, maybe, just maybe, here sits the missing link!* He laughed and slapped his leg. He told Buddy he would walk the remaining distance of 12 or so miles. Adam also told him to tell his boss not to worry about the fare—it was fine. At least this way he wouldn't have to look at the young man's snot-covered face ever again.

Adam's laugh brought Buddy back into the real world. He leaped out, ran to the rear, pointed toward the ruined tire and declared to the world, "We have a blowout. We've gotta change 'er. Yessiree, WE'VE gotta get 'er off."

Adam, too good for his own good, put his pack back into the little truck's bed and accepted the tire wrench and tool Buddy was so perfectly willing to hand him. Adam took the lug wrench and handle, which would be used as a tire tool later to help break down the spare that had to be fixed also. Buddy informed him that the spare had been a running tire last month, but it had gone flat. He'd been "too busy and overworked," and never got around to repairing it. He then let Adam know that as soon as he had the spare broken down, mended, remounted, and ready to be aired up, he would have caught his breath enough to be able to get up off the rock he'd perched himself on and find the air pump for Adam to use.

He told Adam he'd first better break the lugs loose before he jacked the Star's ruined tire off the ground. Adam told Buddy to go fetch the jack. This command made Buddy remember he'd left the jack leaning up against the icehouse's wall last month when he was ordered to fix the flat tire. "We ain't got ary un. Hit broke."

Adam figured he'd break all the lugs loose first, then fix the spare. After everything was ready, he'd find a suitable long pole and large rocks to raise the light rear end of the pickup. He grinned to himself, thinking this was one job Cousin Buddy could do and do well—sit on the end of a pole.

Adam commenced breaking the lugs loose while Buddy sat on his rock. His wide chimp mouth broke into a grin, actually altering his facial expression, which occurred as seldom as a blue moon. His eyes even lost a little of their dull, dead look for a moment.

Adam heaved with all his might, putting legs, back, and shoulders into action. He strained with his arms, locked hands and fingers that were curled around the tempered handle of the lug wrench. This was the last lug nut and as usual the tightest. Adam put out everything he could muster. It broke with such force, he was thrown through the air holding the wrench's handle.

The old man landed hard. When his head cleared, he still felt what he'd feared—the familiar sharp, burning pain once again seared through his chest and he couldn't draw air into his lungs. He heard Cousin Buddy laughing and talking. Through a dense fog, Buddy's snot-covered idiotic face appeared before Adam's. Even though he figured he was about dead, the old trapper grinned, thinking, *Yes, God, if this is my dying look, I reckon I've already paid my dues to hell.* This thought made him chuckle weakly.

When Buddy heard Adam laugh, he thought it time to tell the old man the joke he'd played on him. Buddy explained, saying, "Mister Troop, ye suppose to o' used the cheater pipe o'er the wrench handle." Cousin Buddy then gave one of his rare idiotic laughs that turned his face into the missing link of Darwin's as Adam slipped into unconsciousness.

chapter
FIVE

Postcard from Venezuela

The mail carrier made two runs a week, usually Tuesday and Friday. This week, for personal reasons, he had to make the run on a Monday. This was fortunate for Adam. The mail carrier was likely to be the only one to come along before nightfall when the delivery truck's owner would come in search of Cousin Buddy. George, the mailman, had been seeing sign for some time and thought one of the "good ol' boys" must have been on one hell of a drunk. He could see where the auto's tires had left the road, plowed gravel and dirt, mowed down dead weeds and grass, then swerved back on the gravel roadbed once more, only to repeat the pattern.

While rounding a curve, George's eyes caught sight of what he'd been looking for. The rig had cleared a trail through young pine saplings. Another 50 feet and the rig would've gone over a sharp drop, then rolled down the ridge to the hollow's bottom.

After walking a short distance toward the vehicle, he recognized it as the Salem jitney and delivery truck. George said aloud to himself,

"What in the hell is in old Ben's head letting Cousin Buddy drive when he literally ain't got enough sense to blow his nose?"

Then he smiled thinking what he'd heard so many times whenever Cousin Buddy's name was mentioned. Aunt Sarah Jane Harper was the midwife at Buddy's bornin'. Just as the woods colt popped out into the cruel world, the pregnant girl's mother elbowed her way in and screamed down at her daughter, "I want to know who's the daddy o' this'n?"

Aunt Sarah Jane never looked up as she tied the naval cord for cutting and said, "Law, woman, how could she tell which briar stuck the deepest when she run through a briar patch?"

Well, a young man named Ben knew his briar had been there plenty of times. The girl's mother even came around threatening Ben since the girl was way under the legal age to be married, much less bred. Ben made it right. He took and raised the boy, even gave him his name—Cousin Buddy.

Adam was lying where he'd fallen and had become somewhat conscious. Whenever George talked to him, he answered back in Cheyenne. George took it that Adam was addressing a class. He'd already figured that the old professor, in his semiconscious state, thought he was teaching one of his Latin classes. George knew five or six Latin words and spoke them to the old gentleman. Each time, Adam answered back in the foreign language. This impressed George. He'd heard so much about the professor who not only was an engineer but a famous geologist and renowned cave explorer. George had even taken time to try to meet Mr. Troop. On every calling, there had been someone else occupying the professor's evening. On one morning call, George knew he'd have the "front row." But Ma Terrill had taken "all seats." He even stayed until Ma dragged Adam down to Salem Furniture and Hardware. It was at this point he gave up on ever having the chance to let Adam know about his first and only love—rocks and caves. He was in hopes of sharing some of the caverns he'd discovered over the last two decades.

George turned on Cousin Buddy, demanding, "What in the hell have you done to the professor?"

Cousin Buddy figured the old man was a goner and he'd better cover his ass. "I ain't done nary a thing to the ol' bastard. I wuz a-breakin the nuts loose on the flat casin'. Next thing I knowed, he wuz a-layin' down thar on the ground. I jest figgered the ol' lazy effer wuz takin' 'im a snooze while I worked."

Adam fooled Buddy as he had so many in the last month. He pulled through again, weak but able to sit up and regain his bearings. He even introduced himself. The mail carrier asked, with heartfelt concern, what Adam thought might have brought on his attack. When the old man told of the stuck lugs, then the wrench handle having slipped out of its end under the extreme pressure he'd been applying, George never said one word. He just reached over, grasped Cousin Buddy's snotty shirtfront, and slapped Buddy twice—HARD.

The blows made the snot fly. Cousin Buddy knew what the treatment was about. George had already started feeling guilty for doling it out, and knew he'd better get the old professor loaded up in his Auburn before his guilt overrode his better sense and he ended up repairing this lazy fudger's tire himself.

As the two walked away, Buddy hollered, "Hey, what about me?"

George never looked back. He simply yelled, "We're going the wrong way, Buddy!"

This time Adam's stroke left visual sign, affecting his right side. His hand had lost most of its strength and movement, his eye had closed, and his mouth was drawn down, giving Adam a completely different appearance to those who'd made his acquaintance prior to this morning. The old man knew he wouldn't recover from this one.

George was one of a kind. He'd amassed so many questions—hundreds of things he always wondered and tried learning about through mail order books and literature, but these only confused him more. Here he had the key to all his questions, but would not, could not, ask.

Adam sat, at first, up front in the car's big comfortable seat. George then pulled the big Auburn over and rearranged his mail load. He helped the old sick gentleman from the front to the deep, plush back seat. Adam was too weak to try to refuse help as he would have other-wise. He was always the one doing for all, not asking an aught, giving freely when he couldn't afford to.

On this morning, Adam broke lugs that would take a three-foot cheater bar to loosen in the hands of most men. Hours later, his legs couldn't carry his own weight without assistance. And assist George did. He was as the Adam of old, taking charge when a crisis arose.

George drove as close to the river ford as his car would allow. Here, he left Adam asleep and went on foot to the river's edge. As per usual, when needed most, the wooden johnboat was at the opposite bank. He removed his shoes and clothing and plunged into the cold, swift Current.

George was an old pro at this. He'd made many crossings and knew to go upstream, giving himself plenty of leeway in case he took cramps. This had happened once years before and would have cost him his life had there not been a piece of driftwood nearby afloat that he was able to grasp onto.

The mail carrier hit the water in a shallow dive, wanting to get the shock of the river's cold water over with as soon as possible. He felt the current starting to catch and pull him so he stroked with all his might, wanting to clear its force before he came even with the tied boat.

As soon as he was safe in the old wooden johnboat, he bailed it down until its hull rode high. He then set to paddling upstream, holding close to the Current's edge. Judging again, he repeated the crossing, dressed, crossed again and returned the boat to its moored position. He then headed toward the log fort house the Bealerts and Smiths called home.

George knew how to walk. When he first started his mail route years before, he delivered on foot. He then graduated to horseback. Now it was motor vehicle, which made the work faster. At the same time, life was emptier. It had lost something. The loss outweighed the gain, even on cold rainy days. It was especially during the first snowfall that he felt the hollow feeling due to the loss of his delivery horse's ride.

He was suddenly startled by a young girl on a little chestnut mare. George and the mare sidestepped simultaneously. The girl pulled her mare up to a sliding halt, not recognizing the mail carrier. He'd deliv-ered to the Rector post office throughout Jennie's short life and had been one of her father's pallbearers three years ago. He'd always liked the girl for her wit and spunk. She had whirled the little Arab mare so sharply that Bird stood momentarily on her hind legs as though she was going to walk upright. Then, quick as a flash, her rider leaped her forward. The mare blocked George in the narrow trail. The little mare's rider had a small pistol in her right hand, bridle reigns in the other.

Jennie, seeing who it was, instantly had her little .32 owlshead dropped back into her saddlebag. Both pretended it never happened. The girl spoke first, always having the knack to put things right.

"George, don't tell me you've lost your big shiny limousine and it's strayed over here on this side of the river where there aren't any roads."

The mail carrier laughed heartily, forgetting momentarily what had brought him at a long, fast lope up their narrow trail from the Welch Crossing. George briefly filled her in on Adam's condition and the circumstances that had brought it on. The girl had been hearing reports of Mr. Troop's health all along. She expected to see him again strong and well as she'd always known him.

George, seeing the effect it had on Jennie, said, "Oh, maybe the professor isn't all that bad." Then he shook his head and spoke to the ground more than the girl saying, "No, no, he's in bad shape. May not even live this night through. We'll need your horse to get him home— I mean to his cabin." The man turned and left at a fast pace with the girl and her mare keeping stride.

As soon as Jennie saw Adam, the shock of his altered appearance was too much for her. George let her cry it out, pretending to be readying the wooden johnboat to go back. After he saw the girl waking the old scholar for his river crossing, everything went smoothly. Even in what looked like the old mountain man's dying throws, he still had the grit of ten men, worrying he was putting someone out. Feebly, he'd try to persuade George to go on with his delivery, knowing that assisting him would run George late into the carrier's day, and for Jennie to be on with her trip to wherever she'd been heading.

By the time they made the short distance to the cabin, Adam's strength had waned to a very low ebb. Jennie's mother Susie and her Grandma Bealert had to talk long and hard to convince the mail carrier to go ahead and finish out his run, then go on home. They could manage Adam's sickness fine. Illness had been their companion for several years now. As Grandma Bealert walked out on the porch to fetch cold water to administer to the sick patient, Susie said to George, "Yes, it is our companion now and to come."

George walked over, looked down at the old man in his stupor-like deep sleep, then turned and walked away without saying a word. So many thoughts ran through the amateur geologist and cave explorer's head until his trip became a blur. The next thing George knew, he was back under the steering wheel of his big touring car, bouncing along the chug-filled ruts of the old wagon road that would eventually lead to the county's maintained gravel highway.

Adam was tough as an old boot, but eventually even an old boot wears out beyond repair. This time the seams had broken deep. The old trapper, bison hunter, bounty man, outlaw, professor and cave explorer had lived a life, a tenth of the adventures anyone would've been envious of. Here in his eighties, he felt he'd never done anything. If only he could "crawl back" and do it all over again.

He started thinking of the doeskin map his wife had helped him draw in his youth. In a little over one hand's worth of decades, that vast wilderness had vanished. The sun and moon had looked upon it since creation and were the only witnesses to the extraordinary changes from the time those huge bones at the ancient dry riverbed had been alive and roamed to the time he'd run into Charbonne and Sybane at the very same spot.

Adam couldn't keep from comparing the two worlds. He felt the changes that had and were to come in the next century might even be more devastating than the destruction that had brought the great beast of that age to its ruin.

His thoughts were cut short. Blackness engulfed his brain as his body fell forward out of the large oak rocker.

Jennie and brother Bob found the old drawn man lying on the floor. This put double worries on the family because their Grandma Bealert had also taken sick. She would soon become an invalid, never to recover.

Over the next couple weeks, Adam, to the children and their mother Susie, seemed to be regaining his strength. But Adam knew his clock was ticking down and he may not be fortunate enough to go on out.

Seeing the ailing Grandma Bealert, Adam knew all too well he could place this same type of burden on these fine, hardworking honest people. Even the girl would have to quit school. Adam knew from Jennie about her hopes and dreams of becoming a nurse. This was the reason she was on her little mare the day Adam came back to his rented cabin. She had to ride three days a week to Rector.

On her ride home the week before, she rode up on Osrowl, Cletis, and Clytis.

"I don't think you've ever had the privilege of meeting them, have you Mr. Troop?" asked Jennie.

This made Adam laugh, his first laugh since breaking the lugs loose two weeks ago. His hand never slapped his knee, though, as was his custom when he laughed spontaneously. Realizing that Jennie noticed this also, he said, "Girl, don't ever lose that dream. Dreams are all we have. You go over there, open the top dresser drawer, the little one on the right, and bring me the little navy blue book. Help me write what you and your mother will need to do to get this money transferred into your care."

The next half hour was spent looking in vain for the little book that contained a mountain of wealth.

It would eventually lay in their button box along with several old Spanish gold coins and a silver bullion which had been plowed out of the lower cornfield by the river years before by her father. The gold and silver would meld and return to their mother earth and the little bankbook and papers would all ascend heavenwards in smoke when, years later, the old fort house burned down. They would return to earth in their own form, both proving as useful as the other in time of need. They'd belch up their own type of smoke and fumes to be gone forever, same as the great beast's flesh and hide had perished from their large bones millenniums before.

Jennie raised from her chair to tiptoe out, not wanting to awake Adam from his doze. She had made the door when the old man cleared his throat and spoke again.

"By the way, Jennie, you and your mother are going to be taking your grandmother to see the doctor Saturday, aren't you?"

Jennie answered, "Yes," thinking Mr. Troop might need something from town. She kept standing, waiting to hear his needs.

Finally, Adam spoke. To Jennie's surprise, he said he'd met a friend, and then mumbled a name. This friend was to come Saturday and carry him to some distant place, a place she'd never heard of called Venezuela.

Adam told her that all of his relatives lived there now. "I would deeply appreciate it if you wouldn't mention this to your mother. I'm afraid it would cause her worry and she has enough with her own mother for me to heap my little complaints upon her shoulders."

Then Adam changed the subject to Mr. Mattlock who was courting Jennie's mother, Susie. He knew this would get the girl riled up and she'd forget their conversation about the bankbook till a later date. He knew by then he'd be gone and wouldn't have to answer any questions concerning the huge balance or give them the opportunity to refuse such a large gift.

"Oh, one more thing, Jennie: I did meet the Riley boys. I guess one could say sort of an informal introduction at a 'hen party' one late night." And to her surprise, Adam laughed again. It relieved her to see him laugh. She was in hopes her old friend was on the mend.

He then added, "I'll send you and little Bob a postcard when I find a fitting one."

This is the last time Jennie and her old friend Adam ever spoke.

chapter
SIX

Soaring with Su-li

Next morning before the crack of dawn, Jennie was up. She had all the morning chores done because brother Bob, little sister Imogene, and baby brother J.B. had gone with Aunt Alley Stewart two days before. This gained her the freedom to go also with her mom and sick grandma. She was young and her spirit was high. She'd never seen Rolla, only heard about the paved streets and the hospital there. She would get a chance to see a real nurse, maybe even one in uniform like she'd seen in the magazine. Her teacher had told her how to obtain materials on different topics so she could find out the qualifications to be eligible to enter nurse's training.

Finally, after months it seemed, the day had arrived—all very unexpectedly. Almost as unexpectedly as the Riley boys. Jennie could grin and feel bold about it now. As she walked with the pail of fresh warm milk, she thought back about how she'd been so intensely looking at the pretty nurse in her white, sacred looking uniform, never looking up from the picture and ad.

She had ridden right among the Riley boys before she realized it. If it hadn't been for Bird spooking sideways, Cletis would've got his hands on her. She shivered at the thought of those three vile creatures and remembered the vow she'd made that day after her escape.

Jennie had earlier heard one of the twins say, "Damn me to hell, why didn't I bring my gun?"

"I will bring my gun and it will damn you to your pagan hell," Jennie said aloud to herself, which served to intensify her determination.

Her thoughts were interrupted by the sound of a strange, eerie song. She recognized Adam's voice. This made her spirit rise even more. It soared with "su-li," the great black bird that rides higher than all the rest for it keeps gaining altitude as the currents pull it upward.

"Su-li" was very fitting. Adam's song was the death song of his wife's people, the Cheyenne.

The girl thought her old friend was happy also. She knew today he was going on a journey to meet his kin. Jennie wondered how long it had been since he'd seen any of them. She wished she had asked him when they were talking about the little book she'd absentmindedly put in the button box when she mended her blouse last night.

Oh, well, I'll remember to ask him when he returns from his visit, Jennie thought. *If he does decide to stay, it'll be the first thing I'll inquire about when I post a letter to him.* She giggled, swinging the pail of warm milk merrily as she skipped along excited and hopeful about what the future might hold for her after this day—the day she'd waited so long for. And it all came about seemingly out of the blue.

Grandma Bealert had come to her season's end. She knew, in her sickly little 65-pound frame, it was her time. All the medical profession since time couldn't save her. But she knew her granddaughter's dreams. Her little thin, drawn mouth smiled. Her deep, sunken eyes regained their old sparkle for a second as she thought about Jennie. She always saw so much of herself in this lively girl. Grinning, she reflected—yes, the part of myself I see in her I'd always fought to keep suppressed and hidden from all.

This was the reason she had decided to be taken to Rolla. After Aunt Alley had come to visit and they'd talked of Jennie's dreams, it was what Aunt Alley said that made this day happen. Grandma Bealert recalled again what the old hill woman had spoken:

"Here we are, two ol' women, no different than all them thar field crops. We done and had our season, Mrs. Bealert. The first good hard wind'll blow us o'er and we'll return to the earth. But Jennie thar is like the next season's seed. I'd shore like to see that gal have 'er a chance to be planted somewhor out o' these hills. The soil has to be richer sumwhors else. Law, I know it's took a toll on us both. It'd be something iff'n Jennie could be one o' them registered nurses. Now that's jest a chance in a lifetime and since she can read and write, I don't see ary a thing that can stop 'er exceptin' she'll never git the chance. Livin' here, first thing ye know she'll be hitched up with one o' them local boys toilin' from first light till way after dark jest to try and halfway feed a parcel o' young 'uns, never gettin' enough ahead to put clothes on their backs and shoes on all them lil' feet."

Then the old hill midwife got up and straightened her tired back. She leaned over once again and hugged the little frail woman. Both had tears in their eyes—not of self-pity, not of grief for the ailing one's condition, but tears of "what if" and "if only."

Aunt Alley had delivered Jennie's mother Susie when she wasn't much older than Jennie was now. To the old, looking back, seven decades are like the twinkling of an eye. To the young looking forward, a year seems like an eternity.

Grandma Bealert heard the tinkling of the harness bells of the horses hitched to the cart that would take her on her last trip alive to the wooden johnboat. Across the Current River, this new invention, the automobile, was waiting for them with neither anticipation, nor love, nor dread. She thought about how it never gave any sign of recognition as one approached for it had no master. Even when its cold steel came to life, it merely had an owner. Not like the horse. It has a master—it waits. The auto has an owner—it's parked. The old sick lady chuckled to herself and thought on how the world was changing too fast—was becoming too crazy to live in. "Almost as crazy as my thoughts! What difference does it make if waiting or parked?"

chapter
SEVEN

Adam's Altar

The old silver-headed man now bowed, not under load or millenniums of time as were the stalactite and stalagmite figurines that he'd seen in the cave. Adam was bowed under the curse of age. It's only release—death. He started his slow pilgrimage to see his kin once more. This would be his last journey.

Adam knew if he exerted himself, he'd be found lying paralyzed or dead. Either way, it would place more burden on the backs of these good people who were already laden down to the maximum. He had figured it out days ago to use the girl's horse, knowing Bird would return to her pasture by the log barn. He'd even fashioned a hackamore out of rawhide string from his old pack. The exertion it placed on the aged mountain man to catch up the little mare, then lead her beside the porch, was almost too much. Given his weakened condition, the porch was the only way he could mount. It was just yesterday he had ridden with the Comanche and Cheyenne who the eastern reporters referred to as the "Cossacks of the American plains." Here today, he had to mount the little mare as though he was a small child.

At the cave's tight entrance, the old trapper slipped the rawhide hackamore off the little Arab's head and slapped her rump. The mare trotted a short distance, stopped, and looked back. To her surprise, her old friend had disappeared from the face of the earth. Remembering the oats Adam had put in her feed box, Bird raced toward her reward.

There is an altar that father time has been building since the founding of the earth. The altar lies below the myriad of warriors who march on either side of the old woman and man who are bowed under their load since time. On this altar lies an old silver-headed man in the full dress of the Cheyenne. His once long, blond hair is now as white as the cold wet stone. He will lay until time indefinite. Here, there are no hours, days, weeks, months or years.

Only the steady dripping of water.

chapter
EIGHT

Snakes, Rats, and Life Forces Leaving

The old adage held true. "When the cat's gone, the mice will play." In this case, it was a snake and two rats—Osrowl, the snake, and Cletis and Clytis, the rats. It wasn't long before all in the district knew the old, rich professor had left.

Ma Terrill came to the Smith house the week after Adam Troop had gone to see his kin. She was "concerned" about his well-being and wanted to make sure he was receiving the utmost nursing care—the "same" as she'd administered to the old gentleman "in her own bed," the bed he had "ruined" and replaced. Ma Terrill would grow very excitable while telling the story of her sacrifice and suffering and all the extra labor the old man had placed upon her.

"What thanks did I ever git?" she would proclaim. "Not even a howdie do! Yessirree, the Bible sure talks of me!" she was telling the Smith family. Ma and her bunch arrived a little past 9:00 that morning. In courtesy, breakfast, or whatever meal had just passed, was offered. This was hill custom. The meal was usually refused by the guest.

274

Not so by Ma. She again launched into a loud, lengthy drama about how and why she felt compelled to take up her cross and bear its weight once more for the old man's life she'd saved. "Jest like the Lord God, yes, jest like my Sweet Jesus. I do all things fer everybody and what thanks do I git?"

As the Smith's again prepared breakfast, Ma Terrill was still talking, pausing only to catch her breath. The Smiths soon realized that Ma Terrill never heard a word that was spoken by anyone else or even noticed when any of the household departed or entered. Susie and daughter Jennie soon had the dozen visitors' breakfast feed prepared. They consumed a mountain of pancakes, eggs, a whole large ham, just shy of three gallons of milk, plus several quarts of home-canned juices.

After all the belching and nose blowing ended, Ma let them know in her own "humble" way that they could expect to have the honor of feeding her clan dinner. So, Susie sent Jennie and Bob out to the chicken house to kill and dress ten fryers. They'd managed to raise 100 this year. After Adam left, over half of them disappeared with no sign of varmints—unless they wanted to take into account the Riley boys' boot prints in the chicken lot's soft dirt.

It was a long, long day. Grandma Bealert took a turn for the worse that morning. To make matters worse, they had Ma Terrill sitting in the large parlor rocker shouting in her piercing voice until the inside of their heads became sore from her continuous bellowing.

Jennie's Rolla trip had found her a companion. This new acquaintance wasn't in human form. It was her own inner being, her teenage girl imagination. When the stress of overwork in the fields and sickness at home became too great, she would delve into the temporary world of make believe to make things aright. She looked forward every evening to going over the materials she'd obtained in Rolla. It helped to keep her little vessel afloat and on course, and kept the flame of hope alive—the hope of being accepted for nurse's training.

In this, Grandma Bealert was Jennie's ally. The old woman was the only person Jennie felt she could turn to who would understand. But now, her ally was lying on her divan of illness, more dead than alive. The little sick woman, always strong of spirit, lasted out the week.

As she lay dying that late night, the Riley boys had been to a pie supper and cakewalk. They too were full of spirit—180 proof, double-run spirits. They saw the light on this late night in the Smith house. Their heads were foggy as they took turns from their own jug. Pa's jug was tied securely to Osrowl's saddle horn and out of harm's way from their merry making. When the three saw the dim light of the kerosene lamp shining through the downstairs window, it drew them as the light draws the miller moth. Cletis couldn't resist taking his rifle from its saddle scabbard, aiming at the dim yellow bull's-eye the window reflected, and squeezing the trigger. But because Cletis was so intoxicated, he never realized the rifle was cocked till he felt the kick of the stock's butt into his shoulder. The loud crack of the gun ended with the thud of its heavy lead bullet. It missed its mark of the glass windowpane and buried deep into the log wall.

This act immediately sobered the two other brothers. They set spurs to their steeds and galloped away. Cletis's riding mule following suit without any command from her rider.

Jennie had relieved her mother a quarter hour earlier. Susie was worn out mentally and physically with family sickness, death, and debts that came with the passing of her husband and father. Susie's father, senile and delirious, had also taken all things of value: gold, silver, paper dollar certificates, and jewelry and hid them from the "bush-whackers." This placed them into destitution. Susie was close to a nervous breakdown for lack of rest. It was the first time Susie had left her mother's bedside for three days and nights. She collapsed into a very deep sleep.

Jennie was the only one who heard the crack of the rifle and the sound of the bullet's lead ball striking the old fort's thick pine log wall. She never moved as she heard the animals' hooves pounding the earth in the Rileys' hasty departure. The species of giant timber from which the walls were hued had been wiped out two decades ago. The bullet's life force penetrated deep into the once live timber. Each was dead now, gone forever, neither to do good nor evil.

These were the thoughts going through Jennie's distraught mind as she closed her grandmother's eyes with her little trembling tear-drenched hands. She then laid her head gently upon her grandmother's thin skeletal breast, letting the tears flow. No sound came from the girl's lips. The room, as well as the house, lay in quiet darkness since she had extinguished the lamp's low flame. At least the darkness relieved the sight of death that seemed to engulf her world since the morning her father suddenly died.

chapter
NINE

Damn Thievin' Giverment Fellers

After Grandma Bealert's funeral, the only thing keeping Jennie from succumbing to despair as their world fell apart was her hope. As debts mounted, the family decided to sell their cattle. Actually, a more suitable description would be that they were "forced" to sell. The market for the commodities they had for sale had literally "rolled away" in the form of the Michigan Log Company. The company cut all the old-growth pine, stripping the land bare. They then took up the rails and company stores, never to return—same as the large pine forest. This left the people in as poor of shape as it did the ancient worn-down mountains.

If one could find a paying market, eggs sold for 3 cents a dozen and a corn-fed fat hog, bar or gilt, $3 per 100 pounds. They had to top the scales at 300 pounds to receive the $9. Any swine that weighed less was docked according to its poundage. Then, $17 a head for 5-year-old steers and fresh cows. The cattle couldn't be sold to individual buyers. All cattle, beef or dairy, had to be sold to the U.S. government. This added to their plight, being forced to sell to the dictators. Each warlord in his own district individually set the monetary value in addition to his own standards to be met or docked. "Docking" was short for "thievery." Leave it to the U.S. government to steal, robbing widows and orphans whenever it got a chance.

And they made their chances. When the government buyer's men came, the Smiths were forced to sell by the droves. It was devastating enough to see large steers driven off at $17 a head. They then took the bulls in for nothing. There would also be no pay for dry cows. These were the cows that had no calf running by their side or were giving no milk. At this time of the year, the dry cows made up 75% of the herd. In Susie Smith's own words, "We'd spent $6,000 to get back $200."

Here they were, deep in debt. The Great Depression had just begun—so young it hadn't won a name for itself yet. For the decade it lasted, its name would be branded into the survivors' memories. The generations to come would set all standards by the conditions it left their relatives in financially, both rich and poor. The latter is what beset the masses in the cities, giving rise to the infamous meandering soup lines. In the country, many had nothing to even put into their soup. Here, once again, our trusty U.S. government was making damn sure the Smith family wouldn't have anything left for their pot.

The Smiths sold—or rather "gave"—their beefs to the U.S. government. Over 75% of their herd was taken in for nothing. "Taken in" was another term the government used for "stealing."

This upset the Riley clan also because they had relied on Bert Bealert's steers for beef as long as even old Pa Riley could recollect. This made Pa Riley declare openly to the Rector spit and whittlers, "Hell, we'd take one at a time as we seed fit. Then here come these damn thievin' giverment fellers and stolt the whole shebang right out from under us. What in the hell are we gonna do now fer our meat since all the hogs got collery? They're piled up a-shiverin' and dyin'. In every holler ye look in, thar they are layin' in heaps."

The old man mounted his old gray mule. Each had seen better days. Neither carried his head any higher than necessary to make the forward movement toward home.

chapter
TEN

A Different Sort of Canvas

This was a weekday and one of the three days that Jennie attended Rector's two-year school for the 9th and 10th grades. Being on her little high-spirited Arab mare, she soon overtook old man Riley. She'd ridden a little over an hour and was halfway home. The old man had been riding for over four hours going in the same direction, his place lying north of their farm. Jennie recognized the pair and was relieved it was just the old man and his old, slow gray mule. She rode on past, greeting him with respect in the hill custom. She first started to say, "Hi, Mr. Riley," but for some reason, it came out "Uncle" Riley. This showed respect for his senior age. The word "uncle" shocked the old man, especially coming from one of those "dad-bratted" Smith kids, as he always referred to Jennie and her brother Bob.

Pa Riley had always secretly liked the two youngsters. He wished his three sons were more like them—*wantin' to get ahead, takin' to the schoolhouse and them thar books instead o' the quart fruit jars o' liquor, fightin' and carryin' on.* Cletis had become intoxicated two nights before, roughing the old man up. This was fresh on the old fellow's mind. This may have been what tempted him to say what he next did. He motioned for the girl to rein in Bird. The road ran straight for the next half quarter, so they walked their mounts side by side.

The old man spoke, breaking the silence. "Yer doin' right by yerself. I'm right proud to hear yer gonna be one o' them thar doctorin' people. All I gotta say is, ye watch out fer that Cletis. The other two sons are okay, but Cletis ain't never been right in the head. Sometimes when folks are off that way, they're a heap stronger than us normal ones. Ye watch out fer him, girl. That's all I gotta say. Now, be on your way."

Pa Riley dropped his head once again, letting his long, bearded chin rest on his overall's bibbed front. The little chestnut mare raced down the worn-down trail the county called a road. Bird knew oats would be the reward for her master's ride home. She was as spirited as the girl and stretched out, hitting full gait toward the old ford road on the Current River.

The Riley clan's beef supply, driven away by Uncle Sam, turned the boys' attention toward the Smith's chicken house. It takes many a fowl to equal even a small steer. The chicken house can be compared to a cistern. Unless there is a continuous fresh supply of water, it soon runs low, then dry from the demands placed on the container.

In less than two months, Susie's chicken house had run dry. The Riley brothers had been making frequent visits with their skeleton key that fit the large, rusty lock that secured the heavy hasp to the thick, white oak door of the chicken house. There now was only an old rooster and one guinea left and neither had taken up permanent residence in the large, well built structure. The height of the tree that the odd pair of fowls roosted in wouldn't have been protection enough to keep them out of the stew pot. If it had been any of the other dozen species of trees that grew in the vicinity of the barn lot and chicken yard, the Rileys would've picked the two old tough birds' bones clean days ago. But not even they could tackle the wads of dead and living thorns that studded the tall thorn tree's body, adorning each limb to its tip.

The Riley clan lowered their standards down the food chain from beef to chicken, then from squirrel to rabbit. Now they'd hit rock bottom possum. When Pa Riley forced them out, or hunger for meat made them stir on their own, they couldn't keep from swinging by the old Bert Bealert place, always in hopes the old rooster and guinea had changed roosting trees to something more accessible. On each possum hunt, they'd shine the lantern's feeble light toward the tree. The rooster, catching the dim rays, would crow thinking it was coming morning. Then the guinea would "putt-rack" back in answer. The rooster had been hit in the neck when he was young which injured his voice box and made his crow come out sounding like, "Are they gone yet?" Then the guinea's "putt-rack" sounded like she was answering, "Not yet, not yet!"

Little brother Bob told the spit and whittlers about this one mail day. The story was made more humorous coming from a child. Before the week ended, the hilarious story had spread far and wide, finally coming back home to the Riley brothers. Osrowl and Clytis laughed as hard as the rest, but not Cletis. Cletis took it very personally. He was always overly self-conscious about people possibly laughing at him. This put Cletis into a fighting fury that couldn't be reasoned with. He decided to teach the Smiths a lesson.

The next full moonlit night, Cletis planned to take the family's single shot Stevens .22 and shoot the fowls out of the tree. He would use shorts for the load and rubber nipples as a silencer.

The month dragged on at a slow pace. It seemed even the possum had disappeared. The Riley brothers' tote sack came home empty night after night until even old Pa Riley's wrath wouldn't bring them around for the evening hunt. The moon had eaten its way into darkness and now was growing into its upcoming quarters once again.

This hunting lapse gave Cletis the time his mind needed to kindle its hatred to a roaring bonfire. He intended to burn the Smith's barn and chicken house. He even contemplated killing the boy and girl if they ran down to try and save their outbuildings.

By the time the moon became full, so were the creeks and hollows. It had been raining hard and steady with a fierce wind. The timbers and wooden roof shakes of the structures were soaked, completely saturated to the core. Burning was out.

This only fueled the wrath that possessed Cletis's dull, one-track mind as he made his way toward his destination. This was the first clear night with no rain in over a week. The moon was bright and full, as full as Cletis's head was of hate—not only for the people he imagined were laughing at him, but especially the girl and her little brother who'd brought it all to a head. It seemed even nature had sided against him. Now, it was his turn to get even. He would stop his forward march every so often, walk back and forth under the full moon's bright light, and shake his fist. He would then point his index finger, envisioning he was threateningly aiming the old battered Stevens .22 at his imaginary audience.

The rain had been rough on man and beast alike. Even the large, shaggy Airedale that Susie's sister Sammy brought down to the family had been forced to the drier interior of the barn. The earth in the barn became saturated until it broke the straw and manure dams that were holding the water at bay. It gushed through the stable and stalls, sweeping the barn's floor clean, leaving it as wet as the outside. This forced Airedale to evacuate. He took up quarters temporarily in the chicken house until the box with the bed of straw on the front porch, where he usually slept, was dry once again.

Airedale, lying warm and dry, was in a deep sleep as the muffled footsteps approached the barn lot. He was used to the sound of falling rain, so the slight sucking noise that came to his sleeping ears from the soles of Cletis's shoes didn't register at first. Then as Cletis started circling the thorn tree looking up toward its top branches for the old rooster and guinea, the noise of his clodhoppers brought Airedale fully awake.

Airedale listened at first thinking it was Bird, who so hated him. The mare's lightning quick hooves would strike his furry body when he was least expecting it. She helped him shed his born city ways of open friendliness.

Cletis took aim at the old rooster. He relied on the bright moon's illuminating glow along with the white strip of bed sheet that was tied to the end of the .22 barrel to help the moon reflect its front sight. He'd move the gun slightly, trying to adjust his bead on the old fowl. This made the strip of white sheet dance and wave in the slight breeze.

Airedale had his hackles up. The rough coat around his neck and shoulders was standing at attention, ready either to do battle or flee. Then the scent of Cletis drifted to his nostrils. He remembered this human with dread because Cletis had initiated him at his spring arrival months before. He wouldn't be as foolish as he was on their first meeting. Back then, he had trotted up, trustingly wagging the short stub of his tail. He'd let the stranger grasp his heavy leather collar that had once been a tug for a draft horse's harness. There was no breaking free as Cletis dealt out blow after blow. The man had worked himself up into such a rage it in fact saved Airedale's life. When Cletis kicked with tremendous power, his foot missed its mark—the dog's head. The foot kept traveling skyward until it threw its owner on his back. Cletis lost his grip on the dog's stout collar and Airedale fled back to the safety of his box on the front porch.

Too scared now even to bark, it was Airedale's turn to use the element of surprise. He sank his strong white long teeth into Cletis's leg muscle right below his rear at the same moment the Riley boy squeezed the trigger. The shot went wild, just opposite of Airedale's shot. The dog had hit his mark. Cletis's leg couldn't hold its owner's weight, much less the dog's poundage. Airedale released his leg hold and leaped for the white strip of sheet, tearing it from the gun's barrel. The dog was mauling the rotten, white strip of cloth within ten feet of Cletis, who reached into his overall pocket and grasped the box of .22 shorts, intending to reload and shoot the dog in the head. He placed the .22 rifle stock between his arm and side and opened the box of bullets. He felt the gun slip down and tried to recover its fall, causing his hands to fumble. The short little brass bullets flew through the night air. At the same instant the dog decided to mount another attack.

This time the tables were turned. It was Cletis who fled. The fight had gone out of him as his bullets scattered from hell to creation. The only noise that could be heard was his own panting breath and Airedale's low throaty growl.

Morning found the old tough rooster welcoming the sun's first rays of light, awakening the speckled guinea. He took to the wing and sailed to the ground, peering at the short brass cartridges. Brother Bob, with the 12-quart pail, entered upon the scene on his way to do the morning milking. They only had two cows left but there were three calves since one of the Guernsey's had twins when she freshened. This occurred after the U.S. government had driven the rest of their herd away, leaving them with an abundance of corn to feed out the young future beefs.

The young boy was trying to figure the logic behind the loss of their herd—the herd that had taken two generations to build, but one day to lose—when his eye caught the old guinea scratching and pecking at the shiny brass and lead bullets. Setting his empty pail on top of the lot fence corner post, he knelt down and started gleaning the little bullets from the barn lot's soft earth. He sifted through the yellow, crushed, straw mixed with black composted dirt that had once been the barn's floor before the week's long rain had transferred it to the outside lot.

After retrieving all the little cartridges, he stood up and, walking slowly, searched for bare patches of soft earth that had no straw impregnating the clean blocks of damp dirt. He found the tracks of the one who'd scattered the .22 shorts. To his surprise, the tracks were intermingled with Airedale's. He knew the man's boot imprint as well as he knew their own large dog's track.

When brother Bob returned to the house after finishing his morning chores, he said nothing to his mother. He'd wait until his sister came home. She now stayed with Melissa Akers, one of the three teachers of the 9th and 10th grades at Akers High School. Jennie was gone three days of each week, riding home at the end of the third day. She had to ride back the evening before "books took up." This put all the chores on her kid brother, which he could handle easily until planting and harvest time.

Brother Bob couldn't wait until school was over this day since his sister Jennie would be coming home, her week being completed. He was anxious to tell her about finding the bullets and especially, the tracks. As soon as school let out, the boy raced home. He didn't head straight to the house, as he usually did, to grab a cold biscuit and left-over breakfast sausage before starting his evening chores. He wanted to first swing by the barn lot to look for more of the .22 shorts. He'd become an instant hero to his older Stewart cousin this morning when he handed him the little bullets ideal for hunting squirrel. The shorts had plenty of power for the kill with minimum noise. His older cousin wanted Bob to search once more before the two cows and three calves stomped the lot into oblivion.

He stopped his ground search when his eyes caught sight of what at first appeared to be an old red and brown tote sack hanging from the lot's main gate. He knew he was the last one here this morning and he'd left nothing hanging anywhere, especially an old red and brown gunnysack in such an obvious place.

For some reason, fear gripped the lad. He could feel the fine hair stand up at the nape of his neck, sensing there was something very wrong, even before he understood what he was actually looking at.

There hung one of the twin calves. Its throat had been cut with such force, the vertebrae bones that held the head had been severed. Only the brown hair and a thin strip of flesh and hide held the head to its body. Whoever killed the heifer calf had skinned out its hindquarters, leaving its ribs attached to the front legs and neck. Its entrails hung limp, the guts sticking to the dirt and straw below in a pool of half-dried blood.

Brother Bob backed away slowly, his eyes glued to the grisly sight. He was not in shock of the sight of death since killing and butchering animals had been part of his life since his earliest memories. It wasn't the kill, but the manner of the kill. The little heifer calf's head had been pulverized. She'd been beaten with the bloody iron pipe that someone then stuck down her throat clean through till it was sticking out of the mangled hide's skirted bottom.

Bob felt a fear that he would know only once more in his lifetime. It would then take a full squadron of Japanese soldiers to equal this moment.

When Jennie arrived home, she listened intently to her brother's story. Even before she saw the remains of the calf, she went to the kitchen and retrieved the whetstone and the worn, thin-bladed butcher knife they used for skinning. She took the large granite dish-pan and foot tub and headed for the lot gate that held the calf's man-gled carcass. There she went to work. She skinned out the front quarters and neck and took them to the Blowing Spring. There, she washed them through water after clean water till the meat no longer colored the liquid. Jennie explained to brother Bob that they couldn't afford to let this much meat go to waste, especially now since their herd was gone and their flock of chickens had disappeared. It was either the sight of the calf's mauled head and body or the texture of the young animal's meat, but Jennie was repulsed by veal the rest of her days.

When the Rileys turned their horses and mules into the Smith fod-der patch, this was the last straw—not the straw that broke the camel's back, but the one that lit the flame that set off the powder keg.

Jennie had her brother circle the fenced fodder patch to where the wire had been cut and laid back for the Riley animals' entry. Bob secured the fence wire back in its place so the horses and mules could-n't escape. Jennie first thought of riding and shooting each beast with her Mossberg pump .22. She knew if she shot each animal through the gut wall, they would die days, weeks, sometimes months later. The low caliber bullet would penetrate, doing mortal damage. Then its entry hole would seal, the bullet not having enough power to exit on the opposite side. It would be next to impossible to locate the small lead projectile in the mountain of inflamed entrails.

Jennie caught up Bird as Bob went to the house to fetch the rifle. To the younger brother, Jennie always seemed to have the right answer. The boy wasn't so sure this time. He wished their old friend Adam Troop hadn't left. *If only he hadn't decided to go live with his relatives, Adam would know what to do.*

He was so consumed with what was the right thing to do, it seemed more like a dream when Jennie rode down on him. The girl leaned out of the saddle, snatched the gun out of her brother's hands and wheeled the mare into full gallop. Jennie felt light-headed, her body felt cold— not from the cool fall air that whipped and played with her hair, but with a coldness that comes to the killer before the kill. She was wild. The Arab felt the same rush of wildness she always gained from the girl. However, this time there wasn't the giant white oak tree to race by for the volley of shots to be fired into.

The spirited mare was not being pulled up but encouraged as they approached the weathered, sturdy oak lot gate that led into the five-acre fodder patch. To the surprise of the onlooking lad, his sister and her mare had become one in flight as they cleared the gate with inches to spare. The horse never broke stride as she landed on her feet. Bird seemed to float across the earth as she flew toward the Riley clan's horses and mules.

The wild girl raised her rifle and pumped the first death missile into its chamber. She sighted her weapon into the running herd. They were fleeing in every direction. Her rifle's bead fell on the old gray mule, the same one that old man Riley was perched upon making his slow ride homeward a few weeks ago. As she started to pull the trigger, she remembered the old man's solemn face as he commended her for wanting to be a nurse and warned her about Cletis. For his kind words and show of concern, she couldn't drop the hammer on his old mule.

The girl reined her mare up short of the gate she'd just jumped. Bob was standing there rigid, as though he'd become one of the fodder shocks. Jennie broke her brother's trance with her laughter. Bob figured his sister would start to cry any second. Instead, she laughed so hard, tears did flow, only they were tears of enjoyment. The utter joy was over what she was picturing in her head. As she explained it all to her kid brother, he too laughed till he was limber and had to catch hold of the oak gate for support. The young girl and boy would no sooner get control than each would again get to imagining what Jennie had described: the Riley boys' faces when their trusty steeds wandered their way home. They'd laugh till all they could do was point toward the barn lot and corral.

This is where they set up their art studio to express their creative talent in paint. The horses and mules would serve as the canvas for the young artist's brushes and shears. They exempted only one, the old gray mule. If it hadn't been for this old patriarch, the rest of the herd would be sporting lead within instead of lead paint on their exteriors.

The old gray mule became a Judas. He helped calm the others in the now restless herd, tolling them into the barn lot and corral.

As their paintbrushes and shears went to work, they began to appreciate what other great artists drew from their works of art. They would apply paint to one of their subjects, then stand back and admire their talent before returning to the canvas to complete the masterpiece. As their brushes worked, even their personalities and styles of speech changed. Sometimes they'd speak in phrases of French, German, or Old English, using the appropriate nation's accent—or what they thought it was, anyway. They pretended to be long deceased renowned artists, calling each other Rubens, Rembrandt, Michelangelo, and so on. The two may not have wound up so carried away with the colored lead oils and shears if they hadn't gotten so into character with speech and song as the paint flew and the hair fell.

On some of the poorer horses and mules, hipbones that protruded the highest became mountains topped by white snowcapped peaks. The backbone was colored in to represent the foothills. At the withers and neck, houses and buildings of every description sprung up on backgrounds of green fields populated with daisies and sunflowers growing along brooks. Then they'd gob drops of blue paint representing rain with yellow zigzag streaks of lightning bolts erupting from gray clouds with black circling buzzards and flying crows above and below.

Cletis's prized riding mule was left for last. She was painted in the fashion and form of a fine lady. They'd held back the quarter inch of hard, almost dried red paint that was pooled in the bottom of a rusty quart can. It had been hoarded back, along with a dozen or more different-sized rust-sealed containers. The pile of paint cans had accumulated over the last three decades, either by purchase or gift from one friend or family member to another. They came to final rest up at the old Bert Bealert farm, never to wander again from the grand heap they were now stacked in at the back of the woodshed. Here they would have lain, drying and hardening, had it not been for this glorious day of expression for man and the bothersome beasts that had upset their lives through either the devouring or destruction of their crops since their father's death. Their only break from endless worry and trouble had been Adam's short stay.

They fetched the kerosene can and gathered the special half-dried paints they'd held back especially for Cletis's most cherished possession—Kate, his gaited riding mule. With the kerosene, they stirred the hard pigments until the paint was brought back to life, resurrected once more to glorify and beautify Cletis's cherished ark.

Cletis expected to captain this ark to the biggest doin's of the year—the Old Settler's Reunion at Eminence. Cletis even had a gal lined up to go with him. She'd be the first he'd ever courted. This was the reason he'd decided to swing by the Smith place on foot to cut out his mule and his brother's saddle horses. He wanted to bring them home a couple days early in order to spruce them up. He'd gone to great pains to keep the lice and mites off of Kate's mane and tail throughout the summer just for this special fall doin's. Now, the blossoms of all his work would produce fruit all right, even above and beyond what his imagination could ever conjure up in his slow to almost stagnant mind.

Yes, he would also enter the fairgrounds with a fair maiden riding up front in his highly polished saddle, same as his brothers and their girlfriends. They'd even lined up several other couples to make the ride. It would be on October's full moon of warm days and crisp cool nights. It was such a perfect setting, even Cletis's mind worked steady. Well, almost steady. A feller such as he requires a few hours a day of blank time to keep him from stripping his cogs.

Cletis saw no sign of horse or mule in the fodder lot where he'd left them a week ago. His plan was for the animals to use the sugar, starch, and protein from the cane to gain stamina, strength, and weight. This was especially true for their riding stock since the big doin's was in the making. He saw that the fodder patch's fence had been mended where he'd cut it. He was pleased to see most of the shocks had either been consumed or trampled and was satisfied all had gone according to plan. Wouldn't his brothers be surprised when they saw their riding horses! They'd have to take their hats off to ol' Cletis, thanking him for his foresight when their steeds were packing the extra weight of the girls—especially Clytis, since his gal was on the hefty side. Clytis had to switch to the tall, big-boned bay since he started courtin' just to pack the weight and there was plenty of weight on the bay's back when she straddled its withers.

"Yep, the fodder . . . the fodder . . . the fodder . . ." echoed in Cletis's head like a Victrola with a stuck needle on a record. He then caught sight of their herd grazing in the distant river bottom's grassy field. He shook his head hard to try to clear his vision. He slung his beefy head once more like a bull does before the charge. Then he himself charged forward, runnin' like a blue racer, hoping the scene before his eyes would dissolve like a mirage upon approach.

It wasn't a mirage. It was the expression of two none great young artists. Their lone beholder was now on his hands and knees pawing the earth, making the inhuman sounds that emanate from the insane.

He would leap up in the air, then in spread-eagle fashion fall flat. Then he'd roll up into a fetal position—crying, laughing, cursing God, man, and especially children of all ages when he gazed in a stupor at Kate, his pride and joy riding mule. The valiant steed, Kate, that was going to carry him on his first and only date to this year's big event, stood arrayed and adorned, painted resplendently with red full lips and large white circles around her eyes. Her roached, arched mane was a brilliant blue. She had yellow stockings with black checkers that were held in place by a green band and small red ribbon. Her body had become Joseph's coat of many colors. This was her evening gown. Setting it all off was the bright, sun-yellow tail that had been sheared and shaved to resemble a lion's. The underbelly was a lesser yellow because the young artists ran low on yellow and had to add the last of the white paint, which had been heavily diluted with the remainder of the kerosene. This amplified his horror to greater heights. The patch of oil on the belly seemed to make Cletis come to full pitch in his bellerin', declaring to the heavens the revenge he would wreak and destruction he would bring to the soul and property of the evildoers.

After Cletis got control enough to quit bellerin', leapin' in the air, and pawin' the earth, he caught up Kate and his pa's old gray mule—the only animal that wasn't a walking mural. The Judas that had helped the young artists toll the others into the barn lot would now help Cletis march the painted troop toward home. This short distance gave Cletis time to regain a minute portion of sanity. He held it in until he dismounted in front of their cabin. He was still in such a worked-up state, he never even saw the new black A model Ford parked proudly in the front yard. It glistened from the rear chrome bumper reflecting the sun's rays as would their small parlor mirror.

Cletis came from astride of his mount of many colors. He stood eye to eye and saw once again her gown of glowing array, accented with the bright sun yellow tail and light ivory belly. As she turned her head toward the unfamiliar shiny black metal box with glass windows, her full red-painted lips seemed to turn into a smile, making the white circled eyes dance as she walled her large, dark brown eyes, showing the whites of her eyeballs. She shook her head to rid herself of a deer fly that was pestering her long tapered ears. This made her blue, roached mane ripple like prairie grass before the breeze. The last of the late summer-hatched horseflies buzzed lazily around her hocks, causing her to stomp her small mule hooves, which showed off her new yellow painted stockings held in place with green bands, accented by the small red ribbons.

The dozen other beautifully painted horses and mules grazed at the overgrown yard's grass and weeds. Their kaleidoscope of mixed colors made Pa Riley's plain unpainted mollie mule stand out like a sore thumb at a banjo-pickin' contest.

Pa Riley walked slowly toward the horses and mule. He heard his oldest son Osrowl ease his hickory split, cane-bottomed chair's legs to the rough-sawn planks of the porch's floor, settling his perch good and square, before he attempted to move.

Finally, he drew his tall, lean, gangly form up. He even squared his naturally humped shoulders, rising on his tiptoes. Then, as if on cue, Osrowl and Pa Riley laughed, clapping their hands as their laughter rang out. This made the horses and mules stop their grazing and turn with heads held high as though they were young recruits at attention, blowing their wide-painted nostrils. A few walled their heavily made-up eyes making it all the more hilarious to the old man and his oldest son.

They were the only ones present since Clytis had gone out also in search of his mounts the same morning. Poor Cletis wasn't conscious of any life forms. His eyes kept transferring Kate's image to his foggy brain, then the brain made the vocal cords bring forth unearthly sounds. First came a high-pitched note that would break in its middle. Then it would settle down into a low, gurgling growl that tapered to a moan. Cletis's grunts and growls, mixed with Pa Riley's high-pitched laughter, produced such an uproar the animals were kept at a rigid attention. Osrowl slowly circled their whole herd, ending back up next to his old Pappy who was still studying the distinct art layout of each animal.

Seeing Osrowl standing by his side, Pa Riley pointed to his old gray mollie and said, "She's shore plain, ain't she? Yer ol' hosses are really shinin' boy, I can tell ye!" then went into another fit of laughing and coughing.

When the old man finally got control, Osrowl spoke. "Hell, I always wanted a paint! Now I got one that can top any in these here parts!"

This statement sent their old Pa into another seizure just as Clytis arrived. Clytis thought his Pa and Osrowl were pleased. They were hoorawin', commenting, and pointing like two critics walking through an art gallery. He figured they must have had a hand in making these masterpieces. He even mistook his twin brother Cletis's moans as exclamations of delight.

As Clytis walked among these live art works, he declared aloud, "By Gad, iff'n they's a-givin' away a cake fer color, we damn shore got 'er by the horns, boys!"

Staring at his tall, leggy bay gelding, he spoke in a low tone, more to himself than his family. "You musta used two gallons o' paint to get 'er all drew out. Hey, ain't that building on his ass the Eminence court-house?"

This last statement was too much for the old man and Osrowl. They grew weak with laughter, clutching ahold of one another for support. Cletis was down on all fours, pawin' and bellerin' once more, throwin' dirt and grass up into the air that landed back on his head and out-stretched body as saliva ran from his foaming mouth.

chapter
ELEVEN

Jennie's Shaky Foundation

Two months had come and gone. The Indian summer was still holding on at the end of November. Jennie and brother Bob had been keeping busy with their late fall harvest. They also started a Bible study with the two missionaries who now lived in the cabin formerly occupied by Adam. Jennie, for the sake of herself, couldn't understand how she'd gotten involved in this latest episode, especially since neither she nor her family were believers. Even her mother had become a follower after Mr. and Mrs. Payne cranked up their small hand-operated Victrola. It was spellbinding to hear a voice coming out of the small, square wooden box. As though by magic, the needle brought forth the deep speaking voice from the spinning, flat record. When one side was finished, the missionaries would flip it over and give the box's crank several turns while the listeners remained mesmerized by its spell. This would again start the deep, soothing voice that talked about death and the grand hope of the resurrection of all the dead.

Jennie told the kind little man and woman that her father had been preached to hell to forever burn in brimstone and fire and that's where she wished to be also. She knew these words would elicit just the shock she wanted, ensuring she'd hear no more about their Sweet Jesus.

The little man's face grew twisted, looking quite comical. Jennie knew he was going to cry. He even bit his lower lip and his small frame slightly quivered till it shook. He turned abruptly, trying to hide his grief and tears.

Mr. Payne couldn't hold it in another second. Despite his valiant effort, the tears came. His laugh was not what one expected from someone of such a modest build. His God sure gave him a Herculean noise for his laughter. It came from so deep down in this little man that it became contagious. Now his wife and Jennie were laughing just as hard. The girl wasn't sure why, but it seemed right. It seemed good.

She laughed, then later cried, not in the presence of the man and woman, but that night as she lay in bed in her cool, dark bedroom. She cried a hollow sick cry—the kind that comes with no sound, no relief. Jennie had become a stranger to her own beliefs. The speaker's voice from the little white oak box, with its cast iron crank handle, had thrown her for a loop. In just a few short minutes, it had torn down the strong wall she'd built up, depended on, for the last three years since her father's death.

The earth kept spinning precisely on its axis, keeping the laws of the universe throughout the night. It labored toward the morning sunrise that cast its first yellow rays in long golden shafts, catching the night dew droplets that clung for life on the last of the Indian summer's foliage that refused to give up life and go into dormancy. They in turn glorified the birth of this new day by giving forth a kaleidoscope of colors as the light reflected off the dew that gave their benefactor another day of life.

Jennie's feet perceived none of this glorious grandeur. Thousands of moisture droplets had soaked through her dry, worn-out clodhoppers that turned up at the toes in ski fashion. They were several sizes larger than her small size 4 feet that trudged along through the wet grass and brown dead weeds carrying the 12-quart galvanized milk pail, half full of white, warm liquid crowned with two inches of foam.

Three tabby kittens followed along behind, getting as wet as the girl's old worn boots. The calico mother cat sat in the barn's stall window. She knew there was no use walking the long, wet distance back toward the old fort house since their kind were fed only at the barn in the ancient bone-colored gravy bowl. It would be filled to the vee that had been notched from its top rim lifetimes ago. This vee would dictate the portion of warm, life-giving fluid that was metered into the container every morning and night. The only extra milk they ever received were the long, well-aimed streams the girl or boy would occasionally spray their way. This was the reason they learned to line up side by side, as soldiers standing at parade rest, in hopes of this special treat, only breaking formation after the long white stream of milk came their way no more. The milker would then return to aiming the streams with force toward the bucket's bottom as their work-seasoned hands gripped and squeezed the Guernsey's milk-swollen udder. The foam would rise like the head of a good draught beer, coming to the pail's top, then refuse to separate from its liquid bottom. It would cling to the more stable interior, forming the appearance of fresh-spun cotton candy. This was the cue for all cats to go at-ease. They'd then see which could lick the fastest—first, the wide, hand-planed pine bench they sat upon, then one another's faces.

This show was what always drew the kind missionary woman to the barn at evening milking time. It was a setting that would lift the spirits of the most heavy of hearts. At times, she'd even sing an old ballad, her voice fine and soothing to the ears and soul.

Jennie's thoughts turned toward the Payne's as she strained the morning's milking. She was still thinking of them as she climbed the stairs going to her room to change clothes for her return trip to Rector's two-year high school. This was her last year.

She just knew the missionaries had never had trauma in their lives. They always seemed to be so light-hearted. If only Jennie had any idea of the inferno that consumed their five children and the scandal that drove the little man from his top well-established law practice.

Mr. Payne met Judge Rutherford and became a missionary for the International Bible Students. This gave the couple the hope of the resurrection, the hope that kept them going day to day. There were rivers of tears shed silently, secretively even from each other in the security of darkness when one thought the other was sound asleep. They neither burdened nor tortured anyone with their anguish.

Jennie was deep in thought trying to sort out the meaning of life and creation. Why am I here on this hellhole called earth? At least there would be no more wars. Millions had died in war at the time of her birth and infancy—a war that was fought to end all wars. The League of Nations she'd studied about was established; its power would be humanly impossible to ever be toppled by any one empire. It would bring world peace so war would be one less worry for mankind, at least during her generation. Her history teacher informed the class that in this advanced age of travel and communication, the world could better be kept under control. The League of Nations was all-powerful, right up there with God himself.

"Actually, its purpose will carry out God's will," she told Mr. and Mrs. Payne. She was reminiscing how his rare Herculean laugh had burst forth like a dam of poor construction trying to hold back a deluge.

The girl was standing on firm ground one second then was swept away before she could recover the foundation and protective barriers so carefully erected for her debate with the Paynes. As she pondered about saving the world, she was interrupted by her mare's nicker. Jennie picked up her schoolbooks and saw her pistol lying on the rocking chair's seat. It had been concealed there under the books she'd checked out from the school's library that had to be returned during this week's school stay.

She dropped the loaded pistol into her saddlebags along with her school dresses and one extra change of riding attire consisting of an old red and black plaid wool shirt and one pair of well-mended, patched overalls.

As Jennie approached her little Arab, the mare nickered again. Her nostrils threw forth two clouds of steam into the frosty morning air. This was a white frost—a killing frost—since the night air had fallen well below 32 degrees. It was just chilly enough to make her change her mind about wearing her light denim jacket. Her heavy wool plaid coat was warranted for this week's trip. She hurried back into the house and hung up the denim jacket—the jacket that held her box of extra .32 caliber pistol cartridges—and donned the wool coat.

Lately, instead of being prepared for the worst, as she usually was, she'd let down her guard. Even the Rileys hadn't entered her mind since the missionaries had arrived. There seemed always to be some topic to mull over. Before this subject could be debated, argued, and settled, it would lead to a score of others.

In less than two months, the two families—the Paynes and the Smiths—had become close, drawing strength from one another's different ways of life. Old wounds that never before knew a soothing, healing balm began slowly to mend. It seemed there was nothing that could topple them from this new foundation that had begun on such rocky soil. The missionaries patiently labored over obstacle after obstacle, carefully excavating the larger boulders of doubt that had been ingrained in the mother and daughter, sweeping away even the smallest pebbles.

Jennie had become so caught up with the bible studies she'd laid caution aside. She now considered all her former grievances petty and childish. She was comforted by this newly gained knowledge of creation in which all creatures great and small were originally created to live in love and peace. Even the lion would reside with the bull, eating straw from the same manger. Then, there was the resurrection of all the dead under this new world government that was just on the verge of being set up to bring world peace for a thousand years.

She even reconsidered entering nurse's training since all death and sickness would be eliminated, none for at least a millennium under this inspirational new government that was going to be established under God's son. At the present time, the door was open to one and all. There would be life for those who accepted this free gift; death to the rejecters.

These words had laid the snare that would almost cost the girl her life. Each time she handled her pistol, she felt doomed. Its small, blue-dyed cold metal frame threatened to damn her from this glorious salvation.

This was the reason Jennie stopped carrying her gun to school.

chapter
TWELVE

Adventure on the Way to the Old Settler's Reunion

Cletis's rage had time to ebb and flow for these same two Indian summer months. There were moments, at first, when his anger would turn into hatred, even for his two brothers. This was especially true for Osrowl since everything had turned out so well for him. Osrowl wouldn't have used his saddle horse, even if it hadn't been painted up, to attend the Old Settler's Reunion at Eminence. Cletis thought about how his own brother Osrowl had changed since he'd started working off the farm and bought that damned car. That "no 'count" shiny black flivver stood in the way of Cletis's immediate revenge.

Osrowl's latest means of transportation was in the making to change his lifestyle permanently. He took to the autos, from driving to mechanics, like a dry land duck does to water.

It was finally decided that Cletis and his string-bean girlfriend, along with Clytis and his hefty maiden, would all go the big doin's in Osrowl's new A model Ford. Osrowl was anxious to show it off, having already discovered he could tinker with the carburetor, then fine tune the spark lever at the steering column to increase its power tenfold on a long pull or steep climb. And the more weight to its light rear, the better.

He knew there'd be other owners of motorized vehicles at the Old Settler's Reunion. Some would come in cars, others in pickups with their small handy beds. But the autos he was hoping to see were the dual-rear-tired two-ton trucks. His future father-in-law was on the verge of purchasing one, maybe even two to use in log hauling to his sawmill. This way he could set up his lumber and tie mill on stationary ground, transporting the timber to the permanent site. This is where his son-in-law-to-be would fit into the picture. He craved more than anything else to be the driver of this shiny new powerhouse of a truck.

Osrowl also knew that at the reunion there'd be hours of debate over which auto was the best and would lead the way and which would fold up. This eventually would spark heated discussions culminating in an explosion of red-faced arguments. At that point the dispute could only be settled with fists and elbows a-flyin'.

There had already been two score of men who'd informed Osrowl, or rather, forcefully notified him, that he was foolish to waste his money on a Ford since young Henry Ford "wasn't even building 'em right. Hell, he was using a line of people to assemble just one rig. How in the hell does one feller know what another has done? And some had heard tell, he even used a woman or two on the line. No, you'd better stay clear of a feller like him. He won't be around long, son."

Osrowl had heard these lines so often he knew them by heart. He even knew exactly when the teller was going to purse his mouth, spit, and shake his head. Then they'd give a little low, sarcastic chuckle as they lovingly slapped or fondly rubbed their Star, Auburn, Light, Moon, Studebaker, or any other vehicle manufactured by a number of family-owned companies that have long been out of business. After they finished imparting their wealth of knowledge about the auto industry, they would end with this pearl of wisdom: "Stay with a family-owned outfit. They'll treat ye like one of their own. A man like Ford, yer jest another number, fer he's here today, gone tomorrow."

Osrowl repeated this worldly sounding wisdom to his future father-in-law. Jim laughed, saying, "Damn right! Jest like family. Sell a load of lumber to yer kin 'on the cuff' and ye can kiss its ass goodbye. Thars never even a thin dime gonna come yer way. Then, every time you bump 'em up fer a little pay, they'll get all heated up telling ye, 'Ye ain't got no money in 'er anyway. What the hell are ye squabblin' about, no how!' No, Osrowl, I want to be jest another number. I don't want the bastards to adopt me. I jest want to buy a rig or two from 'em."

Osrowl would find out through life that this was some of the soundest and proven advice to ever come his way.

Friday evening found all in high spirits except for Cletis. He was brooding even more than at first, if this was possible. He hated the car, knowing he could never master the skill of driving. He longed for the chance to repeat the words of an older renowned citizen he'd heard— that the auto was just another fad that would soon vanish because there wasn't enough road that was useable. Besides, their cost and maintenance would put a rich man into the poorhouse.

"Jest wait till the first snow or ice and ye'll be hollerin' fer me to fetch the team to pull ye outta of trouble!" Cletis would say. "Yessir, ye jest wait!"

Osrowl informed Cletis there wasn't any snow or ice tonight and wouldn't be in the near future and he'd better get himself all "gussied up." They were a-headin' out to get his gal. They would then swing by to get the other two and bring them all back to the place before they left out for the doin's. "And tell Clytis to eat, clean up, and git ready for not one but maybe two big nights, thanks to the helpless car that ol' Henry Ford built. I'll be thar and back before ye can ketch up and saddle yer mount!"

Osrowl set the spark, gave the A model a crank, and was off, never telling his sullen brother the reason they were bringing the girls back to the place was because the girls, all three, wanted to see the artwork for themselves.

Osrowl's A model returned packin' the three giggly, teenage maidens. Osrowl's gal, Nadene, had been born with a heap of horse sense. She was mature beyond her years and would eventually, in the coming future, make him a wealthy man.

Clytis's hefty girlfriend of only one night, this night, was very, very, overly sensitive about her weight, dress, looks, and life in general. If allowed, Bertha would take over the floor of conversation and harp for hours on the woes of the world and the twist of fate that had dealt her such a short, shitty hand, blasting out her complaints in order to bend every ear in and out of her vicinity.

Cletis's string bean gal, Sharon, was a box of giggles with a tendency to speak first and cogitate later. Actually, Sharon spoke first and never let the words cross her mind again since she usually was too busy giggling.

Osrowl and Clytis had temporary relief from the worry about Cletis's mood when the giggly girl leaped out of the car's back seat. Her appearance seemed to momentarily take the scowl off of Cletis—until she sniffed the air. She then had Cletis blow his breath into her face. Sharon screwed up her face and screeched, "Gawd! Yer breath smells like rotten meat! Don't ye have any mint a-growin' ye can chew on?" She relapsed into a fit of giggles and walked off demanding to see the paintings.

The word had really gotten around. The whole county had seen, or at least heard about, the Riley's troop of live artwork.

Clytis tried to come to the rescue by saying their herd had grazed their way out and probably wouldn't return this week.

No sooner had he spoken than here came the art gallery on hooves all marching toward the cabin being led, once again, by the old plain gray mollie mule. The horses and mules preferred the short tender blue grass that voluntarily grew at the north end of the cabin. It was also a shady pleasant place for the girls to observe the art. Even Cytis's hefty date of one night lost herself for the next 45 minutes as String Bean and Osrowl's future wife, Nadene, laughed and exclaimed over each grazing live tapestry.

Then, Cletis's gal recognized his own fancy riding mule. She started making comments that had his brothers holding their breath. Osrowl kept hinting at a hasty departure, but String Bean wasn't about to be budged an inch away from this exhibition until she had her say. She asked Cletis why they couldn't go on his mule to the reunion. Osrowl came to his brother's aid, saying it was too late to start out on such a long journey tonight on animal transportation. Only the motorized vehicle could make this trip.

Puffing out his chest as he took his girl's hand, Osrowl added, "We'll make it easily—long as there ain't no snow or ice."

As he added the last part, he aimed a little smirk at Cletis, which only Clytis caught. Sharon was busy telling Cletis that if they'd ride in on his gaily-painted mule, they'd look just like the gypsies she'd seen camped down at Round Springs last summer. "They had their wagons, carts, and animals decorated with paint and cloth and was right proud of it. Why shouldn't we too?"

This question caused Cletis's one-track mind to go blank, then back-track over the complete episode once more for the hundredth time. He had more than seen those damn gypsies with their fancy painted up car-avan. There was a pretty black-headed gal with sparkling dancing eyes. He later felt she'd put a hex on him. After all, what other circumstance could explain how his entire life savings, all $84.35 of it, was gone. Yep, gone. Gone as the wild goose. Just up and flew away right before his eyes. This gypsy gal had taken his hand and peered into his palm. Before you knew it, she had Cletis telling her things even Cletis had never known about himself. Cletis had a secret compartment under his saddle-bags where he kept his life savings secure from all. He didn't trust his brothers or even his own Pa with this secret, figuring the less there were "in the know," the safer his fortune would be. She was the first woman, first *anything*, to ever say the things she'd whispered to him. She did strange things to his fingers, hands, and arms, all the while telling him how strong, brave, and intelligent he was. He knew how strong and brave he was, but the last word sort of lost him. He'd figured she was speaking in her foreign tongue, until he asked her. This made the girl laugh, flashing her pearly white teeth. As she nibbled at his ear, she whispered the magic words, the words he now knew had put him under her hex. She whispered, "It means smart." The word seemed to echo in his head for hours. He remembered how her tongue at the base of his neck and ears started the steam to building just like that J.I. Case 18 at the sawmill two years before when its pop-off valve got stuck. How it trembled, huffed, and shook just before the old 18 blew sky high.

Well, his own pop-off valve worked just fine. It did seem different, lots different, than it was with that damn calf. He felt glad now about taking the iron pipe and beating the calf's head into a pulp before he skinned out its hindquarters.

Cletis was snapped out of his gypsy reverie when the voices of the rest penetrated the fog in his head. They were leaving. If he was going to come, he'd better load up.

The trouble started as soon as they commenced the loading of six adults into the little A model. They tried and succeeded in fitting Cletis and Clytis, along with their dates, into the backseat. Cletis was a hefty boy. Clytis's gal Bertha ran a 100 pounds to the foot, putting plenty of weight to the little Ford's rear. There'd be no traction lacking this night. Clytis and Cletis sat on the outside and the gals sat in the middle. This would've been fine if everyone weighed about the same. Actually, stocky built Cletis and big Bertha should've been on the outside to equalize weight over the rear wheels. But the way it ended up, it threw all the weight to the driver's side rear tire. The little A's rear spring buckled, giving it the appearance of a black dog with a game leg. This made old man Riley laugh as the overloaded car pulled out of his yard. He shook his old, white head, laughed again, and went back into the cabin as a cool nip entered into the late evening air.

Everything went fine till they hit the first creek crossing. On entering its flow, Osrowl braked the car, almost to a stop. Then, he ground the shifting stick into first. This gear was the lowest and slowest with the most power and was nicknamed "granny." This move would've been fine if only the weight to the rear had been equalized from the start.

All went well till the car hit mid-stream. There, the left tire eased up against a piece of submerged timber that some caring citizen had placed to try to fill a chug hole months before. It had accumulated a thick growth of brown and green moss, making the traction purely absent.

The car spun. Being newly acquainted with driving, Osrowl determined that the thing to do was push the gas pedal to the metal stop peg on the floorboard. This resulted in the A spinning furiously, digging out the softer earth and gravel under its high, narrow, spoked wheel.

Then he tried reverse with no success. Osrowl was hung for his first time and he knew it. Inexperienced as he was, he figured all he had to do now was equalize the weight over the rear tires.

At this point, all hell broke loose, for it was much easier said than done.

Osrowl was nervous. His main concern was to keep the engine running. He could tell the tail pipe was underwater, so he used the gas foot pedal to keep the engine revved. Then, after gaining a little confidence, Osrowl eased off, setting the A's throttle wire to keep the RPMs just above normal idle.

All sat staring straight ahead as though they were expecting the front tires would miraculously touch the opposite side. A couple of minutes passed. Osrowl and his gal, Nadene, sat close now since the driver didn't need his space to keep the vehicle on course. All the extra breathing room to the front was desired by the four who were squeezed together in the rear seat.

Nadene whispered to her love, "What now?"

Osrowl, breathing shallow, whispered back, "We've gotta equalize the weight over the rear tires. This'll give us the traction we need to go either forward or backwards."

Sharon, the string bean girl, giggled, making everyone jump as she hollered out, "Ye heard the man. Bertha, ye gotta get yer hulk over that rear tire where yer skinny man's a-settin'!"

Her ensuing giggles mixed with big Bertha's squalls as she bellered and blubbered about her weight, appearance, and dress.

Sharon, with never a thought about what came out of her mouth, blurted out again, "Be thankful, gal, about your poundage. All those pones of flesh is what's gonna get us out of this mess that Osrowl's got us into!" She ended it all in a solo giggling fit as Bertha's sobs came to an abrupt end.

Still, no one moved. Osrowl slowly and stiffly turned his head as though a copperhead snake lay at the base of his ear and was ready to strike. He loosened his grip on Nadene's hand a little and gave a slight motion with his index finger signaling Bertha to change positions with her date.

Clytis sat motionless, perched as a fowl, his rump barely touching the seat's edge. Being unaccustomed to automobiles, not one of the young people thought to have Clytis do the initial changing move so Bertha would've been free to simply scoot across the new slick rear seat.

Bertha stared hard at the interior rearview mirror as though taking a bearing on where she must land. Her breathing started out in short shallow pants. Then, as she gathered up all her strength and will, her panting grew loud and harsh.

Finally, she lunged with the mirror as her target. She was wearing her new crepe dress from Sears and Roebuck. It had full, long, flowing black sleeves with wide, white embroidered cuffs. Her outstretched arms resembled two cavalry banners in full charge and their charge was aimed at the little A's rearview mirror that was now being held in a death grip by each of her chubby hands.

Clytis still sat perched on the seat's edge, and now had even less room to move than before since Bertha was as thick fore and aft as she was from side to side. She held onto the mirror with all her might, holding her breath as though she was underwater. The poor girl had tried to get away back at the Riley's cabin to have a chance to relieve her gas she'd been holding in since Osrowl and the other two girls had picked her up for this evening's date. She'd never gotten her chance because Clytis would never leave her side for a moment.

At this very minute, Clytis was sitting under the gun—"canon" may be more accurate since big Bertha was loaded to the hilt. Under the strain, she could feel the movement of this massive gas bomb. Her legs started to quiver, working up from her swollen ankles to the knees. When the vibration went around each side of her flaring hips, her elbows started to shake. Only the grip of her hands remained firm.

Then, it happened. The laws of motion were put into effect all at once. Sharon, the box of giggles, commanded Clytis to move and move pronto. Clytis had had an upset stomach for the last couple days. He'd just silently belched up an acid burp and was trying to swallow it back down when he heard his name being called by everyone for him to move.

The only one who didn't holler out this order was big Bertha. She was still holding onto the mirror for dear life and trying to hold in her thunderhead of gas. The good trooper Clytis slid back on his seat and lunged to the left toward the narrow ribbon opening between Bertha's rear and the seat's padded back. In his startled, clumsy move, he put extra force into his lunge. This caused him to wedge between his date's rump and his brother's A model seat.

At this same instant, the rearview mirror that was manufactured for sight, not its weight-bearing capacity, gave way. Its sturdy yoke snapped with the sound of a .22 short exploded with the hit of a shop hammer. This sudden release of the strain on the now broken mirror's mount caused Bertha to come backwards with hundreds of pounds of force.

The great cheeks could hold the gas bomb no longer. She clamped them tight, mustering up her last reserve of strength. The release of pent-up gas started out with a shrill whistle. Then, as she lost all power over the situation, it degenerated into a hoarse rumble.

Clytis was penned tight and his face was in the direct line of big Bertha's gas attack. If only he'd been forewarned, he could've held his breath. But there was so much confusion with all the orders being shouted from every direction. To top it all off, he'd just swallowed the soured acidy burp.

It was all too much, even for his cast iron stomach. Clytis felt nauseated and weak. He strained feebly as an injured animal does under a deadfall trap before darkness engulfs its brain into unconsciousness. Vomit spewed forth in a long, hot, acid gush that sprayed all over the A's front, flat windshield where it hung for a second. By the time it ran down the dashboard, another volley was fired, each making a shorter run as the pressure was relieved from the sick man's feverish gut.

Clytis was still heaving—dry heaving. There was nothing left for him to spew forth. The only sounds now were the chug of the A model's submerged tail pipe, Clytis's dry heaving, and Sharon's high-pitched giggling.

Then, as if on cue, Clytis's heaving and Sharon's giggles stopped. There followed a good minute of complete silence. Everyone stayed frozen in place, whether pinned or sitting, as though they were under a spell. The spell was soon enough broken when Sharon said, "Gawd! With Cletis's breath, Clytis's puke, and Bertha's farts all bein' mixed together, it'd stink a dog off a gut wagon! Whee! Stop the world and let me off!"

Then, Cletis remembered. His slow wit tried to assemble the right words for the gouge he'd been waiting SO long to deliver. He wanted desperately to be the one this time to use the goad instead of it being used on him, as usual. He finally straightened up, glanced smugly at everyone in the back seat and said, "Ye ready fer me to go and fetch the team of horses or ye want to wait fer the snow and ice?"

This was the spark that ignited the powder keg. The next instant, fists and elbows were a-flying. If big Bertha hadn't been still hanging over the front seat in everyone's way, still gripping the mirror along with its broken yoke, there would've been hell to pay. Things were bad enough already.

When it was all over, there was the one broken mirror, one door glass gone, and the front windshield had been kicked out. The engine had died and Clytis's puke was smeared from stem to stern. The shiny new model A had been welcomed into the family.

Things kept going from bad to worse. First, as everyone piled out to help push the A out of the hole it had spun itself into, some slipped on the rocks, falling either backwards or down on all fours, eventually regaining their stance only to go down once more. The water at the ford was shallow, but swift. The engine was cold, dead, and wet. Osrowl cranked the engine to no avail. He set the spark in all positions. The fire seemed unable to connect at the right given moment. It would cough, splutter a couple licks, then die. Everyone and everything was saturated, soaked to the bone on this clear night with a full moon.

Now the carburetor was flooded. Gas smells mingled with the brisk fall night air. The owner of the auto quit the strenuous turning of the crank. The compression had kicked the handle counterclockwise several times, giving his hand and lower arm some terrific wallops. They were starting to get sore to the touch. Osrowl decided to go back to the rear tire that was hung and dig out the submerged timber. It turned out to be a buried log so waterlogged that it would weigh almost as much as his car.

Osrowl stood up, trying to relieve the ache in his lower back. He squeezed and released his throbbing hand that the crank handle had made its strikes on. "Whor in the hell is that damn simpleminded brother of mine?" he wondered aloud. "He shoulda been back by now! Damn him to hell no how!"

Earlier, Cletis had left on foot, hastily trotting home, but not out of any great concern for his companions. He was also wet and cold. They'd previously tried to push the car out. Cletis had taken the shiny chrome rear bumper in his large, ape-like hands, hoping he could put enough pressure to either bend or tear it off, not realizing it had been attached to the car's frame in such a way it would take a span of oxen to break it loose, much less a slow ox such as he.

Well, Cletis set his feet and heaved with all his might. The rock he'd braced his feet against shifted out from his boot soles. The next moment, the large hulk of a man was wallerin' and cursin' in the swift flowing shallow water. When he regained his footing, he turned from the A model and its party and waded toward the gravel bar the car had entered from.

Giggles hollered after him, saying, "Hey, Cletis! Where ye a-headin'?"

Cletis stopped, gave one of his rare laughs and shouted, "I'd better go and fetch a team before the snow starts a-fallin'!" He then turned and started out in a long turkey trot.

It was dark by the time Cletis and the team of draft horses arrived. Moonbeams spotlighted the wet, cold party huddled on the bank by their small bonfire. Each was anxious to be on their way home, all figuring as soon as the team of large stout Clydesdales were hitched to the little A, their troubles would be over. But as fate would have it, this only started a new round of troubles.

Cletis had fitted one horse with traces. The other's harness had been fitted with leather tugs. Cletis didn't bring a doubletree to attach to each horse's individual singletree which would've given them full advantage for their pull. He instead looped a short chain around each horse's hames. The chain was to be used later to attach their trace chains and leather tugs to the singletree, then to the front bumper.

This move went over like a lead balloon. Each horse could now pull separately. Despite being hooked in this fashion, they could've probably pulled out the automobile on their first try. That is, if it had been in neutral and the emergency brake lever hadn't been pulled on accidentally after Osrowl had cranked in vain and gave up on his dead, wet engine. Someone, either getting in or out, had knocked both levers out of neutral. The shift lever was in reverse and the handbrake was fully engaged.

The team danced anxiously. They were not only being hooked to this strange metal box, but were also standing on the swift shoal ford— the same ford they'd been used to crossing all their lives at a swift pace, not at a standstill. This made the horses nervous as a whore in church. They were being held in by Cletis since he was the largest and strongest. Osrowl, the car's owner, carefully inspected and hooked the chain where he figured the least damage would occur to his new silver chrome bumper while still giving Short and Dutch, their two Belgiums, the most advantage.

Ol' Short and Dutch had eaten and trampled many a shock of the Smith's rich fodder and were fully rested. The great reserves of strength and energy they'd gained from their master's wrongful entry of the fodder patch were now going to be put to use for the waiting spectators who'd left their toe fire and lined the ford's bank.

Cletis was still at the horses' head, holding them in. Osrowl had wrapped the chains in the dark shadows since the moon's bright illuminating glow couldn't penetrate his location. Feeling all was secure, he told brother Cletis to release his grip and stand clear so the A model wouldn't strike him if the horses veered on their way out. Since he wasn't using a doubletree, Osrowl had decided to rely on one set of check lines instead of trying to use both. This way only one horse would feel the command of a driver. Osrowl figured the other would follow suit. He'd a-better put this one back on the blackboard and ciphered 'er out a few times more.

When Osrowl popped the check lines on ol' Short's rump, 2,000 pounds of muscle and blood, along with a good dose of adrenaline that shot through the big strong horse, lunged forward. A large splash of water flew up from this sudden movement and spooked his matched teammate, causing Dutch to put all his force and power in the opposite direction. Dutch sprung backwards, driving his powerful wide, full rump into the A grill, making the metal pop and buckle. The silver swan hood ornament flew through the air, landing several feet downstream in the fast flowing current now being stirred up by eight large Clydesdale legs and hooves. They'd become very excited during the next few seconds; one lunging forward to the other's backward efforts.

By the time they could be quieted down enough by the three brothers, the horses had bent and broken enough off of Osrowl's "pride and joy" till it was almost ready to be stripped down to use as a means to run a buzz saw. The car was still in its original stuck position, but was now heavily customized. Osrowl had hooked the chains wide, which would've been proper, if only he'd hooked them on the outer side of the frame. But he had each chain hooked to the inside of the bumper's mounts, allowing both chains to run to the bumper's middle when the pulling began.

After they'd quieted the big brutes down, they entered the stream once more to see why the hook chains had come loose.

While the three brothers were trying to figure out what had gone wrong, Sharon giggled, hollering out, "The chains held just fine Osrowl. Ye tied 'em real good fer here lays yer bumper. Ye can use it fer a doubletree and hitch it to yer wagon! It'll be the envy of every gypsy that wanders through these here parts!"

Sure enough, the bumper had been yanked off, leaving the carriage bolts behind with part of the bumper still attached to the A's frame. The remaining strip of metal projected forward like a knight's jousting pole.

Nadene hated to see her love's feathers not just wilt, but plucked clean to the bone, and by a simple, giggly girl at that. This set Nadene's spark. She finally stepped in and went to giving orders. She made all the decisions from this night onwards and for over the next half century. Eventually, her barked commands would make her future mate a wealthy man.

But right now her immediate concern was to get her man's car back on dry land so he could bring it back to life and get everyone back to their homes. She had some of the party find and fetch a strong pole of sizeable length and girth that could stand the A model's weight. Then two large stones were rolled into place topped with a huge chunk of wood, forming a very suitable lifting device. Nadene had Bertha sit to its far end, which suspended the little light A's rear effortlessly. That is, until Giggles made one of her brash comments, making Bertha flee her roost temporarily and race toward the gravel bar, bawling and talking at once.

Again, Nadene helped big Bertha regain her footing. Bertha had only got a couple of short strides on the slippery rocks before she received another impromptu baptism.

As soon as she reestablished the anchor girl back upon her pole, Sharon opened her mouth to comment once more. Nadene turned and slapped the giggly girl full in the face, explaining that the slap wasn't for her dumb mouth, but for the close call she'd made for the others— especially Osrowl, who'd been placing a rock and a piece of flat board in the hole under the lifted wheel.

They again lifted the car. Osrowl got the rock and board in place, forming a flat, smooth surface. They had Short under control, hitching him long with Cletis leading him instead of driving. This too is what Nadene ordered, not proposed.

Nadene was now in full command, making Cletis feel the hate for the auto and hate for the ones he felt had put him into this humiliating situation. It would all have plenty of time over the next couple of months to fester to a full head.

chapter
THIRTEEN

Kill or Be Killed

For these two months, Jennie Smith, his archenemy, never left Cletis's wakening thoughts.

During this same period, the Rileys hadn't crossed the girl's mind. She'd gotten caught up in school, Bible discussions with the missionaries, and the brochures that had been sent to her teacher, Melissa Akers, on the qualifications and advance preparations for acceptance in nursing school. The Rileys had been put aside and so had precaution, up until this week. She'd even quit carrying her pistol to school in her saddlebags. She wouldn't have taken it this week if it hadn't been lying on the oak rocker's seat under the pile of library books that were due to be brought back this week. She had thrown the pistol in without thinking; it was an old habit that used to be second nature.

She'd gone back to the house and changed her light blue denim jacket for the red and black buffalo plaid wool coat. Extra .32 caliber cartridges lay in the button-down pocket of the lighter denim jacket that now hung in the mudroom back at the old fort house as she rode away. This left her with only the five rounds in the gun.

The next three school days flew by as they always did. Learning was Jennie's enjoyment; taking in knowledge was her staff of life. She'd tie the mare's bridle reins together and droop them over the saddle horn on the ride to and from school. One would find her deep in thought or studying, already having her lessons ahead for the month. This week's school-ending ride found her again transfixed. Bird navigated the weekly homeward journey as her master studied the world ancient history book in her hands, trying to figure out the origins of mankind. She never saw Cletis astride of his riding mule until it was too late.

Bird threw her ears forward and gave a nickering call, making Jennie jerk and sit up straight in the saddle. She was startled by the crack of a rifle shot, and simultaneously, the large hardback history book was knocked from her hands and flew through the air.

The mare jumped sideways as the next bullet whistled under her belly, hitting the earth and throwing up small particles of debris. The Arab mare was reined in so sharply that as she did an about-face, she stood momentarily on her hind legs. Her front legs were pawing the air as though already in a hard run. The third bullet was close. Jennie could hear the low whistling whine as it cut the air only inches away.

Bird had been merely startled by the flying book and the small sharp pebbles, sticks and soil that hit her soft underside. She'd heard several thousand shots fired from the .32 pistol and .22 rifle. When the Bible thumpers arrived, the horse had been denied, for a short while, the fun game of target practice. The Paynes made Jennie feel guilty even to handle these instruments of death, much less carry them for the purpose of destruction. Still, the noise of flying projectiles always made Bird come to life, ready for the charge.

When Cletis rounded the sharp bend in the trail, his twin brother Clytis was still some distance to the rear. He'd dismounted to dig out a stone out that had lodged between the shoe and frog of his bay's hoof's rind. This allowed Cletis to get a short distance ahead and time to fire the three shots at Jennie. When Clytis eventually made the same curve, he wasn't aware of what had just happened and wasn't alarmed.

Jennie had no forewarning or time to think. It all happened too fast. First, her history book had been knocked from her grip with the rifle's first shot. Then, before the shot blast had even quit echoing, there was another. Her escape was pure instinct upon hearing the third shot. There was no time to pause and consider the next move or reflect on the scripture she'd learned over the past two months about the grand hope of the resurrection and all the laws and bylaws one had to do to gain this hope—turn the other cheek . . . love they neighbor . . . and let a trigger happy bastard blow you out of the saddle. No, none of these good holy words were recalled to the wild girl's mind.

Then, Adam spoke. His words were as clear to her ears as though they were standing before the giant white oak tree, the tree she'd ridden by on Bird and shot into so many times. The tree died this past year. She pictured the tree as it was trying to cling life while its last huge branch withered and died before the fall colors set in. This is when she heard the old mountain man speak:

"Jennie, you must choose either to kill or be killed."

His voice was clear—TOO clear. She shook her head trying to free herself of distracting thoughts long enough so she could feel fear enough to flee.

Instead, she couldn't muster up any emotions one way or the other. Strange thoughts and memories flowed through her mind as she turned Bird back down the trail. *She could see her father's grave, the watery sepulcher he'd been sunken into and the small bunches of little blue wild flowers she had slipped back and planted before his grave had caved in. She wished now she'd gone back and planted them again after it was mounded up once more.* The Arab's hooves stomping a patch of little wild flowers had dredged up this memory, followed by a story Adam had told around the evening fire—about old Touch The Sky, and how he sent word to his enemy the Crow to meet him for battle. They sent twelve of their strongest, bravest warriors to the challenge. He had slain four of the young braves before they finally killed the ancient dying chief of the Sioux.

Using the same riding trick the old warrior had used, she left the saddle and swung down on her mare's side as low as possible. Using Bird as a shield, she hung on as the horse took off in a full gallop toward her enemy.

Clytis had spurred his bay making him move out when he heard the shots and wondered what the hell his addle-brained brother was shooting at this time. He'd almost reached Cletis and started to open his mouth to shout at him, asking about the shots. Before he could speak, here came Bird! He knew the little chestnut Arab as well as if she was one of his own. He could see the horse bearing down directly toward them . . . *without a rider?*

The racing horse came in full stride, stretching out till her stomach was low to the earth. Her nostrils were flared and her eyes were walled large, showing the whites as they rolled back into her head. Even her teeth were showing, giving her a demonic appearance as the two brothers sat spellbound. Neither could move nor take their eyes off this charging, "riderless" animal.

Something about this riderless horse spooked Clytis's long-legged bay gelding. His horse shied away and off the trail, then started to run off. Each time Clytis tried to pull him in, he'd cat lope, then hit a buck until he was let out.

Then Clytis heard shots, something he thought sounded like small caliber blasts, but he wasn't certain. He had just barely got his horse under control when he again saw the Arab, still charging directly for him. Only now, she wasn't riderless. Jennie Smith was astride Bird's back.

Clytis could see clearly she had a pistol in her hand, although he didn't know it had been emptied—into Cletis. And Jennie had left all her extra cartridges in the denim jacket at home.

"SONS O' BITCH! JESUS H. CHRIST!!" Clytis set spurs to his big bay with such force, he drew blood. The long-legged horse leaped out so suddenly and strongly, he came within a gnat's hair of jumping out from under his rider.

The race was on—the race that held a priceless trophy for each. If Jennie won, she would finally be released from the vermin that had caused her family so much needless adversity. If Clytis was the winner, he would finish with his life, knowing if Jennie caught up, he would lay dead. This was the greatest motivation the young Riley had ever felt before or since. He raked the rowels of his spurs into this horse's ribs, showing no mercy.

The big bay horse became insane in his flight, not from fear of the girl and her chestnut mare, but from the never-ending torture being doled out to his ribs. Although he fled as fast as he could, he couldn't outrun the painful nuisance. The bay was running at such a pace, Clytis knew his horse's wind would break soon if he didn't pull him up. Clytis made a quick glance to his rear, knowing if he spelled his horse, he'd be dead.

He then saw the seemingly impossible—that damn little stunted-looking Arab was gaining on him. Clytis wanted to win his trophy and stand in the winner's circle more than anything else since the day of his birth. He set his spurs hard and quick, rocking with one and nervously gouging with the other as they approached a slick, mucky, narrow seeping branch that tried to run through its marshier bottom. The spring that fed this mess of muck and mire had been opened and cleaned a quarter century ago by a family of squatters. They'd given up on the spring due to death from typhoid. The only sign left of their presence was a large, heavy galvanized bucket that sat at a slant a few feet from the edge of the branch. It's bottom had been eaten away a decade before the birth of either Riley.

Clytis's winded bay never even attempted to clear the seep. The horse's breathing had turned into a hoarse, raspy rattle a quarter mile before they reached the swampy area. When they tried to clear it, they hit it headlong. His front legs buried up to their knees as his back legs entered, putting him into a floundering slide.

When Jennie and Bird approached the seep, Jennie swooped low from the back of her racing horse. Her work-strong little calloused hand grasped the old bucket's upright bail, resurrecting it from the edge of the mire to be used once again.

Bird held true to her name. Her little hooves became airborne to clear the deep muck that lay in wait like a snare. Jennie leaned forward automatically to help her mare complete the jump, still holding the old heavy bucket in her right hand as her mount's hooves touched solid ground on the opposite side.

The exhausted bay pawed and strained against his new adversary—the grey-brownish black muck that had him mired down. It kept the horse from fleeing the constant torment of the spurs that now had his blood flowing freely from his lower rib cage.

Before the bay could upright himself again, Bird was at his side. Jennie smashed the heavy bottomless bucket over Clytis's head. It fit over the scared young man's head perfectly, like the headpiece of a suit of armor.

Jennie held a death grip on the bail as the bay lunged out from under the bucketed rider, yanking the unbalanced, unseeing man from his horse.

Neither Jennie nor Clytis could recall much of what occurred next in this bogged down, murky battle in a swamp. As the milky haze before the girl's eyes cleared, she saw blood floating in the stagnant water.

Clytis Riley lay unmoving before her. Jennie mistook his unconsciousness for death or she would've held his head under the mire longer—as long as it would have taken to kill him.

She walked toward her waiting mare in a daze. Her shoes were a ball of mud and her feet were soaked till the brackish water oozed out from their tops. Her clothing was caked with mud and blood and her pistol was gone. It had become lost, stomped down into the mire to lay there forever.

All of the sudden she felt faint, weak, sick. She started to heave, but nothing came up but hot acid and clear streamers of saliva. She mounted Bird in this dazed and sickened state and rode away.

She rode back the way she had come, riding past the spot where she'd first shot Cletis. It never registered on her mind that both he and his mule were gone. She did stop where Cletis first shot at her. There, she dismounted to retrieve the history book. It was heavily damaged from the rifle slug that tore through part of its opened pages. She remounted, letting the Arab mare choose her own pace for the rest of the way home.

Dark comes early at this time of year. Brother Bob was finishing up his evening chores when Jennie rode in. He saw the mud and blood that covered her clothes and it in turn had given a good plastering to her saddle. He dropped the pitchfork he'd been using and rushed forward, believing she was badly injured. He took her mare's bridle reins from her.

Bob later recalled their conversation. He asked his older sister if she was okay. He'd assumed that her horse had fallen and rolled on top of her several times to get her as bloody and mud-caked as she was. Jennie told her brother she would appreciate it if he would take Bird, give her a good currycombing and rubdown, wipe her saddle clean, and give her extra corn and oats.

Bob replied, "Shore, but are you hurt?"

Jennie gave a strange, hollow-eyed grin that put chills up the boy's spine. He knew now something was bad wrong, even before his big sister spoke.

"I'm fine, Bob. I just killed Cletis and Clytis Riley."

"HOLY SHIT, JENNIE!" Bob blurted out. "We're in big ass trouble now! To hell with your horse and saddle! Let's get to the house! We gotta tell mom!"

For once, Jennie didn't scold him for cursing. He knew by this that her statement was true.

chapter
FOURTEEN

Mr. Payne, the Lawyer

The missionaries, Brother and Sister Payne, had been splitting their time equally staying a week at the Smith's cabin, the next with George, the mailman. George had become a disciple of theirs and would stay in the "door-to-door work," as it was called by the International Bible students, for the next 40 years. George had a large comfortable touring car. The Paynes could carry their message of hope in comfort to all parts of Shannon and Dent County, finishing way ahead of their planned schedule. This left only the river district that they would have to cover by horseback or on foot. On this weekday they were coming back to their original headquarters, the little cabin on the Current River.

George was planning on putting in two or three days with his senior believers. This was fortunate for Jennie since he could provide the fast transportation that would be necessary later on that evening.

In the next thirty minutes, as the story was related, Jennie and the rest would see the frail-looking little missionary man in a completely different light. He didn't enter the old fort house's parlor as "Brother

Payne, the missionary," carrying the message of love and peace for the earth and all mankind; he entered as "Mr. Payne, the LAWYER," a man who'd been in extremely high demand by every corrupt government criminal here and abroad a decade and a half ago.

Even before Jennie completed her account of the episode, Mr. Payne had George the mailman go and get his car ready for their trip to Eminence this late evening. The mother and daughter, at different intervals, tried to ask, "Why?"

Every time they tried, Mr. Payne, the lawyer, cut their questioning off curtly with this stern answer: "There's no time to explain. Now, we must be on our way."

The girl started to leave their presence so she could change clothes and wash the blood and mud off of her hands and face. It was a shock to all when Mr. Payne said, "Absolutely not! The more blood and mud, the better. Be careful not to wipe or scrape any off until we've started our case. We're going to Eminence to have a warrant sworn out against those two young criminals."

The girl looked up at the missionary's face with a puzzled expression of wonderment and again asked, "Why?"

The man's face softened somewhat as he grinned. He even chuckled, saying, "Yes, it's hard to believe, but it's against the law of our land for one to shoot another." Then he added, "Even if you're a woman, or a girl."

He started to say more, then added quickly, "Come! We must be on our way before this matter backlashes on us and we'll be the party being served a warrant instead of the one doing the serving!"

He slapped his hands together with a sharp bang that startled the small party into action as the little lawyer rubbed his hands together as though in preparation for a game of sports. His eyes danced, showing a new light of life, kindled from the banked embers that had been laying in wait for over 15 years.

Whenever those who were born and raised using animal power as their chief means for work and transportation travels in the motorized mechanisms of man's inventions, they always find themselves awestruck at the distance that can be traveled in such a short amount of time. It seemed to Jennie they were there before they even got started, especially since Mr. Payne had sat in the backseat with her. His soothing voice presented her with question after question as he jotted down notes, filling several small pages.

The girl did wonder at times if the old missionary's memory was becoming like that of her grandfather's since he'd quiz her about one aspect of her story, then turn right around and ask about the same thing she had just clarified a few sentences before. Her answers were always the same, although his questions were phrased differently each time. "Poor man," she thought. "It won't be long now until Sister Payne will have her hands full . . ."

Jennie never finished her thoughts as her lawyer slapped his little notebook closed and declared, "Don't worry, girl. We'll take it all the way to the Supreme Court if we have to!"

His next statement made George and the girl catch their breath.

"Yes, we'll make these ignorant BASTARDS who have set themselves up here to administer justice comply with the law for ONCE in their pitiful lives!"

He chuckled, leaned back on the Auburn's comfortable plush leather seat, closed his eyes, and spoke no more. The party rode in complete silence. Only the drone of the engine kept George's big touring car from having the stillness of the tomb.

chapter
FIFTEEN

That Damned Little Bible Thumper

Sheriff Bum Powell was leaving his office as the three arrived in George's touring car. The automobile never failed to turn the heads of all who had a chance to glimpse at such a rarity. Before this evening ended, the High Sheriff would wish he hadn't this particular opportunity to make its acquaintance.

Bum saw the little missionary too late. There wasn't time enough to change course and evade the preacher. He'd been drunk and rude with Brother Payne at their first and only encounter. Tonight the High Sheriff was in no mood to hear about anyone's Sweet Jesus. His wisdom tooth had swollen throughout the day till even Uncle Tuck's best and strongest spirits wouldn't touch the excruciating throb that shot through his skull at each heartbeat.

The little man blocked the way of the hulking sheriff who towered over him. The sheriff started to growl at the missionary about how he could take his savior and shove him up his ass.

Brother Payne, now Lawyer Payne, spoke. His voice no longer held the soothing tone of the missionary. This in itself snapped the sheriff to a startled attention. Even the throb in his jaw was shocked into momentary submission. The commanding voice was at enormous odds with the person it was coming from.

Mr. Payne spoke fast and brief, telling Bum what the nature of his request stemmed from and what the sheriff's obligations were under these circumstances.

As Jennie's attorney was speaking with the sheriff, the judge arrived on the scene. He'd been working late since this was a court day and had overheard the demands of the bible thumper. The judge had also had a run in with the missionaries. It was still fresh in his memory how foolish they'd made him feel in front of his own houseguest. He'd only let them in to have sport with the peasantry. He had indulged in his private chambers, taking on more spirits than usual, which made him feel all-powerful and wise and caused him to let his guard down that night. Here was a second chance to put this bible thumping little bastard in his place.

Sheriff Powell hailed his judge and friend and told him the news of not one, but two victims. Bum had been on his way to Doc Oody's office. Doc had sent word for Bum to come and make a report since it involved a shooting. The messenger told the sheriff one man had taken five slugs: two in the gut, and three flesh wounds. Ol' Doc didn't figure the man would make it at first. Must have been a family brawl since the other man had the pure hell beat right out of him. Doc was just now getting around to cleaning and sewing the hide back in place.

"His brother give him a good threshing," Bum explained to the judge, "either while he wuz bein' shot or jest after, we figgered, since neither one has spoke a word. Their brother Osrowl Riley hauled 'em in then left. Ne'er spoke nary a word either."

Damned lucky coincidence Mr. Payne had run into Bum and the judge, because he now knew the condition of the Rileys and what the scuttlebutt was. They weren't dead, and no one yet knew what had happened.

Mr. Payne knew he'd have to put his foot down right here and now if he was going to establish a firm case against Jennie's assailants. He knew it was more than rumor how corrupt the judge, and especially the sheriff, had been in the past. He was sure they hadn't changed a lick.

The lawyer proceeded to speak of abilities and connections he'd never mentioned or bragged about before or since, and were aimed purely at the judge. He knew the sheriff was way too ignorant to comprehend even the smallest aspect of his opening speech.

The judge's initial annoyance with Mr. Payne had boiled over into a seething rage. He knew Mr. Payne realized that he and Bum were planning to brush him off as a "nobody" and carry on as usual. The judge didn't have a shadow of a doubt this little man could and would do what he had spoken about not only to him, but to his cronies, too. The judge wound up petrified, seeing his career, power, and reputation gone. He was afraid he couldn't hide his intimidation, so he decided the best way to conceal it was to take it out on Bum.

The judge growled at Bum to return to the sheriff's office so they could get this process over with. Bum hadn't heard much of anything except that he had to return to his office. *Damn this little bible thumper to hell*, Bum thought as his throbbing jaw reached a new tempo of pain.

Jennie's friend and lawyer never revealed the minutest detail about her run in with the Rileys until he'd obtained every legal document that he demanded. Mr. Payne helped Bum get them filled out by dictating the wording of each form. He carefully crafted Jennie's defense, making sure the warrants were sworn out on the Rileys and not on her.

The sheriff, even with his swollen jaw and throbbing head, was beginning to add things up. The mud and blood-caked girl was tied in heavily somehow with the victims laying over in Doc's spare bed above his office. Not only had one been shot, the other was beaten, and he now was supposed to serve papers against the two of them.

Mr. Payne, in his familiar soothing tone, told his young client that she had not killed Cletis or Clytis, knowing this would relieve her.

The judge now realized for the first time Jennie was of the opposite gender. He looked at her, then addressed the mud-caked girl before him.

"Well, young lady, what do you think about that?" the judge said with a sneer that said, "It will all come out what sort of hanky-panky has been going on between you three."

Jennie gave the judge a cold, piercing stare. She knew what he was implying. She looked down for a few seconds before she spoke. Then, the high-spirited girl lifted her head, looked the judge square in the eye and said, "Just shows you some are too damned mean to die."

This even made the sheriff laugh, despite his throbbing jaw.

chapter
SIXTEEN

The "Wise" Judge
at Jennie's Trial

The case never came to an official trial because of Mr. Payne's knowl-edge and foresight. It was, as they say, "kicked out." The only thing worth mentioning was one statement made by Cletis at the hearing. When asked if he'd ever before felt that his life was in danger prior to the shooting, he answered, "Hale, yes! One late night in their chicken house!"

This made a stir. All eyes turned toward Jennie. Then Mr. Payne asked Cletis, who was frail and crippled now, to answer in more detail.

"Yep! That ol' longhaired mountain man that called hisself Adam Troop put his long pig sticker to my throat! Drew blood, he did, and said, 'Ye boys come anytime. Always liked company at these late night hen parties.' Then he laughed like a crazy feller and put his moccasin in the small of my back. Next thing I knowed, I was a-layin' face down in the chicken yard!"

The courtroom erupted in laughter

Jennie's lawyer asked what happened next.

Cletis answered, "I don't rightly know. I never hung around to see!"

This statement brought another volley of laughter. Cletis looked around the room wondering what was so funny. He pretended to laugh also, not knowing why. He was relieved when the bible man said, "No more questions for the present time."

And there weren't any more questions or statements from anyone else either. The judge did not merely wield power in this little town; he was THE power, ALL-SUPREME. He had "wisely" used the lapse of time between the night Mr. Payne and the mud-caked girl first showed up to the day of this official hearing to determine the case's stature. As soon as the Most High Supreme Judge realized who this lowly bible thumper REALLY was, he was sorely and purely relieved to have this incident swept under and away and never recorded. His superior position in society no longer threatened, he once again looked forward to basking in the awe and admiration he imagined he inspired in the fine citizens of Eminence. If he never has to have another meeting with this frail-looking man on the subjects of religion or law, so much the better.

Each party dropped their charges and the State of Missouri never took it up. As far as the judge was concerned, the State of Missouri—hell, even the whole United States, the WORLD—only existed within the boundaries of HIS Shannon County, known to the residents as "Booger County."

Old Pa Riley died less than six months after the shooting and beating of his twin boys. The kinfolks and friends who had gathered at his bedside related later that his last thoughts and words were of Jennie and her younger brother Bob. Those words were, "I wushed I could o' jest lived long enough to o' got even with those dad-bratted Smith kids. Hale, I reckon I'd o' lived forever."

Witnesses claimed a spark of life shown in his old dying eyes just for a second. He then gave a low chuckle and died.

With Pa Riley dead and buried, Osrowl married and left, leaving the twins to fend for themselves. Cletis was now referred to as "poor Cletis" since the two bullets he'd taken through the guts had left him almost an invalid. He never recovered fully. Five years to the day of the fracas, he had a temper fit that caused an artery to burst in his brain. He died instantly at his brother's garage.

Osrowl and his wife Nadene had earlier taken in poor Cletis and gave him a job. In actuality, they just made him a job. The day he'd thrown the temper fit over the T model's rust-seized muffler clamp bolt that sent him to his final resting place, Osrowl and Nadene were having no rest. They'd just returned from Kansas City where they had purchased another garage. One brother was on his way to prosperity and wealth, the other to his grave.

Clytis was riding the rails looking for work during the full heat of the Depression. He was broke and too proud to return to his prosperous brother for employment. It would be several decades before he'd return from Oregon. Even then, it was only for a short visit. He too would prosper at the expense of our vast, seemingly endless, old-growth forest. His crews of men, with their Chinook crosscuts and felling axes, destroyed tenfold the giants for each tree they salvaged.

Jennie completed the two years of high school that Rector provided and was enrolled in the school of nursing in Springfield, Missouri.

She offered to pay for the damaged history book Cletis had shot out of her hands. Her teacher, Melissa Akers, just hugged her and cried.

Epilogue

We are certain Jennie now knows why Adam never sent the postcard from Venezuela.

The old fort house, awarded to Jennie's Great-Grandpa Bealert for fighting in the Black Hawk Wars, was on property that was eventually stolen by the federal government to create the Ozark National Scenic Riverways.

The Toll of the Eddy

"Edd Self was no stranger to hunger . . ."

So begins the next book, *The Toll of Eddy*, which delves more deeply into the young life of Adam Troop and Jim Butler (Jim Self) including their involvement in the Sam Bass gang. There is a detailed description of the Sam Bass shootout at Round Rock, Texas. There is also a very bizarre aspect surrounding the entire story from the time leading up to the shootout as well as after.

It also ties in such subjects as King Arthur and the Current River, Catholics, Masons, Hernando Desoto and the true identity of the Queen of Confitachiqui, the purpose of the mounds, and many more diverse, mysterious and often outlandish topics.

About the Author

Ray Self was in 1943 born at home on Upper Shawnee in Shannon County, Missouri. Before leaving for the Navy, he lived in Eminence, then Bartlett.

He currently resides on a small farm in Tennessee on the Buffalo River with his wife, Amy.

Aside from writing, building, farming, sawmilling, and a little black-smithing, he is currently working on reestablishing the Whig Party and becoming its 2004 presidential candidate.

"If ye love wealth greater than liberty, the tranquility of servitude better than the animating contest for freedom, go from us in peace.

We ask not your counsels or arms.

Crouch down and lick the hand that feeds you

. . . and may posterity forget that you were our countrymen."

—SAM ADAMS

The Wicked Current
Ray Self

Available at *www.amazon.com*

Credit card orders: 1–800–431–1579

To order by mail, send check or money order for $22.95
($19.95 plus $3.00 s/h) to:
Buffalo Mill Press
P.O. Box 87
Hohenwald, TN 38462

Contact author at above address
or at wickedcurrent@aol.com

Published by Buffalo Mill Press
P.O. Box 87
Hohenwald, TN 38462
931–796–0048
BuffaloMill@djis.net